NOBEL LECTURES PHYSICS

NOBEL LECTURES

INCLUDING PRESENTATION SPEECHES
AND LAUREATES' BIOGRAPHIES

PHYSICS

CHEMISTRY

PHYSIOLOGY OR MEDICINE

LITERATURE

PEACE

PUBLISHED FOR THE NOBEL FOUNDATION
BY
ELSEVIER PUBLISHING COMPANY
AMSTERDAM – LONDON – NEW YORK

NOBEL LECTURES

INCLUDING PRESENTATION SPEECHES
AND LAUREATES' BIOGRAPHIES

PHYSICS

1922-1941

PUBLISHED FOR THE NOBEL FOUNDATION
IN 1965 BY
ELSEVIER PUBLISHING COMPANY
AMSTERDAM - LONDON - NEW YORK

ELSEVIER PUBLISHING COMPANY
335 JAN VAN GALENSTRAAT, P.O. BOX 211, AMSTERDAM

AMERICAN ELSEVIER PUBLISHING COMPANY, INC.
52 VANDERBILT AVENUE, NEW YORK, N.Y. 10017

ELSEVIER PUBLISHING COMPANY LIMITED
RIPPLESIDE COMMERCIAL ESTATE
BARKING, ESSEX

LIBRARY OF CONGRESS CATALOG CARD NUMBER 63–22072

WITH 107 ILLUSTRATIONS

PRINTED IN THE NETHERLANDS BY
N.V. DRUKKERIJ G.J. THIEME, NIJMEGEN
BOOK DESIGN: HELMUT SALDEN

Foreword

The Nobel Foundation has, by agreement, granted the Elsevier Publishing Company of Amsterdam the right to publish in English language the Nobel Lectures for 1901–1962. The lectures in the five Nobel Prize domains: Physics, Chemistry, Physiology or Medicine, Literature, and Peace will appear separately, according to the subject. The scientific lectures will each cover three volumes and those in literature and peace one volume each. Short biographical notes and the presentation speeches will also be included.

The Nobel Foundation has since 1901 each year published *Les Prix Nobel* which contains all Nobel Lectures of that year, always in the language in which they were given, as well as short biographies of the laureates. In addition an account is given of the prize-award ceremonies in Stockholm and in Oslo, including presentation addresses and after-dinner speeches, etc., thus covering the whole field of Nobel Prize events of one particular year.

In the Elsevier series the Nobel Lectures, presentation addresses, and biographies will now be more readily accessible to those who wish to follow the development in only certain of the Nobel subjects, as reflected in the prize awards during the years passed. For practical reasons English has been chosen as common language for this series.

It is the hope of the Nobel Foundation that the volumes to be published by Elsevier Publishing Company will supplement *Les Prix Nobel* and that together they will serve to spread knowledge of those landmarks on the road of human progress that have been honoured by Nobel Prizes.

Arne Tiselius – President, Nobel Foundation

Publisher's Note

During the realization of this work we have been confronted by many problems. In solving the great majority of them we have relied heavily upon assistance, both invited and spontaneously offered, from many quarters.

To some problems there was no solution to be found; in particular, it proved impossible to obtain, for some of the lectures, the original photographs or blocks used for the illustrations. As an inevitable consequence of this it was found necessary to reproduce these illustrations from a printed original; this naturally renders them less perfect than we would have wished. We thank those who were able to lend us original material.

The translations of those lectures which were delivered in a language other than English were prepared by the Babylon Translation Service, London. We are indebted to the Editor of *Nature* for the reproduction of the translation of Bohr's Lecture, which appeared in the issue of July 7, 1923, of this journal. Our acknowledgement is due to Mr. D. F. Styles and Mr. M. Fedorski (both of Manchester), and to the Babylon Translation Service, for research on, and preparation of, most of the biographies. Completion of these, and the addition of much detail, was achieved with the cooperation of many of the laureates themselves, their colleagues and assistants, and other individuals whose help was requested. To all of them we would like to offer our sincerest thanks in appreciation of their efforts.

Elsevier Publishing Company

Contents

Physics 1922

NIELS BOHR

«for his services in the investigation of the structure of atoms, and of the radiation emanating from them»

Physics 1922

Presentation Speech by Professor S.A. Arrhenius, Chairman of the Nobel Committee for Physics of the Royal Swedish Academy of Sciences

Your Majesty, Your Royal Highnesses, Ladies and Gentlemen.

Ever since Kirchhoff and Bunsen (1860) introduced spectral analysis, that extremely important aid to investigation has produced the finest results. To begin with, material was collected and spectra were investigated not only from terrestrial objects but also from the heavenly bodies. There was a splendid harvest. Then came the second stage of research. Attempts were made to find regularities in the structure of the spectra. To begin with, it was natural to try to compare the different spectral lines which are emitted by a glowing gas with the different notes that could be produced by a vibrating solid. The vibrating bodies in a glowing gas would in that case be its atoms and molecules. But little progress could be made on this track. It was necessary to fall back on another method, namely to try by calculation to establish the connection between the various vibrations which could be emitted by a gas. Hydrogen ought to be the simplest of all gases. The Swiss Balmer in 1885 found a simple formula for the connection mentioned between the lines of hydrogen as then known. There followed a large number of investigators, such as Kayser and Runge, Ritz, Deslandres, and especially our compatriot Rydberg, who sought for similar regularities in the spectra of the other chemical elements. Rydberg succeeded in representing their light vibrations by means of formulae which exhibited a certain resemblance to Balmer's formula. These formulae contain a constant which has afterwards acquired extremely great importance and has been recorded amongst the universal and fundamental values of physics under the name of the Rydberg constant.

Now, if it were possible to obtain an idea of the structure of the atom, of course, that would form a good starting-point to create a conception of the possible light vibrations that can be emitted by an atom of hydrogen. Rutherford, who has to such an extraordinary degree wrung their secrets from the atoms, had constructed such «atom models». According to his conception, the atom of hydrogen should consist of a positive nucleus, with a unit charge, of extremely small dimensions, and about this a negatively charged electron should describe an orbit. As probably only electric forces are at work between the nucleus and the electron, and as these electric forces follow the same law as the attraction of gravity between two masses, the path of the electron ought to be elliptical or circular, and the nucleus to be situated either in one of the foci of the ellipse or in the centre of the circle. The nucleus would be comparable to the sun and the electron to a planet. In accordance with the classical theory of Maxwell, therefore, these orbit movements should emit rays and consequently cause a loss of energy, and the electron would describe smaller and smaller tracks with a declining period of revolution and finally rush in towards the positive nucleus. Thus the track would be a spiral, and the rays of light emitted, which will require a steadily declining period of vibration, would correspond to a continuous spectrum, which, of course, is characteristic of a glowing solid or liquid body, but not at all of a glowing gas. Consequently, either the atom model must be false, or else the classical theory of Maxwell must be incorrect in this case. Ten years or so previously there would have been no hesitation in the choice between these alternatives, but the atom model would have been declared to be inapplicable. But in 1913, when Bohr began to work at this problem, the great physicist Planck of Berlin had traced his law of radiation, which could be explained only on the assumption, which was in conflict with all preceding notions, that the energy of heat is given off in the form of «quanta», that is to say small portions of heat, just as matter consists of small portions, i.e. the atoms. With the help of this assumption Planck succeeded, in complete accordance with experience, in calculating the distribution of energy in radiation from a hypothetically completely black body. Afterwards (in 1905 and 1907) Einstein had perfected the quantum theory and deduced therefrom several laws, such as the diminution of the specific heat of solid bodies with declining temperature and the photoelectric effect, for which discovery he has this day been awarded the Nobel Prize.

Accordingly, Bohr had no need to hesitate in his choice: he assumed that Maxwell's theory does not hold good in the present case, but that the atom model of Rutherford is correct. Thus the electrons do not emit light when they move in their tracks round the positive nucleus, tracks which we begin by assuming to be circular. The emission of light would take place when the electron jumps from one track to another. The quantity of energy which is thus radiated is a quantum. As, according to Planck, the quantum of energy is the product of the number of light vibrations with the Planckian constant, which is denoted by the letter h, it is possible to calculate the number of vibrations which corresponds to a given passing from one orbit to another. The regularity which Balmer found for the spectrum of hydrogen requires that the radii of the different orbits should be proportional to the squares of the whole numbers, that is to say as 1 to 4 to 9, and so on. And indeed Bohr succeeded, in his first treatise on this question, in calculating the Rydberg constant from other known magnitudes, namely the weight of an atom of hydrogen, the Planckian constant, and the value of the electric unit of charge. The difference between the value found by observation and the calculated value of the Rydberg constant amounted to only 1 percent; and this has been diminished by more recent measurements.

This circumstance at once attracted the admiring attention of the scientific world to Bohr's work and made it possible to foresee that he would to a great extent solve the problem before him. Sommerfeld showed that what is known as the fine structure of the hydrogen lines, by which is meant that the lines observed with a strongly dispergent spectroscope are divided up into several closely adjacent lines, can be explained in accordance with Bohr's theory in the following way. The various stationary tracks for the movement of the electrons – if we leave out of account the innermost one, which is the ordinary one, and is called the « orbit of rest » – may be not only circular but also elliptical, with a major axis equal to the diameter of the corresponding circular orbit. When an electron passes from an elliptical orbit to another track, the change in the energy, and consequently the number of vibrations for the corresponding spectral lines, is somewhat different from what it is when it passes from the corresponding circular orbit to the other track. Consequently we get two different spectral lines, which nevertheless lie very close to one another. Yet we observe only a smaller number of lines than we should expect according to this view of things.

The difficulties thus revealed, however, Bohr succeeded in removing by the introduction of what is known as the principle of correspondence, which opened up entirely new prospects of great importance. This principle to some extent brings the new theory nearer to the old classical theory. According to this principle, a certain number of transitions are impossible. The principle in question is of great importance in the determination of the tracks of electrons which are possible within atoms that are heavier than the atom of hydrogen. The nuclear charge of the atom of helium is twice as great as that of the atom of hydrogen: in a neutral condition it is encircled by two electrons. It is the lightest atom next that of hydrogen. It occurs in two different modifications: one is called parhelium, and is the more stable, and the other is called orthohelium – these were supposed at first to be two different substances. The principle of correspondence states that the two electrons in parhelium in their tracks of rest run along two circles, which form an angle of 60° to one another. In orthohelium, on the other hand, the tracks of the two electrons lie in the same plane, the one being circular, while the other is elliptical. The following element with an atomic weight which is next in magnitude to helium is lithium, with three electrons in a neutral state. According to the principle of correspondence, the tracks of the two innermost electrons lie in the same way as the tracks of the two electrons in parhelium, while the track of the third is elliptical and is of far greater dimensions than the inner tracks.

In a similar manner Bohr is able, with the help of the principle of correspondence, to establish, in the most important points, the situation of the various tracks of electrons in other atoms. It is on the positions of the outermost electron tracks that the chemical properties of the atoms depend, and it is on this ground that their chemical valency has partly been determined. We may entertain the best hopes of the future development of this great work.

Professor Bohr. You have carried to a successful solution the problems that have presented themselves to investigators of spectra. In doing so you have been compelled to make use of theoretical ideas which substantially diverge from those which are based on the classical doctrines of Maxwell. Your great success has shown that you have found the right roads to fundamental truths, and in so doing you have laid down principles which have led to the most splendid advances, and promise abundant fruit for the work of the future. May it be vouchsafed to you to cultivate for yet a long time to come, to the advantage of research, the wide field of work that you have opened up to Science.

NIELS BOHR

The structure of the atom

Nobel Lecture, December 11, 1922

Ladies and Gentlemen. Today, as a consequence of the great honour the Swedish Academy of Sciences has done me in awarding me this year's Nobel Prize for Physics for my work on the structure of the atom, it is my duty to give an account of the results of this work and I think that I shall be acting in accordance with the traditions of the Nobel Foundation if I give this report in the form of a survey of the development which has taken place in the last few years within the field of physics to which this work belongs.

The general picture of the atom

The present state of atomic theory is characterized by the fact that we not only believe the existence of atoms to be proved beyond a doubt, but also we even believe that we have an intimate knowledge of the constituents of the individual atoms. I cannot on this occasion give a survey of the scientific developments that have led to this result; I will only recall the discovery of the electron towards the close of the last century, which furnished the direct verification and led to a conclusive formulation of the conception of the atomic nature of electricity which had evolved since the discovery by Faraday of the fundamental laws of electrolysis and Berzelius's electrochemical theory, and had its greatest triumph in the electrolytic dissociation theory of Arrhenius. This discovery of the electron and elucidation of its properties was the result of the work of a large number of investigators, among whom Lenard and J. J. Thomson may be particularly mentioned. The latter especially has made very important contributions to our subject by his ingenious attempts to develop ideas about atomic constitution on the basis of the electron theory. The present state of our knowledge of the elements of atomic structure was reached, however, by the discovery of the atomic nucleus, which we owe to Rutherford, whose work on the radioactive substances discovered towards the close of the last century has much enriched physical and chemical science.

According to our present conceptions, an atom of an element is built up
of a nucleus that has a positive electrical charge and is the seat of by far the
greatest part of the atomic mass, together with a number of electrons, all
having the same negative charge and mass, which move at distances from
the nucleus that are very great compared to the dimensions of the nucleus
or of the electrons themselves. In this picture we at once see a striking resemblance to a planetary system, such as we have in our own solar system. Just
as the simplicity of the laws that govern the motions of the solar system is
intimately connected with the circumstance that the dimensions of the moving bodies are small in relation to the orbits, so the corresponding relations
in atomic structure provide us with an explanation of an essential feature of
natural phenomena in so far as these depend on the properties of the elements. It makes clear at once that these properties can be divided into two
sharply distinguished classes.

To the first class belong most of the ordinary physical and chemical properties of substances, such as their state of aggregation, colour, and chemical
reactivity. These properties depend on the motion of the electron system
and the way in which this motion changes under the influence of different
external actions. On account of the large mass of the nucleus relative to that
of the electrons and its smallness in comparison to the electron orbits, the
electronic motion will depend only to a very small extent on the nuclear
mass, and will be determined to a close approximation solely by the total
electrical charge of the nucleus. Especially the inner structure of the nucleus
and the way in which the charges and masses are distributed among its
separate particles will have a vanishingly small influence on the motion of
the electron system surrounding the nucleus. On the other hand, the structure of the nucleus will be responsible for the second class of properties that
are shown in the radioactivity of substances. In the radioactive processes we
meet with an explosion of the nucleus, whereby positive or negative particles, the so-called α- and β-particles, are expelled with very great velocities.

Our conceptions of atomic structure afford us, therefore, an immediate
explanation of the complete lack of interdependence between the two classes
of properties, which is most strikingly shown in the existence of substances
which have to an extraordinarily close approximation the same ordinary
physical and chemical properties, even though the atomic weights are not
the same, and the radioactive properties are completely different. Such substances, of the existence of which the first evidence was found in the work of
Soddy and other investigators on the chemical properties of the radioactive

elements, are called isotopes, with reference to the classification of the elements according to ordinary physical and chemical properties. It is not necessary for me to state here how it has been shown in recent years that isotopes are found not only among the radioactive elements, but also among ordinary stable elements; in fact, a large number of the latter that were previously supposed simple have been shown by Aston's well-known investigations to consist of a mixture of isotopes with different atomic weights.

The question of the inner structure of the nucleus is still but little understood, although a method of attack is afforded by Rutherford's experiments on the disintegration of atomic nuclei by bombardment with α-particles. Indeed, these experiments may be said to open up a new epoch in natural philosophy in that for the first time the artificial transformation of one element into another has been accomplished. In what follows, however, we shall confine ourselves to a consideration of the ordinary physical and chemical properties of the elements and the attempts which have been made to explain them on the basis of the concepts just outlined.

It is well known that the elements can be arranged as regards their ordinary physical and chemical properties in a *natural system* which displays most suggestively the peculiar relationships between the different elements. It was recognized for the first time by Mendeleev and Lothar Meyer that when the elements are arranged in an order which is practically that of their atomic weights, their chemical and physical properties show a pronounced periodicity. A diagrammatic representation of this so-called Periodic Table is given in Fig. 1, where, however, the elements are not arranged in the ordinary way but in a somewhat modified form of a table first given by Julius Thomsen, who has also made important contributions to science in this domain. In the figure the elements are denoted by their usual chemical symbols, and the different vertical columns indicate the so-called periods. The elements in successive columns which possess homologous chemical and physical properties are connected with lines. The meaning of the square brackets around certain series of elements in the later periods, the properties of which exhibit typical deviations from the simple periodicity in the first periods, will be discussed later.

In the development of the theory of atomic structure the characteristic features of the natural system have found a surprisingly simple interpretation. Thus we are led to assume that the ordinal number of an element in the Periodic Table, the so-called atomic number, is just equal to the number of electrons which move about the nucleus in the neutral atom. In an imperfect

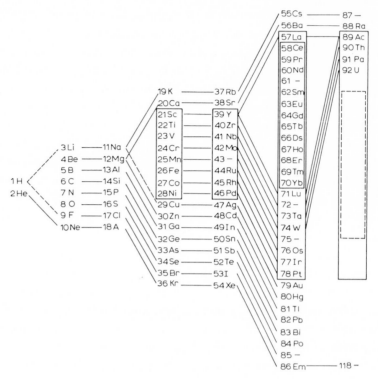

Fig. 1.

form, this law was first stated by Van den Broek; it was, however, fore-shadowed by J. J. Thomson's investigations of the number of electrons in the atom, as well as by Rutherford's measurements of the charge on the atomic nucleus. As we shall see, convincing support for this law has since been obtained in various ways, especially by Moseley's famous investigations of the X-ray spectra of the elements. We may perhaps also point out, how the simple connexion between atomic number and nuclear charge offers an explanation of the laws governing the changes in chemical properties of the elements after expulsion of α- or β-particles, which found a simple formulation in the so-called radioactive displacement law.

Atomic stability and electrodynamic theory

As soon as we try to trace a more intimate connexion between the properties of the elements and atomic structure, we encounter profound difficulties, in that essential differences between an atom and a planetary system show themselves here in spite of the analogy we have mentioned.

The motions of the bodies in a planetary system, even though they obey the general law of gravitation, will not be completely determined by this law alone, but will depend largely on the previous history of the system. Thus the length of the year is not determined by the masses of the sun and the earth alone, but depends also on the conditions that existed during the formation of the solar system, of which we have very little knowledge. Should a sufficiently large foreign body some day traverse our solar system, we might among other effects expect that from that day the length of the year would be different from its present value.

It is quite otherwise in the case of atoms. The definite and unchangeable properties of the elements demand that the state of an atom cannot undergo permanent changes due to external actions. As soon as the atom is left to itself again, its constituent particles must arrange their motions in a manner which is completely determined by the electric charges and masses of the particles. We have the most convincing evidence of this in spectra, that is, in the properties of the radiation emitted from substances in certain circumstances, which can be studied with such great precision. It is well known that the wavelengths of the spectral lines of a substance, which can in many cases be measured with an accuracy of more than one part in a million, are, in the same external circumstances, always exactly the same within the limit of error of the measurements, and quite independent of the previous treatment of this substance. It is just to this circumstance that we owe the great importance of spectral analysis, which has been such an invaluable aid to the chemist in the search for new elements, and has also shown us that even on the most distant bodies of the universe there occur elements with exactly the same properties as on the earth.

On the basis of our picture of the constitution of the atom it is thus impossible, so long as we restrict ourselves to the ordinary mechanical laws, to account for the characteristic atomic stability which is required for an explanation of the properties of the elements.

The situation is by no means improved if we also take into consideration the well-known electrodynamic laws which Maxwell succeeded in formulating on the basis of the great discoveries of Oersted and Faraday in the first half of the last century. Maxwell's theory has not only shown itself able to account for the already known electric and magnetic phenomena in all their details, but has also celebrated its greatest triumph in the prediction of the electromagnetic waves which were discovered by Hertz, and are now so extensively used in wireless telegraphy.

For a time it seemed as though this theory would also be able to furnish a basis for an explanation of the details of the properties of the elements, after it had been developed, chiefly by Lorentz and Larmor, into a form consistent with the atomistic conception of electricity. I need only remind you of the great interest that was aroused when Lorentz, shortly after the discovery by Zeeman of the characteristic changes that spectral lines undergo when the emitting substance is brought into a magnetic field, could give a natural and simple explanation of the main features of the phenomenon. Lorentz assumed that the radiation which we observe in a spectral line is sent out from an electron executing simple harmonic vibrations about a position of equilibrium, in precisely the same manner as the electromagnetic waves in radiotelegraphy are sent out by the electric oscillations in the antennæ. He also pointed out how the alteration observed by Zeeman in the spectral lines corresponded exactly to the alteration in the motion of the vibrating electron which one would expect to be produced by the magnetic field.

It was, however, impossible on this basis to give a closer explanation of the spectra of the elements, or even of the general type of the laws holding with great exactness for the wavelengths of lines in these spectra, which had been established by Balmer, Rydberg, and Ritz. After we obtained details as to the constitution of the atom, this difficulty became still more manifest; in fact, so long as we confine ourselves to the classical electrodynamic theory we cannot even understand why we obtain spectra consisting of sharp lines at all. This theory can even be said to be incompatible with the assumption of the existence of atoms possessing the structure we have described, in that the motions of the electrons would claim a continuous radiation of energy from the atom, which would cease only when the electrons had fallen into the nucleus.

The origin of the quantum theory

It has, however, been possible to avoid the various difficulties of the electro-dynamic theory by introducing concepts borrowed from the so-called quantum theory, which marks a complete departure from the ideas that have hitherto been used for the explanation of natural phenomena. This theory was originated by Planck, in the year 1900, in his investigations on the law

of heat radiation, which, because of its independence of the individual properties of substances, lent itself peculiarly well to a test of the applicability of
the laws of classical physics to atomic processes.

Planck considered the equilibrium of radiation between a number of systems with the same properties as those on which Lorentz had based his theory
of the Zeeman effect, but he could now show not only that classical physics
could not account for the phenomena of heat radiation, but also that a complete agreement with the experimental law could be obtained if – in pronounced contradiction to classical theory – it were assumed that the energy
of the vibrating electrons could not change continuously, but only in such
a way that the energy of the system always remained equal to a whole
number of so-called energy-quanta. The magnitude of this quantum was
found to be proportional to the frequency of oscillation of the particle,
which, in accordance with classical concepts, was supposed to be also the
frequency of the emitted radiation. The proportionality factor had to be
regarded as a new universal constant, since termed Planck's constant, similar
to the velocity of light, and the charge and mass of the electron.

Planck's surprising result stood at first completely isolated in natural science, but with Einstein's significant contributions to this subject a few years
after, a great variety of applications was found. In the first place, Einstein
pointed out that the condition limiting the amount of vibrational energy of
the particles could be tested by investigation of the specific heat of crystalline
bodies, since in the case of these we have to do with similar vibrations, not
of a single electron, but of whole atoms about positions of equilibrium in the
crystal lattice. Einstein was able to show that the experiment confirmed
Planck's theory, and through the work of later investigators this agreement
has proved quite complete. Furthermore, Einstein emphasized another consequence of Planck's results, namely, that radiant energy could only be emitted or absorbed by the oscillating particle in so-called «quanta of radiation»,
the magnitude of each of which was equal to Planck's constant multiplied
by the frequency.

In his attempts to give an interpretation of this result, Einstein was led to
the formulation of the so-called «hypothesis of light-quanta», according to
which the radiant energy, in contradiction to Maxwell's electromagnetic
theory of light, would not be propagated as electromagnetic waves, but
rather as concrete light atoms, each with an energy equal to that of a quantum of radiation. This concept led Einstein to his well-known theory of the
photoelectric effect. This phenomenon, which had been entirely unexplain-

able on the classical theory, was thereby placed in a quite different light, and
the predictions of Einstein's theory have received such exact experimental
confirmation in recent years, that perhaps the most exact determination of
Planck's constant is afforded by measurements on the photoelectric effect.
In spite of its heuristic value, however, the hypothesis of light-quanta, which
is quite irreconcilable with so-called interference phenomena, is not able to
throw light on the nature of radiation. I need only recall that these interference phenomena constitute our only means of investigating the properties
of radiation and therefore of assigning any closer meaning to the frequency
which in Einstein's theory fixes the magnitude of the light-quantum.

In the following years many efforts were made to apply the concepts of
the quantum theory to the question of atomic structure, and the principal
emphasis was sometimes placed on one and sometimes on the other of the
consequences deduced by Einstein from Planck's result. As the best known
of the attempts in this direction, from which, however, no definite results
were obtained, I may mention the work of Stark, Sommerfeld, Hasenöhrl,
Haas, and Nicholson.

From this period also dates an investigation by Bjerrum on infrared absorption bands, which, although it had no direct bearing on atomic structure,
proved significant for the development of the quantum theory. He directed
attention to the fact that the rotation of the molecules in a gas might be
investigated by means of the changes in certain absorption lines with temperature. At the same time he emphasized the fact that the effect should not
consist of a continuous widening of the lines such as might be expected from
classical theory, which imposed no restrictions on the molecular rotations,
but in accordance with the quantum theory he predicted that the lines should
be split up into a number of components, corresponding to a sequence of
distinct possibilities of rotation. This prediction was confirmed a few years
later by Eva von Bahr, and the phenomenon may still be regarded as one
of the most striking evidences of the reality of the quantum theory, even
though from our present point of view the original explanation has undergone a modification in essential details.

The quantum theory of atomic constitution

The question of further development of the quantum theory was in the
meantime placed in a new light by Rutherford's discovery of the atomic nu-

cleus (1911). As we have already seen, this discovery made it quite clear that by classical conceptions alone it was quite impossible to understand the most essential properties of atoms. One was therefore led to seek for a formulation of the principles of the quantum theory that could immediately account for the stability in atomic structure and the properties of the radiation sent out from atoms, of which the observed properties of substances bear witness. Such a formulation was proposed (1913) by the present lecturer in the form of two postulates, which may be stated as follows:

(1). Among the conceivably possible states of motion in an atomic system there exist a number of so-called *stationary states* which, in spite of the fact that the motion of the particles in these states obeys the laws of classical mechanics to a considerable extent, possess a peculiar, mechanically unexplainable stability, of such a sort that every permanent change in the motion of the system must consist in a complete transition from one stationary state to another.

(2). While in contradiction to the classical electromagnetic theory no radiation takes place from the atom in the stationary states themselves, a process of transition between two stationary states can be accompanied by the emission of electromagnetic radiation, which will have the same properties as that which would be sent out according to the classical theory from an electrified particle executing an harmonic vibration with constant frequency. This frequency v has, however, no simple relation to the motion of the particles of the atom, but is given by the relation

$$hv = E' - E'',$$

where h is Planck's constant, and E' and E'' are the values of the energy of the atom in the two stationary states that form the initial and final state of the radiation process. Conversely, irradiation of the atom with electromagnetic waves of this frequency can lead to an absorption process, whereby the atom is transformed back from the latter stationary state to the former.

While the first postulate has in view the general stability of the atom, the second postulate has chiefly in view the existence of spectra with sharp lines. Furthermore, the quantum-theory condition entering in the last postulate affords a starting-point for the interpretation of the laws of series spectra.

The most general of these laws, the combination principle enunciated by Ritz, states that the frequency v for each of the lines in the spectrum of an element can be represented by the formula

$$v = T'' - T',$$

where T'' and T' are two so-called «spectral terms» belonging to a manifold of such terms characteristic of the substance in question.

According to our postulates, this law finds an immediate interpretation in the assumption that the spectrum is emitted by transitions between a number of stationary states in which the numerical value of the energy of the atom is equal to the value of the spectral term multiplied by Planck's constant. This explanation of the combination principle is seen to differ fundamentally from the usual ideas of electrodynamics, as soon as we consider that there is no simple relation between the motion of the atom and the radiation sent out. The departure of our considerations from the ordinary ideas of natural philosophy becomes particularly evident, however, when we observe that the occurrence of two spectral lines, corresponding to combinations of the same spectral term with two other different terms, implies that the nature of the radiation sent out from the atom is not determined only by the motion of the atom at the beginning of the radiation process, but also depends on the state to which the atom is transferred by the process.

At first glance one might, therefore, think that it would scarcely be possible to bring our formal explanation of the combination principle into direct relation with our views regarding the constitution of the atom, which, indeed, are based on experimental evidence interpreted on classical mechanics and electrodynamics. A closer investigation, however, should make it clear that a definite relation may be obtained between the spectra of the elements and the structure of their atoms on the basis of the postulates.

The hydrogen spectrum

The simplest spectrum we know is that of hydrogen. The frequencies of its lines may be represented with great accuracy by means of Balmer's formula:

$$v = K \left(\frac{1}{n''^2} - \frac{1}{n'^2} \right),$$

where K is a constant and n' and n'' are two integers. In the spectrum we accordingly meet a single series of spectral terms of the form K/n^2, which decrease regularly with increasing term number n. In accordance with the postulates, we shall therefore assume that each of the hydrogen lines is emitted by a transition between two states belonging to a series of stationary states of the hydrogen atom in which the numerical value of the atom's energy is equal to hK/n^2.

Following our picture of atomic structure, a hydrogen atom consists of a positive nucleus and an electron which – so far as ordinary mechanical conceptions are applicable – will with great approximation describe a periodic elliptical orbit with the nucleus at one focus. The major axis of the orbit is inversely proportional to the work necessary completely to remove the electron from the nucleus, and, in accordance with the above, this work in the stationary states is just equal to hK/n^2. We thus arrive at a manifold of stationary states for which the major axis of the electron orbit takes on a series of discrete values proportional to the squares of the whole numbers. The accompanying Fig. 2 shows these relations diagrammatically. For the sake of simplicity the electron orbits in the stationary states are represented by circles, although in reality the theory places no restriction on the eccentricity of the orbit, but only determines the length of the major axis. The arrows represent the transition processes that correspond to the red and

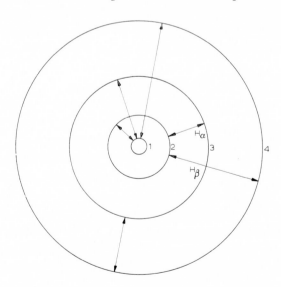

Fig. 2.

green hydrogen lines, H_α and H_β, the frequency of which is given by means of the Balmer formula when we put $n'' = 2$ and $n' = 3$ and 4 respectively. The transition processes are also represented which correspond to the first three lines of the series of ultraviolet lines found by Lyman in 1914, of which the frequencies are given by the formula when n is put equal to 1, as well as to the first line of the infrared series discovered some years previously by Paschen, which are given by the formula if n'' is put equal to 3.

This explanation of the origin of the hydrogen spectrum leads us quite naturally to interpret this spectrum as the manifestation of a process whereby the electron is bound to the nucleus. While the largest spectral term with term number 1 corresponds to the final stage in the binding process, the small spectral terms that have larger values of the term number correspond to stationary states which represent the initial states of the binding process, where the electron orbits still have large dimensions, and where the work required to remove an electron from the nucleus is still small. The final stage in the binding process we may designate as the normal state of the atom, and it is distinguished from the other stationary states by the property that, in accordance with the postulates, the state of the atom can only be changed by the addition of energy whereby the electron is transferred to an orbit of larger dimensions corresponding to an earlier stage of the binding process.

The size of the electron orbit in the normal state calculated on the basis of the above interpretation of the spectrum agrees roughly with the value for the dimensions of the atoms of the elements that have been calculated by the kinetic theory of matter from the properties of gases. Since, however, as an immediate consequence of the stability of the stationary states that is claimed by the postulates, we must suppose that the interaction between two atoms during a collision cannot be completely described with the aid of the laws of classical mechanics, such a comparison as this cannot be carried further on the basis of such considerations as those just outlined.

A more intimate connexion between the spectra and the atomic model has been revealed, however, by an investigation of the motion in those stationary states where the term number is large, and where the dimensions of the electron orbit and the frequency of revolution in it vary relatively little when we go from one stationary state to the next following. It was possible to show that the frequency of the radiation sent out during the transition between two stationary states, the difference of the term numbers of which is small in comparison to these numbers themselves, tended to coincide in frequency with one of the harmonic components into which the electron motion could be resolved, and accordingly also with the frequency of one of the wave trains in the radiation which would be emitted according to the laws of ordinary electrodynamics.

The condition that such a coincidence should occur in this region where the stationary states differ but little from one another proves to be that the constant in the Balmer formula can be expressed by means of the relation

$$K = \frac{2\pi^2 e^4 m}{h^3},$$

where e and m are respectively the charge and mass of the electron, while h is Planck's constant. This relation has been shown to hold to within the considerable accuracy with which, especially through the beautiful investigations of Millikan, the quantities e, m, and h are known.

This result shows that there exists a connexion between the hydrogen spectrum and the model for the hydrogen atom which, on the whole, is as close as we might hope considering the departure of the postulates from the classical mechanical and electrodynamic laws. At the same time, it affords some indication of how we may perceive in the quantum theory, in spite of the fundamental character of this departure, a natural generalization of the fundamental concepts of the classical electrodynamic theory. To this most important question we shall return later, but first we will discuss how the interpretation of the hydrogen spectrum on the basis of the postulates has proved suitable in several ways, for elucidating the relation between the properties of the different elements.

Relationships between the elements

The discussion above can be applied immediately to the process whereby an electron is bound to a nucleus with any given charge. The calculations show that, in the stationary state corresponding to a given value of the number n, the size of the orbit will be inversely proportional to the nuclear charge, while the work necessary to remove an electron will be directly proportional to the square of the nuclear charge. The spectrum that is emitted during the binding of an electron by a nucleus with charge N times that of the hydrogen nucleus can therefore be represented by the formula:

$$v = N^2 K \left(\frac{1}{n''^2} - \frac{1}{n'^2} \right).$$

If in this formula we put $N = 2$, we get a spectrum which contains a set of lines in the visible region which was observed many years ago in the spectrum of certain stars. Rydberg assigned these lines to hydrogen because of the close analogy with the series of lines represented by the Balmer formula. It was never possible to produce these lines in pure hydrogen, but just before the theory for the hydrogen spectrum was put forward, Fowler succeeded in observing the series in question by sending a strong discharge through a mixture of hydrogen and helium. This investigator also assumed that the lines were hydrogen lines, because there existed no experimental evidence from which it might be inferred that two different substances could show properties resembling each other so much as the spectrum in question and that of hydrogen. After the theory was put forward, it became clear, however, that the observed lines must belong to a spectrum of helium, but that they were not like the ordinary helium spectrum emitted from the neutral atom. They came from an ionized helium atom which consists of a single electron moving about a nucleus with double charge. In this way there was brought to light a new feature of the relationship between the elements, which corresponds exactly with our present ideas of atomic structure, according to which the physical and chemical properties of an element depend in the first instance only on the electric charge of the atomic nucleus.

Soon after this question was settled the existence of a similar general relationship between the properties of the elements was brought to light by Moseley's well-known investigations on the characteristic X-ray spectra of the elements, which was made possible by Laue's discovery of the interference of X-rays in crystals and the investigations of W. H. and W. L. Bragg on this subject. It appeared, in fact, that the X-ray spectra of the different elements possessed a much simpler structure and a much greater mutual resemblance than their optical spectra. In particular, it appeared that the spectra changed from element to element in a manner that corresponded closely to the formula given above for the spectrum emitted during the binding of an electron to a nucleus, provided N was put equal to the atomic number of the element concerned. This formula was even capable of expressing, with an approximation that could not be without significance, the frequencies of the strongest X-ray lines, if small whole numbers were substituted for n' and n''.

This discovery was of great importance in several respects. In the first place, the relationship between the X-ray spectra of different elements proved so simple that it became possible to fix without ambiguity the atomic number for all known substances, and in this way to predict with certainty the atomic number of all such hitherto unknown elements for which there is a place in the natural system. Fig. 3 shows how the square root of the frequency for two characteristic X-ray lines depends on the atomic number. These lines belong to the group of so-called K-lines, which are the most penetrating of the characteristic rays. With very close approximation the points lie on straight lines, and the fact that they do so is conditioned not only by our taking account of known elements, but also by our leaving an open place between molybdenum (42) and ruthenium (44), just as in Mendeleev's original scheme of the natural system of the elements.

Further, the laws of X-ray spectra provide a confirmation of the general theoretical conceptions, both with regard to the constitution of the atom and the ideas that have served as a basis for the interpretation of spectra. Thus

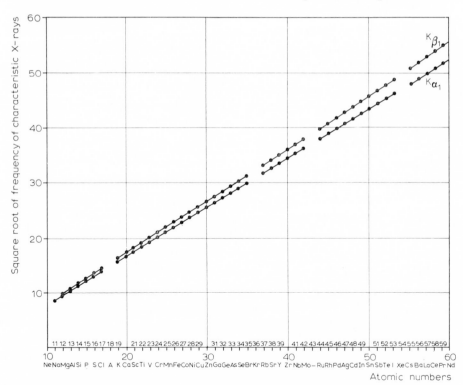

Fig. 3.

the similarity between X-ray spectra and the spectra emitted during the binding of a single electron to a nucleus may be simply interpreted from the fact that the transitions between stationary states with which we are concerned in X-ray spectra are accompanied by changes in the motion of an electron in the inner part of the atom, where the influence of the attraction of the nucleus is very great compared with the repulsive forces of the other electrons.

The relations between other properties of the elements are of a much more complicated character, which originates in the fact that we have to do with processes concerning the motion of the electrons in the outer part of the atom, where the forces that the electrons exert on one another are of the same order of magnitude as the attraction towards the nucleus, and where, therefore, the details of the interaction of the electrons play an important part. A characteristic example of such a case is afforded by the spatial extension of the atoms of the elements. Lothar Meyer himself directed attention to the characteristic periodic change exhibited by the ratio of the atomic weight to the density, the so-called atomic volume, of the elements in the natural system. An idea of these facts is given by Fig. 4, in which the atomic volume is represented as a function of the atomic number. A greater difference be-

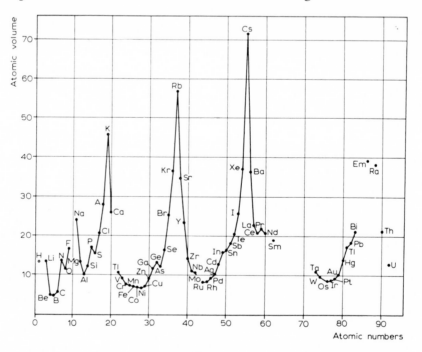

Fig. 4.

tween this and the previous figure could scarcely be imagined. While the X-ray spectra vary uniformly with the atomic number, the atomic volumes show a characteristic periodic change which corresponds exactly to the change in the chemical properties of the elements.

Ordinary optical spectra behave in an analogous way. In spite of the dissimilarity between these spectra, Rydberg succeeded in tracing a certain general relationship between the hydrogen spectrum and other spectra. Even though the spectral lines of the elements with higher atomic number appear as combinations of a more complicated manifold of spectral terms which is not so simply co-ordinated with a series of whole numbers, still the spectral terms can be arranged in series each of which shows a strong similarity to the series of terms in the hydrogen spectrum. This similarity appears in the fact that the terms in each series can, as Rydberg pointed out, be very accurately represented by the formula $K/(n + \alpha)^2$, where K is the same constant that occurs in the hydrogen spectrum, often called the Rydberg constant, while n is the term number, and α a constant which is different for the different series.

This relationship with the hydrogen spectrum leads us immediately to regard these spectra as the *last step of a process whereby the neutral atom is built up by the capture and binding of electrons to the nucleus*, one by one. In fact, it is clear that the last electron captured, so long as it is in that stage of the binding process in which its orbit is still large compared to the orbits of the previously bound electrons, will be subjected to a force from the nucleus and these electrons, that differs but little from the force with which the electron in the hydrogen atom is attracted towards the nucleus while it is moving in an orbit of corresponding dimensions.

The spectra so far considered, for which Rydberg's laws hold, are excited by means of electric discharge under ordinary conditions and are often called arc spectra. The elements emit also another type of spectrum, the so-called spark spectra, when they are subjected to an extremely powerful discharge. Hitherto it was impossible to disentangle the spark spectra in the same way as the arc spectra. Shortly after the above view on the origin of arc spectra was brought forward, however, Fowler found (1914) that an empirical expression for the spark spectrum lines could be established which corresponds exactly to Rydberg's laws with the single difference that the constant K is replaced by a constant four times as large. Since, as we have seen, the constant that appears in the spectrum sent out during the binding of an electron to a helium nucleus is exactly equal to $4\,K$, it becomes evident that spark spectra are due to the ionized atom, and that their emission corresponds to *the last step but one in the formation of the neutral atom* by the successive capture and binding of electrons.

Absorption and excitation of spectral lines

The interpretation of the origin of the spectra was also able to explain the characteristic laws that govern absorption spectra. As Kirchhoff and Bunsen had already shown, there is a close relation between the selective absorption of substances for radiation and their emission spectra, and it is on this that the application of spectrum analysis to the heavenly bodies essentially rests. Yet on the basis of the classical electromagnetic theory, it is impossible to understand why substances in the form of vapour show absorption for certain lines in their emission spectrum and not for others.

On the basis of the postulates given above we are, however, led to assume that the absorption of radiation corresponding to a spectral line emitted by a transition from one stationary state of the atom to a state of less energy is brought about by the return of the atom from the last-named state to the first. We thus understand immediately that in ordinary circumstances a gas or vapour can only show selective absorption for spectral lines that are produced by a transition from a state corresponding to an earlier stage in the binding process to the normal state. Only at higher temperatures or under the influence of electric discharges whereby an appreciable number of atoms are being constantly disrupted from the normal state, can we expect absorption for other lines in the emission spectrum in agreement with the experiments.

A most direct confirmation for the general interpretation of spectra on the basis of the postulates has also been obtained by investigations on the excitation of spectral lines and ionization of atoms by means of impact of free electrons with given velocities. A decided advance in this direction was marked by the well-known investigations of Franck and Hertz (1914). It appeared from their results that by means of electron impacts it was impossible to impart to an atom an arbitrary amount of energy, but only such amounts as corresponded to a transfer of the atom from its normal state to another stationary state of the existence of which the spectra assure us, and the energy of which can be inferred from the magnitude of the spectral term.

Further, striking evidence was afforded of the independence that, according to the postulates, must be attributed to the processes which give rise to the emission of the different spectral lines of an element. Thus it could be shown directly that atoms that were transferred in this manner to a stationary state of greater energy were able to return to the normal state with emission of radiation corresponding to a single spectral line.

Continued investigations on electron impacts, in which a large number of physicists have shared, have also produced a detailed confirmation of the theory concerning the excitation of series spectra. Especially it has been possible to show that for the *ionization* of an atom by electron impact an amount of energy is necessary that is exactly equal to the work required, according to the theory, to remove the last electron captured from the atom. This work can be determined directly as the product of Planck's constant and the spectral term corresponding to the normal state, which, as mentioned above, is equal to the limiting value of the frequencies of the spectral series connected with selective absorption.

The quantum theory of multiply-periodic systems

While it was thus possible by means of the fundamental postulates of the quantum theory to account directly for certain general features of the properties of the elements, a closer development of the ideas of the quantum theory was necessary in order to account for these properties in further detail. In the course of the last few years a more general theoretical basis has been attained through the development of formal methods that permit the fixation of the stationary states for electron motions of a more general type than those we have hitherto considered. For a simply periodic motion such as we meet in the pure harmonic oscillator, and at least to a first approximation, in the motion of an electron about a positive nucleus, the manifold of stationary states can be simply co-ordinated to a series of whole numbers. For motions of the more general class mentioned above, the so-called *multiply-periodic* motions, however, the stationary states compose a more complex manifold, in which, according to these formal methods, each state is characterized by several whole numbers, the so-called « quantum numbers ».

In the development of the theory a large number of physicists have taken part, and the introduction of several quantum numbers can be traced back to the work of Planck himself. But the definite step which gave the impetus to further work was made by Sommerfeld (1915) in his explanation of the fine structure shown by the hydrogen lines when the spectrum is observed with a spectroscope of high resolving power. The occurrence of this fine structure must be ascribed to the circumstance that we have to deal, even in hydrogen, with a motion which is not exactly simply periodic. In fact, as a consequence of the change in the electron's mass with velocity that is claimed by the theory of relativity, the electron orbit will undergo a very slow precession in the orbital plane. The motion will therefore be doubly periodic, and besides a number characterizing the term in the Balmer formula, which we shall call the *principal quantum number* because it determines in the main the energy of the atom, the fixation of the stationary states demands another quantum number which we shall call the *subordinate quantum number*.

A survey of the motion in the stationary states thus fixed is given in the diagram (Fig. 5), which reproduces the relative size and form of the electron orbits. Each orbit is designated by a symbol n_k, where n is the principal quantum number and k the subordinate quantum number. All orbits with the same principal quantum number have, to a first approximation, the same major axis, while orbits with the same value of k have the same parameter, i.e. the same value for the shortest chord through the focus. Since the energy values for different states with the same value of n but different values of k differ a little from each other, we get for each hydrogen line corresponding to definite values of n' and n'' in the Balmer formula a number of different transition processes, for which the frequencies of the emitted radia-

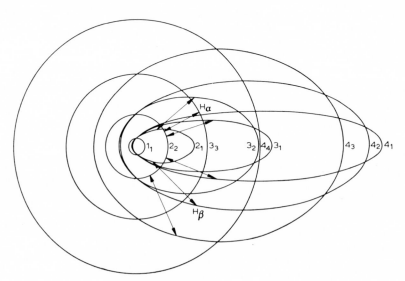

Fig. 5.

tion as calculated by the second postulate are not exactly the same. As Sommerfeld was able to show, the components this gives for each hydrogen line agree with the observations on the fine structure of hydrogen lines to within the limits of experimental error. In the figure the arrows designate the processes that give rise to the components of the red and green lines in the hydrogen spectrum, the frequencies of which are obtained by putting $n'' = 2$ and $n' = 3$ or 4 respectively in the Balmer formula.

In considering the figure it must not be forgotten that the description of the orbit is there incomplete, in so much as with the scale used the slow precession does not show at all. In fact, this precession is so slow that even for the orbits that rotate most rapidly the electron performs about 40,000 revolutions before the perihelion has gone round once. Nevertheless, it is this precession alone that is responsible for the multiplicity of the stationary states characterized by the subordinate quantum number. If, for example, the hydrogen atom is subjected to a small disturbing force which perturbs the regular precession, the electron orbit in the stationary states will have a form altogether different from that given in the figure. This implies that the fine structure will change its character completely, but the hydrogen spectrum will continue to consist of lines that are given to a close approximation by the Balmer formula, due to the fact that the approximately periodic character of the motion will be retained. Only when the disturbing forces become so large that even during a single revolution of the electron the orbit is appreciably disturbed, will the spectrum undergo essential changes. The statement often advanced that the introduction of two quantum numbers should be a necessary condition for the explanation of the Balmer formula must therefore be considered as a misconception of the theory.

Sommerfeld's theory has proved itself able to account not only for the fine structure of the hydrogen lines, but also for that of the lines in the helium spark spectrum. Owing to the greater velocity of the electron, the intervals between the components into which a line is split up are here much greater and can be measured with much greater accuracy. The theory was also able to account for certain features in the fine structure of X-ray spectra, where we meet frequency differences that may even reach a value more than a million times as great as those of the frequency differences for the components of the hydrogen lines.

Shortly after this result had been attained, Schwarzschild and Epstein (1916) simultaneously succeeded, by means of similar considerations, in accounting for the characteristic changes that the hydrogen lines undergo in an electric field, which had been discovered by Stark in the year 1914. Next, an explanation of the essential features of the Zeeman effect for the hydrogen lines was worked out at the same time by Sommerfeld and Debye (1917). In this instance the application of the postulates involved the consequence that only certain orientations of the atom relative to the magnetic field were allowable, and this characteristic consequence of the quantum theory has quite recently received a most direct confirmation in the beautiful researches of Stern and Gerlach on the deflexion of swiftly moving silver atoms in a nonhomogenous magnetic field.

The correspondence principle

While this development of the theory of spectra was based on the working out of formal methods for the fixation of stationary states, the present lecturer succeeded shortly afterwards in throwing light on the theory from a new viewpoint, by pursuing further the characteristic connexion between the quantum theory and classical electrodynamics already traced out in the hydrogen spectrum. In connexion with the important work of Ehrenfest and Einstein these efforts led to the formulation of the so-called *correspondence principle*, according to which the occurrence of transitions between the stationary states accompanied by emission of radiation is traced back to the harmonic components into which the motion of the atom may be resolved and which, according to the classical theory, determine the properties of the radiation to which the motion of the particles gives rise.

According to the correspondence principle, it is assumed that every transition process between two stationary states can be co-ordinated with a corresponding harmonic vibration component in such a way that the probability of the occurrence of the transition is dependent on the amplitude of the vibration. The state of polarization of the radiation emitted during the transition depends on the further characteristics of the vibration, in a manner analogous to that in which on the classical theory the intensity and state of polarization in the wave system emitted by the atom as a consequence of the presence of this vibration component would be determined respectively by the amplitude and further characteristics of the vibration.

With the aid of the correspondence principle it has been possible to confirm and to extend the above-mentioned results. Thus it was possible to develop a complete quantum theory explanation of the Zeeman effect for the hydrogen lines, which, in spite of the essentially different character of the assumptions that underlie the two theories, is very similar throughout to Lorentz's original explanation based on the classical theory. In the case of the Stark effect, where, on the other hand, the classical theory was completely at a loss, the quantum theory explanation could be so extended with the help of the correspondence principle as to account for the polarization of the different components into which the lines are split, and also for the characteristic intensity distribution exhibited by the components. This last question has been more closely investigated by Kramers, and the accompanying figure will give some impression of how completely it is possible to account for the phenomenon under consideration.

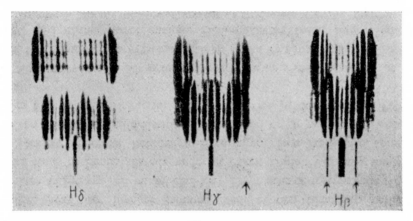

Fig. 6.

Fig. 6 reproduces one of Stark's well-known photographs of the splitting up of the hydrogen lines. The picture displays very well the varied nature of the phenomenon, and shows in how peculiar a fashion the intensity varies from component to component. The components below are polarized perpendicular to the field, while those above are polarized parallel to the field.

Fig. 7 gives a diagrammatic representation of the experimental and theoretical results for the line Hγ, the frequency of which is given by the Balmer formula with $n'' = 2$ and $n' = 5$. The vertical lines denote the components into which the line is split up, of which the picture on the right gives the components which are polarized parallel to the field and that on the left those that are polarized perpendicular to it. The experimental results are represented in the upper half of the diagram, the distances from the dotted line representing the measured displacements of the components, and the lengths of the lines being proportional to the relative intensity as estimated by Stark from the blackening of the photographic plate. In the lower half is given for comparison a representation of the theoretical results from a drawing in Kramers' paper.

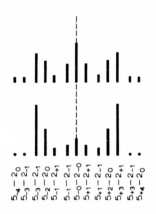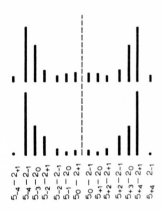

Fig. 7.

The symbol $(n'_{s'} - n''_{s''})$ attached to the lines gives the transitions between the stationary states of the atom in the electric field by which the components are emitted. Besides the principal quantum integer n, the stationary states are further characterized by a subordinate quantum integer s, which can be negative as well as positive and has a meaning quite different from that of the quantum number k occurring in the relativity theory of the fine structure of the hydrogen lines, which fixed the form of the electron orbit in the undisturbed atom. Under the influence of the electric field both the form of the orbit and its position undergo large changes, but certain properties of the orbit remain unchanged, and the surbordinate quantum number s is connected with these. In Fig. 7 the position of the components corresponds to the frequencies calculated for the different transitions, and the lengths of the lines are proportional to the probabilities as calculated on the basis of the correspondence principle, by which also the polarization of the radiation is determined. It is seen that the theory reproduces completely the main feature of the experimental results, and in the light of the correspondence principle we can say that the Stark effect reflects down to the smallest details the action of the electric field on the orbit of the electron in the hydrogen atom, even though in this case the reflection is so distorted that, in contrast with the case of the Zeeman effect, it would scarcely be possible directly to recognize the motion on the basis of the classical ideas of the origin of electromagnetic radiation.

Results of interest were also obtained for the spectra of elements of higher atomic number, the explanation of which in the meantime had made important progress through the work of Sommerfeld, who introduced several quantum numbers for the description of the electron orbits. Indeed, it was possible, with the aid of the correspondence principle, to account completely for the characteristic rules which govern the seemingly capricious occurrence of combination lines, and it is not too much to say that the quantum theory has not only provided a simple interpretation of the combination principle, but has further contributed materially to the clearing up of the mystery that has long rested over the application of this principle.

The same viewpoints have also proved fruitful in the investigation of the so-called band spectra. These do not originate, as do series spectra, from individual atoms, but from molecules; and the fact that these spectra are so rich in lines is due to the complexity of the motion entailed by the vibrations of the atomic nuclei relative to each other and the rotations of the molecule as a whole. The first to apply the postulates to this problem was Schwarzschild, but the important work of Heurlinger especially has thrown much light on the origin and structure of band spectra. The considerations employed here can be traced back directly to those discussed at the beginning of this lecture in connexion with Bjerrum's theory of the influence of molecular rotation on the infrared absorption lines of gases. It is true we no longer think that the rotation is reflected in the spectra in the way claimed by classical electrodynamics, but rather that the line components are due to transitions between stationary states which differ as regards rotational motion. That the phenomenon retains its essential feature, however, is a typical consequence of the correspondence principle.

The natural system of the elements

The ideas of the origin of spectra outlined in the preceding have furnished the basis for a theory of the structure of the atoms of the elements which has shown itself suitable for a general interpretation of the main features of the properties of the elements, as exhibited in the natural system. This theory is based primarily on considerations of the manner in which the atom can be imagined to be built up by the capture and binding of electrons to the nucleus, one by one. As we have seen, the optical spectra of elements provide us with evidence on the progress of the last steps in this building-up process.

An insight into the kind of information that the closer investigation of the spectra has provided in this respect may be obtained from Fig. 8, which gives a diagrammatic representation of the orbital motion in the stationary states corresponding to the emission of the arc-spectrum of potassium. The curves show the form of the orbits described in the stationary states by the last electron captured in the potassium atom, and they can be considered as stages in the process whereby the 19th electron is bound after the 18 previous electrons have already been bound in their normal orbits. In order not to complicate the figure, no attempt has been made to draw any of the orbits of these inner electrons, but the region in which they move is enclosed by a dotted circle. In an atom with several electrons the orbits will, in general, have a complicated character. Because of the symmetrical nature of the field of force about the nucleus, however, the motion of each single electron can be approximately described as a plane periodic motion on which is super-imposed a uniform rotation in the plane of the orbit. The orbit of each electron will therefore be to a first approximation doubly periodic, and will be fixed by two quantum numbers, as are the stationary states in a hydrogen atom when the relativity precession is taken into account.

In Fig. 8, as in Fig. 5, the electron orbits are marked with the symbol n_k,

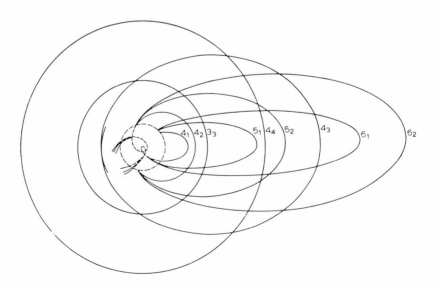

Fig. 8.

where n is the principal quantum number and k the subordinate quantum number. While for the initial states of the binding process, where the quantum numbers are large, the orbit of the last electron captured lies completely outside of those of the previously bound electrons, this is not the case for the last stages. Thus, in the potassium atom, the electron orbits with subordinate quantum numbers 2 and 1 will, as indicated in the figure, penetrate partly into the inner region. Because of this circumstance, the orbits will deviate very greatly from a simple Kepler motion, since they will consist of a series of successive outer loops that have the same size and form, but each of which is turned through an appreciable angle relative to the preceding one. Of these outer loops only one is shown in the figure. Each of them coincides very nearly with a piece of a Kepler ellipse, and they are connected, as indicated, by a series of inner loops of a complicated character in which the electron approaches the nucleus closely. This holds especially for the orbit with subordinate quantum number 1, which, as a closer investigation shows, will approach nearer to the nucleus than any of the previously bound electrons.

On account of this penetration into the inner region, the strength with which an electron in such an orbit is bound to the atom will – in spite of the fact that for the most part it moves in a field of force of the same character as that surrounding the hydrogen nucleus – be much greater than for an electron in a hydrogen atom that moves in an orbit with the same principal quantum number, the maximum distance of the electron from the nucleus at the same time being considerably less than in such a hydrogen orbit. As we shall see, this feature of the binding process in atoms with many electrons is of essential importance in order to understand the characteristic periodic way in which many properties of the elements as displayed in the natural system vary with the atomic number.

In the accompanying table (Fig. 9) is given a summary of the results concerning the structure of the atoms of the elements to which the author has been led by a consideration of successive capture and binding of electrons to the atomic nucleus. The figures before the different elements are the atomic numbers, which give the total number of electrons in the neutral atom. The figures in the different columns give the number of electrons in orbits corresponding to the values of the principal and subordinate quantum numbers standing at the top. In accordance with ordinary usage we will, for the sake of brevity, designate an orbit with principal quantum number n as an n-quantum orbit. The first electron bound in each atom moves in an orbit

	1_1	2_1	2_2	3_1	3_2	3_3	4_1	4_2	4_3	4_4	5_1	5_2	5_3	5_4	5_5	6_1	6_2	6_3	6_4	6_5	6_6	7_1	7_2
1 H	1																						
2 He	2																						
3 Li	2	1																					
4 Be	2	2																					
5 B	2	2	(1)																				
− −	−	−	−																				
10 Ne	2	4	4																				
11 Na	2	4	4	1																			
12 Mg	2	4	4	2																			
13 Al	2	4	4	2	1																		
− −	−	−	−	−	−																		
18 A	2	4	4	4	4																		
19 K	2	4	4	4	4		1																
20 Ca	2	4	4	4	4		2																
21 Sc	2	4	4	4	4	1	(2)																
22 Ti	2	4	4	4	4	2	(2)																
− −	−	−	−	−	−	−																	
29 Cu	2	4	4	6	6	6	1																
30 Zn	2	4	4	6	6	6	2																
31 Ga	2	4	4	6	6	6	2	1															
− −	−	−	−	−	−	−	−	−															
36 Kr	2	4	4	6	6	6	4	4															
37 Rb	2	4	4	6	6	6	4	4			1												
38 Sr	2	4	4	6	6	6	4	4			2												
39 Y	2	4	4	6	6	6	4	4	1		(2)												
40 Zr	2	4	4	6	6	6	4	4	2		(2)												
− −	−	−	−	−	−	−	−	−	−		−												
47 Ag	2	4	4	6	6	6	6	6	6		1												
48 Cd	2	4	4	6	6	6	6	6	6		2												
49 In	2	4	4	6	6	6	6	6	6		2	1											
− −	−	−	−	−	−	−	−	−	−		−	−											
54 X	2	4	4	6	6	6	6	6	6		4	4											
55 Cs	2	4	4	6	6	6	6	6	6		4	4				1							
56 Ba	2	4	4	6	6	6	6	6	6		4	4				2							
57 La	2	4	4	6	6	6	6	6	6		4	4	1			(2)							
58 Ce	2	4	4	6	6	6	6	6	6	1	4	4	1			(2)							
59 Pr	2	4	4	6	6	6	6	6	6	2	4	4	1			(2)							
− −	−	−	−	−	−	−	−	−	−	−	−	−	−			−							
71 Cp	2	4	4	6	6	6	8	8	8	8	4	4	1			(2)							
72 −	2	4	4	6	6	6	8	8	8	8	4	4	2			(2)							
− −	−	−	−	−	−	−	−	−	−	−	−	−	−			−							
79 Au	2	4	4	6	6	6	8	8	8	8	6	6	6			1							
80 Hg	2	4	4	6	6	6	8	8	8	8	6	6	6			2							
81 Tl	2	4	4	6	6	6	8	8	8	8	6	6	6			2	1						
− −	−	−	−	−	−	−	−	−	−	−	−	−	−			−	−						
86 Em	2	4	4	6	6	6	8	8	8	8	6	6	6			4	4						
87 −	2	4	4	6	6	6	8	8	8	8	6	6	6			4	4					1	
88 Ra	2	4	4	6	6	6	8	8	8	8	6	6	6			4	4					2	
89 Ac	2	4	4	6	6	6	8	8	8	8	6	6	6			4	4	1				(2)	
90 Th	2	4	4	6	6	6	8	8	8	8	6	6	6			4	4	2				(2)	
− −	−	−	−	−	−	−	−	−	−	−	−	−	−			−	−	−				−	
118 ?	2	4	4	6	6	6	8	8	8	8	8	8	8	8		6	6	6				4	4

Fig. 9.

that corresponds to the normal state of the hydrogen atom with quantum symbol 1_1. In the hydrogen atom there is of course only one electron; but we must assume that in the atoms of other elements the next electron also will be bound in such a 1-quantum orbit of type 1_1. As the table shows, the following electrons are bound in 2-quantum orbits. To begin with, the binding will result in a 2_1 orbit, but later electrons will be bound in 2_2 orbits, until, after binding the first 10 electrons in the atom, we reach a closed configuration of the 2-quantum orbits in which we assume there are four orbits of each type. This configuration is met for the first time in the neutral neon atom, which forms the conclusion of the second period in the system of the elements. When we proceed in this system, the following electrons are bound in 3-quantum orbits, until, after the conclusion of the third period of the system, we encounter for the first time, in elements of the fourth period, electrons in 4-quantum orbits, and so on.

This picture of atomic structure contains many features that were brought forward by the work of earlier investigators. Thus the attempt to interpret the relations between the elements in the natural system by the assumption of a division of the electrons into groups goes as far back as the work of J. J. Thomson in 1904. Later, this viewpoint was developed chiefly by Kossel (1916), who, moreover, has connected such a grouping with the laws that investigations of X-ray spectra have brought to light.

Also G. R. Lewis and I. Langmuir have sought to account for the relations between the properties of the elements on the basis of a grouping inside the atom. These investigators, however, assumed that the electrons do not move about the nucleus, but occupy positions of equilibrium. In this way, though, no closer relation can be reached between the properties of the elements and the experimental results concerning the constituents of the atoms. Statical positions of equilibrium for the electrons are in fact not possible in cases in which the forces between the electrons and the nucleus even approximately obey the laws that hold for the attractions and repulsions between electrical charges.

The possibility of an interpretation of the properties of the elements on the basis of these latter laws is quite characteristic for the picture of atomic structure developed by means of the quantum theory. As regards this picture, the idea of connecting the grouping with a classification of electron orbits according to increasing quantum numbers was suggested by Moseley's discovery of the laws of X-ray spectra, and by Sommerfeld's work on the fine structure of these spectra. This has been principally emphasized by Vegard,

who some years ago in connexion with investigations of X-ray spectra proposed a grouping of electrons in the atoms of the elements, which in many
ways shows a likeness to that which is given in the above table.

A satisfactory basis for the further development of this picture of atomic
structure has, however, only recently been created by the study of the binding processes of the electrons in the atom, of which we have experimental
evidence in optical spectra, and the characteristic features of which have
been elucidated principally by the correspondence principle. It is here an
essential circumstance that the restriction on the course of the binding process, which is expressed by the presence of electron orbits with higher quantum numbers in the normal state of the atom, can be naturally connected
with the general condition for the occurrence of transitions between stationary states, formulated in that principle.

Another essential feature of the theory is the influence, on the strength
of binding and the dimensions of the orbits, of the penetration of the later
bound electrons into the region of the earlier bound ones, of which we have
seen an example in the discussion of the origin of the potassium spectrum.
Indeed, this circumstance may be regarded as the essential cause of the pronounced periodicity in the properties of the elements, in that it implies that
the atomic dimensions and chemical properties of homologous substances in
the different periods, as, for example, the alkali-metals, show a much greater
similarity than that which might be expected from a direct comparison of
the orbit of the last electron bound with an orbit of the same quantum
number in the hydrogen atom.

The increase of the principal quantum number which we meet when we
proceed in the series of the elements, affords also an immediate explanation
of the characteristic deviations from simple periodicity which are exhibited
by the natural system and are expressed in Fig. 1 by the bracketing of certain
series of elements in the later periods. The first time such a deviation is met
with is in the 4th period, and the reason for it can be simply illustrated by
means of our figure of the orbits of the last electron bound in the atom of
potassium, which is the first element in this period. Indeed, in potassium we
encounter for the first time in the sequence of the elements a case in which
the principal quantum number of the orbit of the last electron bound is, in
the normal state of the atom, larger than in one of the earlier stages of the
binding process. The normal state corresponds here to a 4_1 orbit, which,
because of the penetration into the inner region, corresponds to a much
stronger binding of the electron than a 4-quantum orbit in the hydrogen

atom. The binding in question is indeed even stronger than for a 2-quantum orbit in the hydrogen atom, and is therefore more than twice as strong as in the circular 3_3 orbit which is situated completely outside the inner region, and for which the strength of the binding differs but little from that for a 3-quantum orbit in hydrogen.

This will not continue to be true, however, when we consider the binding of the 19th electron in substances of higher atomic number, because of the much smaller relative difference between the field of force outside and inside the region of the first eighteen electrons bound. As is shown by the investigation of the spark spectrum of calcium, the binding of the 19th electron in the 4_1 orbit is here but little stronger than in 3_3 orbits, and as soon as we reach scandium, we must assume that the 3_3 orbit will represent the orbit of the 19th electron in the normal state, since this type of orbit will correspond to a stronger binding than a 4_1 orbit. While the group of electrons in 2-quantum orbits has been entirely completed at the end of the 2nd period, the development that the group of 3-quantum orbits undergoes in the course of the 3rd period can therefore only be described as a provisional completion, and, as shown in the table, this electron group will, in the bracketed elements of the 4th period, undergo a stage of further development in which electrons are added to it in 3-quantum orbits.

This development brings in new features, in that the development of the electron group with 4-quantum orbits comes to a standstill, so to speak, until the 3-quantum group has reached its final closed form. Although we are not yet in a position to account in all details for the steps in the gradual development of the 3-quantum electron group, still we can say that with the help of the quantum theory we see at once why it is in the 4th period of the system of the elements that there occur for the first time successive elements with properties that resemble each other as much as the properties of the *iron group*; indeed, we can even understand why these elements show their well-known paramagnetic properties. Without further reference to the quantum theory, Ladenburg had on a previous occasion already suggested the idea of relating the chemical and magnetic properties of these elements with the development of an inner electron group in the atom.

I will not enter into many more details, but only mention that the peculiarities we meet with in the 5th period are explained in much the same way as those in the 4th period. Thus the properties of the bracketed elements in the 5th period as it appears in the table, depend on a stage in the development of the 4-quantum electron group that is initiated by the entrance in the normal state of electrons in 4_3 orbits. In the 6th period, however, we meet new features. In this period we encounter not only a stage of the development of the electron groups with 5- and 6-quantum orbits, but also the final completion of the development of the 4-quantum electron group, which is initiated by the entrance for the first time of electron orbits of the 4_4 type in the normal state of the atom. This development finds its characteristic expression in the occurrence of the peculiar family of elements in the 6th period, known as the *rare-earths*. These show, as we know, a still greater mutual similarity in their chemical properties than the elements of the iron family. This must be ascribed to the fact that we have here to do with the development of an electron group that lies deeper in the atom. It is of interest to note that the theory can also naturally account for the fact that these elements, which resemble each other in so many ways, still show great differences in their magnetic properties.

The idea that the occurrence of the rare-earths depends on the development of an inner electron group has been put forward from different sides. Thus it is found in the work of Vegard, and at the same time as my own work, it was proposed by Bury in connexion with considerations of the systematic relation between the chemical properties and the grouping of the electrons inside the atom from the point of view of Langmuir's static atomic model. While until now it has not been possible, however, to give any theoretical basis for such a development of an inner group, we see that our extension of the quantum theory provides us with an unforced explanation. Indeed, it is scarcely an exaggeration to say that if the existence of the rare-earths had not been established by direct chemical investigation, the occurrence of a family of elements of this character within the 6th period of the natural system of the elements might have been theoretically predicted.

When we proceed to the 7th period of the system, we meet for the first time with 7-quantum orbits, and we shall expect to find within this period features that are essentially similar to those in the 6th period, in that besides the first stage in the development of the 7-quantum orbits, we must expect to encounter further stages in the development of the group with 6- or 5-quantum orbits. However, it has not been possible directly to confirm this expectation, because only a few elements are known in the beginning of the 7th period. The latter circumstance may be supposed to be intimately connected with the instability of atomic nuclei with large charges, which is expressed in the prevalent radioactivity among elements with high atomic number.

X-ray spectra and atomic constitution

In the discussion of the conceptions of atomic structure we have hitherto placed the emphasis on the formation of the atom by successive capture of electrons. Our picture would, however, be incomplete without some reference to the confirmation of the theory afforded by the study of X-ray spectra. Since the interruption of Moseley's fundamental researches by his untimely death, the study of these spectra has been continued in a most admirable way by Prof. Siegbahn in Lund. On the basis of the large amount of experimental evidence adduced by him and his collaborators, it has been possible recently to give a classification of X-ray spectra that allows an immediate interpretation on the quantum theory. In the first place it has been possible, just as in the case of the optical spectra, to represent the frequency of each of the X-ray lines as the difference between two out of a manifold of spectral terms characteristic of the element in question. Next, a direct connexion with the atomic theory is obtained by the assumption that each of these spectral terms multiplied by Planck's constant is equal to the work which must be done on the atom to remove one of its inner electrons. In fact, the removal of one of the inner electrons from the completed atom may, in accordance with the above considerations on the formation of atoms by capture of electrons, give rise to transition processes by which the place of the electron removed is taken by an electron belonging to one of the more loosely bound electron groups of the atom, with the result that after the transition an electron will be lacking in this latter group.

The X-ray lines may thus be considered as giving evidence of stages in a process by which the atom undergoes a *reorganization* after a disturbance in its interior. According to our views on the stability of the electronic configuration such a disturbance must consist in the removal of electrons from the atom, or at any rate in their transference from normal orbits to orbits of higher quantum numbers than those belonging to completed groups; a circumstance which is clearly illustrated in the characteristic difference between selective absorption in the X-ray region, and that exhibited in the optical region.

The classification of the X-ray spectra, to the achievement of which the above-mentioned work of Sommerfeld and Kossel has contributed materially, has recently made it possible, by means of a closer examination of the manner in which the terms occurring in the X-ray spectra vary with the atomic number, to obtain a very direct test of a number of the theoretical

conclusions as regards the structure of the atom. In Fig. 9 the abscissæ are
the atomic numbers and the ordinates are proportional to the square roots
of the spectral terms, while the symbols K, L, M, N, O, for the individual

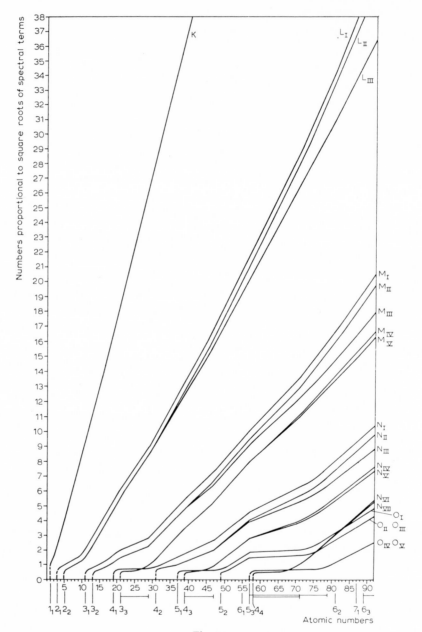

Fig. 10.

terms refer to the characteristic discontinuities in the selective absorption of the elements for X-rays; these were originally found by Barkla before the discovery of the interference of X-rays in crystals had provided a means for the closer investigation of X-ray spectra. Although the curves generally run very uniformly, they exhibit a number of deviations from uniformity which have been especially brought to light by the recent investigation of Coster, who has for some years worked in Siegbahn's laboratory.

These deviations, the existence of which was not discovered until after the publication of the theory of atomic structure discussed above, correspond exactly to what one might expect from this theory. At the foot of the figure the vertical lines indicate where, according to the theory, we should first expect, in the normal state of the atom, the occurrence of n_k orbits of the type designated. We see how it has been possible to connect the occurrence of every spectral term with the presence of an electron moving in an orbit of a definite type, to the removal of which this term is supposed to correspond. That in general there corresponds more than one curve to each type of orbit n_k is due to a complication in the spectra which would lead us too far afield to enter into here, and may be attributed to the deviation from the previously described simple type of motion of the electron arising from the interaction of the different electrons within the same group.

The intervals in the system of the elements, in which a further development of an inner electron group takes place because of the entrance into the normal atom of electron orbits of a certain type, are designated in the figure by the horizontal lines, which are drawn between the vertical lines to which the quantum symbols are affixed. It is clear that such a development of an inner group is everywhere reflected in the curves. Particularly the course of the N- and O-curves may be regarded as a direct indication of that stage in the development of the electron groups with 4-quantum orbits of which the occurrence of the rare-earths bears witness. Although the apparent complete absence of a reflection in the X-ray spectra of the complicated relationships exhibited by most other properties of the elements was the typical and important feature of Moseley's discovery, we can recognize, nevertheless, in the light of the progress of the last years, an intimate connexion between the X-ray spectra and the general relationships between the elements within the natural system.

Before concluding this lecture I should like to mention one further point in which X-ray investigations have been of importance for the test of the theory. This concerns the properties of the hitherto unknown element with

atomic number 72. On this question opinion has been divided in respect to
the conclusions that could be drawn from the relationships within the Periodic Table, and in many representations of the table a place is left open for
this element in the rare-earth family. In Julius Thomsen's representation of
the natural system, however, this hypothetical element was given a position
homologous to titanium and zirconium in much the same way as in our
representation in Fig. 1. Such a relationship must be considered as a necessary consequence of the theory of atomic structure developed above, and is
expressed in the table (Fig. 9) by the fact that the electron configurations for
titanium and zirconium show the same sort of resemblances and differences as
the electron configurations for zirconium and the element with atomic number 72. A corresponding view was proposed by Bury on the basis of his
above-mentioned systematic considerations of the connexion between the
grouping of the electrons in the atom and the properties of the elements.

Recently, however, a communication was published by Dauvillier announcing the observation of some weak lines in the X-ray spectrum of a
preparation containing rare-earths. These were ascribed to an element with
atomic number 72 assumed to be identical with an element of the rare-earth
family, the existence of which in the preparation used had been presumed
by Urbain many years ago. This conclusion would, however, if it could be
maintained, place extraordinarily great, if not unsurmountable, difficulties
in the way of the theory, since it would claim a change in the strength of the
binding of the electrons with the atomic number which seems incompatible
with the conditions of the quantum theory. In these circumstances Dr. Coster
and Prof. Hevesy, who are both for the time working in Copenhagen, took
up a short time ago the problem of testing a preparation of zircon-bearing
minerals by X-ray spectroscopic analysis. These investigators have been able
to establish the existence in the minerals investigated of appreciable quantities
of an element with atomic number 72, the chemical properties of which
show a great similarity to those of zirconium and a decided difference from
those of the rare-earths.*

I hope that I have succeeded in giving a summary of some of the most
important results that have been attained in recent years in the field of atomic
theory, and I should like, in concluding, to add a few general remarks concerning the viewpoint from which these results may be judged, and par-

---

* For the result of the continued work of Coster and Hevesy with the new element,
for which they have proposed the name hafnium, the reader may be referred to their
letters in *Nature* of January 20, February 10 and 24, and April 7.

ticularly concerning the question of how far, with these results, it is possible to speak of an explanation, in the ordinary sense of the word. By a theoretical explanation of natural phenomena we understand in general a classification of the observations of a certain domain with the help of analogies pertaining to other domains of observation, where one presumably has to do with simpler phenomena. The most that one can demand of a theory is that this classification can be pushed so far that it can contribute to the development of the field of observation by the prediction of new phenomena.

When we consider the atomic theory, we are, however, in the peculiar position that there can be no question of an explanation in this last sense, since here we have to do with phenomena which from the very nature of the case are simpler than in any other field of observation, where the phenomena are always conditioned by the combined action of a large number of atoms. We are therefore obliged to be modest in our demands and content ourselves with concepts which are formal in the sense that they do not provide a visual picture of the sort one is accustomed to require of the explanations with which natural philosophy deals. Bearing this in mind I have sought to convey the impression that the results, on the other hand, fulfil, at least in some degree, the expectations that are entertained of any theory; in fact, I have attempted to show how the development of atomic theory has contributed to the classification of extensive fields of observation, and by its predictions has pointed out the way to the completion of this classification. It is scarcely necessary, however, to emphasize that the theory is yet in a very preliminary stage, and many fundamental questions still await solution.

Biography

Niels Henrik David Bohr was born in Copenhagen on October 7, 1885, as the son of Christian Bohr, Professor of Physiology at Copenhagen University, and his wife Ellen, *née* Adler. Niels, together with his younger brother Harald (the future Professor in Mathematics), grew up in an atmosphere most favourable to the development of his genius – his father was an eminent physiologist and was largely responsible for awakening his interest in physics while still at school, his mother came from a family distinguished in the field of education.

After matriculation at the Gammelholm Grammar School in 1903, he entered Copenhagen University where he came under the guidance of Professor C. Christiansen, a profoundly original and highly endowed physicist, and took his Master's degree in Physics in 1909 and his Doctor's degree in 1911.

While still a student, the announcement by the Academy of Sciences in Copenhagen of a prize to be awarded for the solution of a certain scientific problem, caused him to take up an experimental and theoretical investigation of the surface tension by means of oscillating fluid jets. This work, which he carried out in his father's laboratory and for which he received the prize offered (a gold medal), was published in the *Transactions of the Royal Society*, 1908.

Bohr's subsequent studies, however, became more and more theoretical in character, his doctor's disputation being a purely theoretical piece of work on the explanation of the properties of the metals with the aid of the electron theory, which remains to this day a classic on the subject. It was in this work that Bohr was first confronted with the implications of Planck's quantum theory of radiation.

In the autumn of 1911 he made a stay at Cambridge, where he profited by following the experimental work going on in the Cavendish Laboratory under Sir J. J. Thomson's guidance, at the same time as he pursued own theoretical studies. In the spring of 1912 he was at work in Professor Rutherford's laboratory in Manchester, where just in those years such an intensive scientific life and activity prevailed as a consequence of that investigator's fundamental inquiries into the radioactive phenomena. Having there carried out a theoretical piece of work on the absorption of alpha rays which was published in the *Philosophical Magazine*, 1913, he passed on to a study of the structure of atoms on the basis of Rutherford's discovery of the atomic nucleus. By introducing conceptions borrowed from the Quantum Theory as established by Planck, which had gradually come to occupy a prominent position in the science of theoretical physics, he succeeded in working out and presenting a picture of atomic structure that, with later improvements (mainly as a result of Heisenberg's ideas in 1925), still fitly serves as an elucidation of the physical and chemical properties of the elements.

In 1913–1914 Bohr held a Lectureship in Physics at Copenhagen University and in 1914–1916 a similar appointment at the Victoria University in Manchester. In 1916 he was appointed Professor of Theoretical Physics at Copenhagen University, and since 1920 (until his death in 1962) he was at the head of the Institute for Theoretical Physics, established for him at that university.

Recognition of his work on the structure of atoms came with the award of the Nobel Prize for 1922.

Bohr's activities in his Institute were since 1930 more and more directed to research on the constitution of the atomic nuclei, and of their transmutations and disintegrations. In 1936 he pointed out that in nuclear processes the smallness of the region in which interactions take place, as well as the strength of these interactions, justify the transition processes to be described more in a classical way than in the case of atoms (Cf. « Neutron capture and nuclear constitution », *Nature*, 137 (1936) 344).

A liquid drop would, according to this view, give a very good picture of the nucleus. This so-called *liquid droplet theory* permitted the understanding of the mechanism of nuclear fission, when the splitting of uranium was discovered by Hahn and Strassmann, in 1939, and formed the basis of important theoretical studies in this field (among others, by Frisch and Meitner).

Bohr also contributed to the clarification of the problems encountered in quantum physics, in particular by developing the *concept of complementarity*. Hereby he could show how deeply the changes in the field of physics have affected fundamental features of our scientific outlook and how the consequences of this change of attitude reach far beyond the scope of atomic physics and touch upon all domains of human knowledge. These views are discussed in a number of essays, written during the years 1933–1962. They are available in English, collected in two volumes with the title *Atomic Phys-*

ics and Human Knowledge and *Essays 1958–1962 on Atomic Physics and Human Knowledge*, edited by John Wiley and Sons, New York and London, in 1958 and 1963, respectively.

Among Professor Bohr's numerous writings (some 115 publications), three appearing as books in the English language may be mentioned here as embodying his principal thoughts: *The Theory of Spectra and Atomic Constitution*, University Press, Cambridge, 1922/2nd. ed., 1924; *Atomic Theory and the Description of Nature*, University Press, Cambridge, 1934/reprint 1961; *The Unity of Knowledge*, Doubleday & Co., New York, 1955.

During the Nazi occupation of Denmark in World War II, Bohr escaped to Sweden and spent the last two years of the war in England and America, where he became associated with the Atomic Energy Project. In his later years, he devoted his work to the peaceful application of atomic physics and to political problems arising from the development of atomic weapons. In particular, he advocated a development towards full openness between nations. His views are especially set forth in his *Open Letter to the United Nations*, June 9, 1950.

Until the end, Bohr's mind remained alert as ever; during the last few years of his life he had shown keen interest in the new developments of molecular biology. The latest formulation of his thoughts on the problem of Life appeared in his final (unfinished) article, published after his death: «Licht und Leben – noch einmal», *Naturwiss.*, 50 (1963) 725 (in English: «Light and Life revisited», *ICSU Rev.*, 5 (1963) 194).

Niels Bohr was President of the Royal Danish Academy of Sciences, of the Danish Cancer Committee, and Chairman of the Danish Atomic Energy Commission. He was a Foreign Member of the Royal Society (London), the Royal Institution, and Academies in Amsterdam, Berlin, Bologna, Boston, Göttingen, Helsingfors, Budapest, München, Oslo, Paris, Rome, Stockholm, Upsala, Vienna, Washington, Harlem, Moscow, Trondhjem, Halle, Dublin, Liége, and Cracow. He was Doctor, *honoris causa*, of the following universities, colleges, and institutes: *(1923–1939)* – Cambridge, Liverpool, Manchester, Oxford, Copenhagen, Edinburgh, Kiel, Providence, California, Oslo, Birmingham, London; *(1945–1962)* – Sorbonne (Paris), Princeton, Mc. Gill (Montreal), Glasgow, Aberdeen, Athens, Lund, New York, Basel, Aarhus, Macalester (St. Paul), Minnesota, Roosevelt (Chicago, Ill.), Zagreb, Technion (Haifa), Bombay, Calcutta, Warsaw, Brussels, Harvard, Cambridge (Mass.), and Rockefeller (New York).

Professor Bohr was married, in 1912, to Margrethe Nørlund, who was for him an ideal companion. They had six sons, of whom they lost two; the other four have made distinguished careers in various professions – Hans Henrik (M.D.), Erik (chemical engineer), Aage (Ph.D., theoretical physicist, following his father as Director of the Institute for Theoretical Physics), Ernest (lawyer).

Niels Bohr died in Copenhagen on November 18, 1962.

Physics 1923

ROBERT ANDREWS MILLIKAN

*«for his work on the elementary charge of electricity and on the
photoelectric effect»*

Physics 1923

*Presentation Speech by Professor A. Gullstrand, Chairman of the Nobel Com-
mittee for Physics of the Royal Swedish Academy of Sciences*

Your Majesty, Your Royal Highnesses, Ladies and Gentlemen.

The Royal Academy of Sciences has awarded this year's Nobel Prize for Physics to Doctor Robert Andrews Millikan for his work on the elementary charge of electricity and on the photoelectric effect.

We speak of an electric charge when electricity is accumulated on a body, and of an electric current when it spreads along a metallic wire. But when electricity passes through water or water solutions there is no current in the same sense of the word; there is a convection of charges combined with chemical decomposition – electrolysis. Thus water is decomposed into its constituents, hydrogen and oxygen, and metallic silver is deposited from solutions of silver salts. If one and the same current is used to cause these decompositions, the weight of hydrogen liberated in a certain time bears the same ratio to the weight of silver deposited as the atomic weight of hydrogen to the atomic weight of silver, and a current of a given strength in a given time always causes the appearance of a constant quantity of hydrogen and the depositing of a corresponding quantity of silver. As the strength of the current indicates the quantity of electricity passing through the fluids in a given time, it follows that the hydrogen atom and the silver atom carry the same charge, and this charge is what is meant by the unit of electric charge. The same laws hold good for all electrolytic processes, different atoms carrying as many units as are indicated by their valency. The charged atoms are called ions, but this word is used also in a wider signification.

It follows from these laws of electrolysis that it was possible to calculate the unit of electric charge with the same degree of probability with which the number of atoms in a gram of hydrogen could be estimated, and as early as 1874 an approximate value of the unit was arrived at in this way, equalling about two thirds of the exact value now known through the researches of Millikan. The word electron was proposed later as a name for the unit of charge, but now that the discovery of cathode rays has brought to our knowledge free units of negative electricity, an electron means an amount of negative electricity equalling the unit of charge.

Electricity does not pass through gases under normal conditions, but when a gas is exposed to X-rays it acquires the power of transmitting a current. It was soon proved that under the influence of these rays, positive and negative ions are formed, conveying charges of electricity in the same way as in the case of electrolysis. The discovery of radioactive elements provided still more powerful means for such an ionization of gases.

With the methods that were now available it could be shown that the unit of charge of the gas ions was approximately the same as the unit known from electrolysis. Ionization was also observed in monatomic inert gases, which proves that the unit of electric charge is a constituent of the atom that is liberated from it by ionization. Eager attempts were now made to obtain a more exact value for the unit of charge, but the results were not much better than before – until Millikan took up the problem.

Millikan's aim was to prove that electricity really has the atomic structure, which, on the base of theoretical evidence, it was supposed to have. To prove this it was necessary to ascertain, not only that electricity, from whatever source it may come, always appears as a unit of charge or as an exact multiple of units, but also that the unit is not a statistical mean, as, for instance, has of late been shown to be the case with atomic weights. In other words it was necessary to measure the charge of a single ion with such a degree of accuracy as would enable him to ascertain that this charge is always the same, and it was necessary to furnish the same proofs in the case of free electrons. By a brilliant method of investigation and by extraordinarily exact experimental technique Millikan reached his goal.

In his fundamental experiments he had two horizontal metal plates, one a short distance above the other, and by means of a switch he could join them with the poles of a source of high-tension current or short-circuit them. The air between the plates was ionized by radium that could be screened off. There was a minute pin-hole in the middle of the top plate, and over it he had arranged a spray of oil droplets with a radius of about one thousandth of a millimeter. Sooner or later such an oil droplet must fall through the pin-hole and enter the space between the plates, where it was illuminated in such a way that Millikan could see it in a telescope like a bright star on a black background. In the eyepiece of this telescope were placed three cross-hairs, and Millikan measured the time which the droplet required to pass between them. In this way he measured the velocity of fall, which for such small droplets is only a fraction of a millimeter a second. The droplet had been charged with electricity by the frictional process involved in blowing the spray, and when it had fallen down, Millikan switched on the source of current so as to cause the drop to be pulled up by the attraction of the upper plate. The droplet rose, and its velocity was measured during its rise; then the plates were short-circuited, and the drop turned again and began to fall. In this way he kept the drop travelling up and down, many times during several hours, and measured its velocity again and again by means of a stop-watch or, later, a chronoscope. The velocity of fall was constant, but on the way up the velocity varied, which means that the drop had captured one or more of the ions spread in the air between the plates. Now in this experiment the difference of velocity is proportional to the charge captured, and the results showed that the difference of velocity always had the same value or an exact multiple of that value. In other words: the drop had caught one or more units of electrical charge, all exactly equal, however the experiments were varied. In this way the charge of a single ion could be measured in a very large number of cases, and it was determined with an exactitude of one in a thousand.

When the source of current is switched on, the positive ions are driven with a high speed towards the negative plate, and *vice versa*. Thus Millikan only needed to have the droplet near one of the plates at the moment when he switched on the source of current, if he wished to expose it to a shower of positive or negative ions and in this way alter its charge. By this method he proved that the electric charge which the drop had acquired by friction was an exact multiple of the unit.

To give unimpeachable proof Millikan was obliged to make similar experiments with cathode rays and with alpha- and beta-rays and, moreover, to investigate the law of fall of small bodies through gases and the law of their Brownian movements.

Even leaving out of consideration the fact that Millikan has proved by these researches that electricity consists of equal units, his exact evaluation of the unit has done physics an inestimable service, as it enables us to calculate with a higher degree of exactitude a large number of the most important physical constants.

In justifying the reward of Millikan the Academy has not omitted to refer also to his investigations of photoelectric effect. Without going into details I will only state that, if these researches of Millikan had given a different result, the law of Einstein would have been without value, and the theory of Bohr without support. After Millikan's results both were awarded a Nobel Prize for Physics last year.

ROBERT A. MILLIKAN

The electron and the light-quant from the experimental point of view

Nobel Lecture, May 23, 1924

The fact that Science walks forward on two feet, namely theory and experiment, is nowhere better illustrated than in the two fields for slight contributions to which you have done me the great honour of awarding me the Nobel Prize in Physics for the year 1923.

Sometimes it is one foot which is put forward first, sometimes the other, but continuous progress is only made by the use of both – by theorizing and then testing, or by finding new relations in the process of experimenting and then bringing the theoretical foot up and pushing it on beyond, and so on in unending alternations.

The terms of this year's award state that it is given for work on the fundamental electrical unit and on photoelectricity. In both fields my own work has been that of the mere experimentalist whose main motive has been to devise, if possible, certain crucial experiments for testing the validity or invalidity of conceptions advanced by others.

The conception of electrical particles or atoms goes back a hundred and seventy years to Benjamin Franklin who wrote about 1750: « The electrical matter consists of particles extremely subtle since it can permeate common matter, even the densest, with such freedom and ease as not to receive any appreciable resistance. »

This theoretical conception was developed in no little detail by Wilhelm Weber[1] in papers written in 1871. The numerical value of the ultimate electrical unit was first definitely estimated by G. Johnstone Stoney[2] in 1881, and in 1891 this same physicist gave to it the name *the electron**.

---

* It is highly desirable that this historically correct, etymologically most suitable, and authoritatively recognized nomenclature (see among many others Rutherford's Presidential Addresses at the British Association 1923, Nernst's *Theoretical Chemistry*, last edition, etc., etc.) be retained. When used without a prefix or qualifying adjective, the word *electron* may signify, if we wish, as it does in common usage, both the generic thing, the unit charge, and also the negative member of the species, precisely as the word «man» in English denotes both the genus homo and the male of mankind. There is no gain in convenience in replacing «positive electron» by «proton», but on the other hand a distinct loss logically, etymologically, and historically.

In 1897 the experimental foot came forward with J. J. Thomson's and Zeeman's determinations of e/m by two wholly distinct methods. It was these experiments and others like them which in a few years gained nearly universal acceptance among physicists for the electron theory.

There remained, however, some doubters, even among those of scientific credentials, for at least two decades – men who adopted the view that the apparent unitary character of electricity was but a statistical phenomenon; and as for educated people of the non-scientific sort, there exists today among them a very general and a very serious misconception as to the character of the present evidence. A prominent literary writer recently spoke of the electron as « only the latest scientific hypothesis which will in its turn give way to the abra-ca-da-bra of tomorrow ».

It is perhaps not inappropriate then to attempt to review today as precisely as possible a few features of the existing experimental situation and to endeavour to distinguish as sharply as may be between theory and some newly established *facts*.

The most direct and unambiguous proof of the existence of the electron will probably be generally admitted to be found in an experiment which for convenience I will call the oil-drop experiment. But before discussing the significance of that advance I must ask you to bear with me while I give the experimentalist's answer to the very fundamental but very familiar query: « What is electricity? » His answer is naïve, but simple and definite. He admits at once that as to the *ultimate* nature of electricity he knows nothing.

He begins rather with a few simple and familiar experiments and then sets up some definitions which are only descriptions of the experiments and therefore involve no hypothetical elements at all.

He first notes the fact that a pith ball, after contact with a glass rod that has been rubbed with silk, is found to be endowed with the new and striking property that it tends to move away from the rod with a surprisingly strong and easily measurable force. He describes that fact, and affirms at the same time his ignorance of all save the existence of this force, by inventing a new word and saying that the pith ball has been put into a *positively electrified state*, or simply has received a *charge of positive electricity*. He then measures the amount of its charge by the strength of the observed force.

Similarly he finds that the pith ball, after contact with an ebonite rod that has been rubbed with cat's fur is attracted, and he proceeds to describe this experiment by saying that it has now received a *charge of negative electricity*. Whenever the pith ball is found to have been put, by contact with any body

or by any other process, into a condition to behave in either of the foregoing
ways, it has, *by definition*, received a charge of either positive or negative
electricity. The whole of our thinking about electrical matters starts with
these two simple experiments and these two definitions.

In order now to get the most crucial possible test of the correctness or in-
correctness of Franklin's conception of a particle, or an atom, of electricity it
was clearly necessary to reduce the charge on the pith ball to the smallest
possible amount, to change that charge by the most minute possible steps,
and then to see whether the forces acting upon it at a given distance from the
glass rod (i.e. in a constant field) had any tendency to increase or decrease
by *unitary* steps.

The success of the experiments first performed in 1909, was wholly due to
the design of the apparatus, i.e. to the relation of the parts.

The pith ball itself which was to take on the smallest possible charge had
of course to be the smallest spherical body which could be found and yet
which would remain of constant mass; for a continuously changing gravitational force would be indistinguishable, in its effect upon the motion of the
charged body, from a continuously changing electrical charge.

A non-homogeneous or non-spherical body also could not be tolerated;
for the force acting on the pith ball had to be measured by the speed of motion imparted to it by the field, and this force could not be computed from
the speed unless the shape was spherical and the density absolutely constant.
This is why the body chosen to replace the pith ball was an individual oil-
droplet about a thousandth of a millimeter in diameter blown out of an
ordinary atomizer and kept in an atmosphere from which convection currents had been completely removed by suitable thermostatic arrangements.
The glass rod, the purpose of which was to produce a constant electrical
field, was of course replaced by the two metal plates C and D (Fig. 1) of
an air condenser, one of the plates (D) being attached to the positive, the

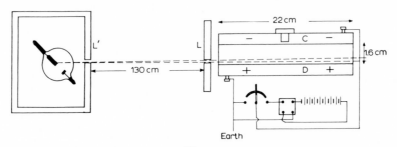

Fig. 1.

other (C) to the negative terminal of a battery, and a switch being added, as shown in the figure, so as to make it possible to throw the field on or off at will.

In order to be able to measure very accurately the force acting upon the charged oil-droplet it was necessary to give it about a centimeter of path in which the speed could be measured. This is one of the most important elements in the design, the overlooking of which has caused some subsequent observers to fall into error. The centimeter of path and the constancy of field then fixed the approximate size of the plates the diameter of which was actually 22 cm. They were placed 16 mm apart.

The field strength too, about 6,000 volts per cm, was vital, and new in work of anything like this kind. It was the element which turned possible failure into success. Indeed, Nature here was very kind. She left only a narrow range of field strengths within which such experiments as these are all possible. They demand that the droplets be large enough so that the Brownian movements are nearly negligible, that they be round and homogeneous, light and non-evaporable, that the distance be long enough to make the timing accurate, and that the field be strong enough to more than balance gravity by its pull on a drop carrying but one or two electrons. Scarcely any other combination of dimensions, field strengths and materials, could have

Table 1.

Time of fall 1.303 cm under gravity (sec)	Time of rise 1.303 cm in field (sec)	Mean times of rise in field (sec)	Divisors for speeds due to field	The electron in terms of a speed
120.8	26.2			
121.0	11.9			
121.2	16.5	67.73	1	3.007
120.1	16.3	26.40	2	3.009
120.2	26.4	16.50	3	2.993
119.8	67.4	11.90	4	3.008
120.1	26.6			
—	16.6			
120.2	16.6	Mean time		
—	16.4	of fall under		
120.2	68.0	gravity		
119.9	67.8	120.35		
—	26.4			

yielded the results obtained. Had the electronic charge been one-tenth its actual size, or the sparking potential in air a tenth of what it is, no such experimental facts as are here presented would ever have been seen.

The observations which gave an unambiguous answer to the questions as to the atomic nature of electricity consisted in putting a charge upon the drop, in general by the frictional process involved in blowing the spray, letting the charged drop drift through a pin-hole in the center of plate C into the space between C and D, and then in changing its charge in a considerable number of different ways; for example, by ionizing the air just beneath it by alpha, beta, or gamma rays from radium and letting the field throw these ions into the drop; by illuminating the surface of the drop itself with ultraviolet light; by shooting X-rays both directly at it and beneath it, etc. The results of those changes in charge in a constant field, as is now well-known, and as is shown in particular cases in the accompanying Table 1, were

(1) that it was found possible to discharge the droplet completely so that within the limits of observational error – a small fraction of one per cent – *it fell its centimeter under gravity, when the 6,000 volt electrical field was on, in precisely the same time required to fall the same distance when there was no field;*

(2) that it could become endowed with a particular speed in the electrical field (corresponding to 67.7 sec in the particular case shown), which *could be reproduced as often as desired, but which was the smallest speed that the given field ever communicated to it* – nor was this change in speed due to the capture of an electron a small one, difficult to observe and measure. It was often larger than the speed due to gravity itself and represented, as in this case shown, a reversal in *direction* so that it was striking and unmistakable;

(3) that *speeds exactly two times, three times, four times, five times, etc.* (always within the limits of observational error – still less than a percent) *could be communicated to the droplet, but never any fraction of these speeds.*

He who has seen that experiment, and hundreds of investigators have observed it, has literally *seen* the electron. For he has measured (in terms of a speed) the smallest of the electrical forces which a given electrical field ever exerts upon the pith ball with which he is working and with the aid of whose movements he defines electricity itself. Further, he has found that that something which he has chosen to call electricity may be placed upon or removed from his pith ball only in quantities which cause the force acting upon it either to drop to zero, or else to go up by definite integral multiples of the smallest observed force.

If a man had seen a football which someone told him was the electron he would be far less certain that what he had seen corresponded to reality, than is the man who has become familiar with the foregoing experiment. *By its aid he can count the number of electrons in a given small electrical charge with exactly as much certainty as he can attain in counting his fingers and his toes.* It is true that when he has counted up to 200 electrons in a given charge, his observational error begins to make it impossible to distinguish between 200 and 201; so that the conclusion that large electrical charges are built up in the same manner as are the charges that he can count is of course in the nature of a generalization, but obviously not one of much uncertainty.

But the electron itself, which man has measured, as in the case shown in the table, is neither an uncertainty nor an hypothesis. It is a new experimental fact that this generation in which we live has for the first time seen, but which anyone who wills may henceforth see.

The measurement of the electron, not as above in terms of the speed that it imparts to a given oil-drop, but in absolute electrostatic units, involved observations of the foregoing sort upon thousands of drops of various sizes, made from a number of different substances, surrounded by a large number of different gases at widely differing pressures, varying from atmospheric down to a millimeter and a half of mercury.

It involved also years of work in finding accurate values of gaseous viscosities, and in determining just how « Stokes' law » must be modified to yield the complete law of fall of a particle through a gas at any density whatever.

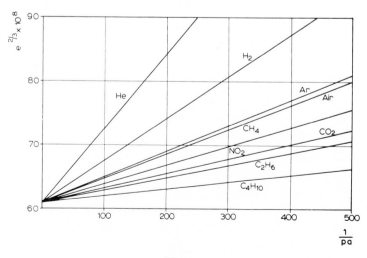

Fig. 2.

But all this is only of interest here in showing, as Fig. 2 does*, *how inevitably all observations on all gases and all substances converge upon the same absolute value of the electron at the intercept on the $e^{\frac{2}{3}}$ axis of the figure.* It is from this intercept that the value of the electron $e = 4.774\,(\pm 0.005) \times 10^{-10}$ absolute electrostatic units is directly obtained.

After ten years of work in other laboratories in checking the methods and the results obtained in connection with the oil-drop investigation published from 1909 to 1923, there is practically universal concurrence upon their correctness, despite the vigorous gauntlet of criticism which they have had to run.

Electrons, of both the positive and negative variety, are then merely observed centers of electrical force, just as was the charged pith ball from which we got our original definition of an electric charge, the difference being that electrons are invariable in their charge while pith-ball charges are built up out of them.

The dimensions of electrons may in general be ignored; i.e. they may both, for practical purposes, be considered as point charges, though, as is well known, the positive has a mass 1,845 times that of the negative. Why this is so no one knows. It is another experimental fact.

It is also well-known that we can now count the exact number of positives and of negatives in every atom; that we can locate all the positives in the nucleus; that we find the negatives scattered partly through the outer regions and partly held within the nucleus; that the number of outer negatives varies from 1 in hydrogen by unit steps up to 92 in uranium, and that the number of negatives in the nucleus is given by the difference between the atomic weight and the atomic number.

Shall we ever find that either positive or negative electrons are divisible? Again no one knows; but we can draw some inferences from the history of the chemical atom. This is sometimes said by the unthinking to have exploded, but of course every scientist knows that it has never lost an iota of its old reality nor of its old vitality. From an experimental point of view the atom of the chemist was all contained in the facts of definite and multiple proportions in combining powers. For the purposes for which the concept was used, viz. those of chemical combination, the chemical atom is just as much the ultimate unit now as it ever has been.

* This is taken from a repetition of my observations in different gases by my assistant Dr. Yoshio Ishida. For similar observations upon different drop-substances, see *The Electron*, rev. ed., University of Chicago Press, 1924.

Similarly it is not likely that the field in which the electron has already been found to be the unit, namely that of atomic structure, will ever have to seek another unit. The new *facts* which this generation has discovered are certainly the permanent heritage of the race. If the electron is ever subdivided it will probably be because man, with new agencies as unlike X-rays and radioactivity as these are unlike chemical forces, opens up still another field where electrons may be split up without losing any of the unitary properties which they have now been found to possess in the relationships in which we have thus far studied them.

The second domain in which, as your award indicates, I have been attempting to take another step, and to assist in bringing the experimental foot up to parallelism at least with the theoretical, is the field of ether waves. In this domain I have been seeking since the year 1904 to find some crucial test for the Thomson-Planck-Einstein conception of localized radiant energy.

This conception in its most general form was introduced by J. J. Thomson[3] in 1903 to account for two newly discovered experimental facts, viz.:

(1) that X-rays pass over all but an exceedingly minute fraction, say one in a billion, of the atoms contained in the space traversed without spending any energy upon them, but here and there find an atom from which they hurl an electron with enormous speed;

(2) that ultraviolet light has the amazing property, discovered by Lenard[4] in 1902, of ejecting electrons from metal surfaces with an energy which is independent of the intensity of the source.

This Thomson semicorpuscular conception of localized radiant energy was taken up in 1905 by Einstein[5] who, by combining it with the facts of quanta discovered by Planck[6] through his analysis of black-body radiation, obtained an equation which should govern, from his viewpoint, the interchange of energy between ether waves and electrons, viz. $\frac{1}{2}mv^2 = h\nu - P$, the first term representing the energy with which the electron escapes, the second term Planck's energy quantum for the particular light employed, and the last the work necessary to get the electron out of the metal.

After ten years of testing and changing and learning and sometimes blundering, all efforts being directed from the first toward the accurate experimental measurement of the energies of emission of photoelectrons, now as a function of temperature, now of wavelength, now of material (contact e.m.f. relations), this work resulted, contrary to my own expectation, in the first direct experimental proof[7] in 1914 of the exact validity, within

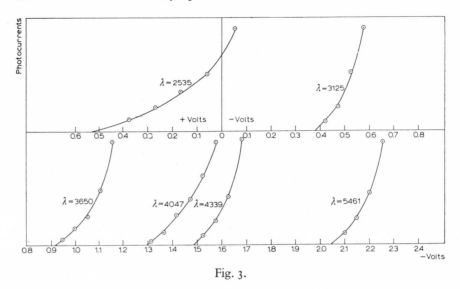

Fig. 3.

narrow limits of experimental error, of the Einstein equation, and the first direct photoelectric determination of Planck's h. The accuracy obtained was about 0.5% which was much the best available at the time. Figs. 3 and 4, which represent the most accurate work done on an individual metal (sodium), will illustrate the entire lack of ambiguity of the result.

This work, like that on the electron, has had to run the gauntlet of severe criticism, for up to 1916 not only was discussion active as to whether there were any limiting velocity of emission, but other observers who had thought that a linear relation existed between energy and frequency had not found the invariable constant h appearing as the ratio. But at the present time it is not too much to say, that the altogether overwhelming proof furnished by the experiments of many different observers, working by different methods in many different laboratories, that Einstein's equation is one of exact validity (always within the present small limits of experimental error) and of very general applicability, is perhaps the most conspicuous achievement of Experimental Physics during the past decade.

A brief historical summary of this advance is as follows: A year or two after the foregoing photoelectric work was completed, Duane[8] and his associates found unambiguous proof of a relation which is just the inverse of Einstein's. They bombarded a metal target with electrons of known and constant energy and found that the maximum frequency of the ether waves (general X-radiation) thereby excited was given, with much precision, by $\frac{1}{2} mv^2 = h\nu$.

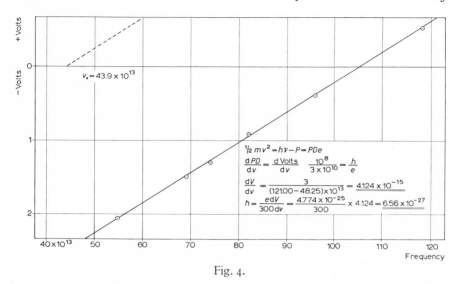

Fig. 4.

D. L. Webster[9] then proved that the characteristic X-ray frequencies of atoms begin to be excited at just the potential at which the energy of the stream of electrons which is bombarding the atoms has reached the value given by $h\nu = \frac{1}{2}mv^2$ in which ν is now the frequency of an absorption edge.

De Broglie[10] and Ellis[11], on the other hand, measured with great precision the speed of electrons ejected from different atomic levels by high-frequency radiations and thus beautifully verified, in this high-frequency field, precisely the same Einstein equation $\frac{1}{2}mv^2 = h\nu - P$ which I had found to hold for ultraviolet and visible frequencies.

Parallel with these developments has come the very full working out of the large field of ionizing and radiating potentials. This has also involved the utilization and verification of the same reciprocal relation between frequency and electronic energy which is stated in the Einstein equation and which constitutes in its inverse form the cornerstone of Bohr's epoch-making treatment of spectral lines. This work all takes its start in Franck and Hertz' fundamental experiments[12], but the field has been most actively and successfully explored since 1916 in America, especially by Foote and Mohler, Wood, Davis and Goucher, McLennan, and others[13].

In view of all these methods and experiments the general validity of Einstein's equation is, I think, now universally conceded, and *to that extent the reality of Einstein's light-quanta may be considered as experimentally established*. But the conception of *localized* light-quanta out of which Einstein got his equation must still be regarded as far from being established. Whether the mechanism of interaction between ether waves and electrons has its seat in the unknown conditions and laws existing within the atom, or is to be looked for primarily in the essentially corpuscular Thomson-Planck-Einstein conception as to the nature of radiant energy is the all-absorbing uncertainty upon the frontiers of modern Physics.

In 1921[14] I thought I had taken another step toward its solution in proving that in the photoelectric process the light energy hv is taken up, not only by electrons within atoms, but also by the free (i.e. the conduction) electrons in metals. For this seemed to take the absorbing mechanism out of the atom entirely and to make the property of imparting the energy hv to an electron, whether free or bound, an intrinsic property of light itself.

But a beautiful discovery by Klein and Rosseland[15] a year later in Bohr's Institute made this conclusion unnecessary. For it showed, as Dr. Epstein first pointed out, that there was an intermediate process, namely a collision of the second kind, by which the energy might be transferred, without loss, *indirectly* from the light wave to the conduction electron, thus obviating the necessity of a *direct* transfer. The act of absorption could still, then, be an atomic process and the absorbed energy be afterward passed on by a collision of the second kind to a free electron. This important discovery then left the evidence for localized light-quanta just where it was before.

Within the past year, however, a young American physicist, Arthur H. Compton[16] of the University of Chicago, by using the conception of localized light-quanta, has brought forward another new phenomenon which at least shows the fecundity of the Einstein hypothesis. Compton goes a step farther than Einstein in that he assumes not only the existence of light-quanta but also that in the impact between a light-quant and a free electron the laws of conservation of energy and of conservation of momentum both hold. This assumption enables him to compute exactly how much the frequency of ether waves which have collided with free electrons will be lowered because of the energy which they have given up to the electron in the act of collision, and therefore the loss which their own hv has experienced. He then finds experimentally that there is approximately the computed lowering in frequency when monochromatic X-rays from molybdenum are scattered by carbon. Further Ross[17] at Stanford University has checked this result by the photographic method.

On account of the fact that Duane and his co-workers at Harvard University could not find a trace of the Compton effect, Messrs. Becker[18], Watson, and Smythe have within a month, at the California Institute at Pasadena, repeated the same type of scattering experiments as those made by Ross, using however aluminium as a scatterer, and *have found on one plate, taken with high resolution, the alpha doublet line of molybdenum shifted as a clearly observable doublet toward longer wavelengths.* Further the amount of the shift was here measurable with an accuracy of about 1% and agreed within this narrow limit with that predicted by Compton's equations. Fig. 5 shows one of these

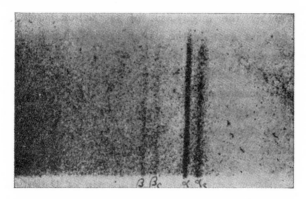

Fig. 5.

new photographs in which both the α and β lines of molybdenum are shifted toward longer wavelengths the correct amount, i.e. to α_c and β_c, through being scattered by aluminium. It may be said then without hesitation that it is not merely the Einstein equation which is having extraordinary success at the moment, but the Einstein conception as well.

But until it can account for the facts of interference and the other effects which have seemed thus far to be irreconcilable with it, we must withhold our full assent. Possibly the recent steps taken by Duane[19], Compton[20], Epstein and Ehrenfest[21] may ultimately bear fruit in bringing even interference under the control of localized light-quanta. But as yet the path is dark.

1. W. Weber, *Werke*, Vol. 4 (1871), p. 281.
2. G. J. Stoney, *Phil. Mag.*, 11 (1881) 384.
3. J. J. Thomson, *Silliman Lectures*, Yale University, 1903.
4. P. E. A. Lenard, *Ann. Physik*, 8 (1902) 149.
5. A. Einstein, *Ann. Physik*, 17 (1905) 132; 20 (1906) 199.
6. M. Planck, *Verhandl. Deut. Phys. Ges.*, Dec. 14 (1900).

7. R. A. Millikan, *Phys. Rev.*, 4 (1914) 73; 6 (1915) 55; 7 (1916) 362.

8. W. Duane *et al.*, *Phys. Rev.*, 6 (1915) 66; 7 (1916) 599; 9 (1917) 568; 10 (1917) 624; *Proc. Natl. Acad. Sci.*, 2 (1916) 90.

9. D. L. Webster, *Proc. Natl. Acad. Sci.*, 3 (1917) 181; 6 (1920) 26, 39.

10. L. de Broglie, paper read before the Third Solvay Congress, 1921.

11. C. D. Ellis, *Proc. Roy. Soc.*, A 99 (1921) 261; C. D. Ellis and H. W. B. Skinner, *ibid.*, A 105 (1924) 165, 185.

12. J. Franck and G. Hertz, *Verhandl. Deut. Phys. Ges.*, 15 and 16 (1914).

13. *Report Photoelectric Conference*, Natl. Research Council, 1921; see also: P. D. Foote and F. L. Mohler, *The Origin of Spectra*, New York, 1922.

14. R. A. Millikan, *Phys. Rev.*, 18 (1921) 236.

15. O. Klein and S. Rosseland, *Z. Physik*, 4 (1921) 46.

16. A. H. Compton, *Phys. Rev.*, 21 (1923) 483; 22 (1923) 409.

17. P. A. Ross, *Proc. Natl. Acad. Sci.*, 9 (1923) 246.

18. J. A. Becker, *Proc. Phys. Soc. (London)*, April 25 (1924); *Phys. Rev.*, 24 (1924) 478.

19. W. Duane, *Proc. Natl. Acad. Sci.*, 9 (1923) 158.

20. A. H. Compton, *ibid.*, 9 (1923) 359.

21. P. S. Epstein and P. Ehrenfest, *ibid.*, 10 (1924) 133.

Biography

Robert Andrews Millikan was born on the 22nd of March, 1868, in Morrison, Ill. (U.S.A.), as the second son of the Reverend Silas Franklin Millikan and Mary Jane Andrews. His grandparents were of the Old New England stock which had come to America before 1750, and were pioneer settlers in the Middle West. He led a rural existence in childhood, attending the Maquoketa High School (Iowa). After working for a short time as a court reporter, he entered Oberlin College (Ohio) in 1886. During his undergraduate course his favourite subjects were Greek and mathematics; but after his graduation in 1891 he took, for two years, a teaching post in elementary physics. It was during this period that he developed his interest in the subject in which he was later to excel. In 1893, after obtaining his mastership in physics, he was appointed Fellow in Physics at Columbia University. He afterwards received his Ph.D. (1895) for research on the polarization of light emitted by incandescent surfaces – using for this purpose molten gold and silver at the U.S. Mint.

On the instigation of his professors, Millikan spent a year (1895–1896) in Germany, at the Universities of Berlin and Göttingen. He returned at the invitation of A. A. Michelson, to become assistant at the newly established Ryerson Laboratory at the University of Chicago (1896). Millikan was an eminent teacher, and passing through the customary grades he became professor at that university in 1910, a post which he retained till 1921. During his early years at Chicago he spent much time preparing textbooks and simplifying the teaching of physics. He was author or co-author of the following books: *A College Course in Physics*, with S. W. Stratton (1898); *Mechanics, Molecular Physics, and Heat* (1902); *The Theory of Optics*, with C. R. Mann – translated from the German (1903); *A First Course in Physics*, with H. G. Gale (1906); *A Laboratory Course in Physics for Secondary Schools*, with H. G. Gale (1907); *Electricity, Sound, and Light*, with J. Mills (1908); *Practical Physics* – revision of *A First Course* (1920); *The Electron* (1917; rev. eds. 1924, 1935).

As a scientist, Millikan made numerous momentous discoveries, chiefly in the fields of electricity, optics, and molecular physics. His earliest major success was the accurate determination of the charge carried by an electron, using the elegant «falling-drop method»; he also proved that this quantity was a constant for all electrons (1910), thus demonstrating the atomic structure of electricity. Next, he verified experimentally Einstein's all-important photoelectric equation, and made the first direct photoelectric determination of Planck's constant h (1912–1915). In addition his studies of the Brownian movements in gases put an end to all opposition to the atomic and kinetic theories of matter. During 1920–1923, Millikan occupied himself with work concerning the hot-spark spectroscopy of the elements (which explored the region of the spectrum between the ultraviolet and X-radiation), thereby extending the ultraviolet spectrum downwards far beyond the then known limit. The discovery of his law of motion of a particle falling towards the earth after entering the earth's atmosphere, together with his other investigations on electrical phenomena, ultimately led him to his significant studies of cosmic radiation (particularly with ionization chambers).

Throughout his life Millikan remained a prolific author, making numerous contributions to scientific journals. He was not only a foremost scientist, but his religious and philosophic nature was evident from his lectures on the reconciliation of science and religion, and from his books: *Science and Life* (1924); *Evolution in Science and Religion* (1927); *Science and the New Civilization* (1930); *Time, Matter, and Values* (1932). Shortly before his death he published *Electrons (+ and —), Protons, Photons, Neutrons, Mesotrons, and Cosmic Rays* (1947; another rev. ed. of *The Electron*, previously mentioned,) and his *Autobiography* (1950).

During World War I, Millikan was Vice-Chairman of the National Research Council, playing a major part in developing anti-submarine and meteorological devices. In 1921, he was appointed Director of the Norman Bridge Laboratory of Physics at the California Institute of Technology, Pasadena; he was also made Chairman of the Executive Council of that institute. In 1946 he retired from this post. Professor Millikan has been President of the American Physical Society, Vice-President of the American Association for the Advancement of Science, and was the American member of the Committee on Intellectual Cooperation of the League of Nations, and the American representative at the International Congress of Physics, known as the Solvay Congress, at Brussels in 1921. He held honorary doctor's degrees of some twenty-five universities, and was a member or honorary member of many learned institutions in his country and abroad. He has been the recipient of the Comstock Prize of the National Academy of Sciences, of the

Edison Medal of the American Institute of Electrical Engineers, of the Hughes Medal of the Royal Society of Great Britain, and of the Nobel Prize for Physics 1923. He was also made Commander of the Legion of Honour, and received the Chinese Order of Jade.

Millikan was an enthusiastic tennis player, and golf was also one of his recreations.

Professor Millikan married Greta Erwin Blanchard in 1902; they had three sons: Clark Blanchard, Glenn Allen, and Max Franklin.

He died on the 19th of December, 1953, in San Marino, California.

Physics 1924

KARL MANNE GEORG SIEGBAHN

«for his discoveries and research in the field of X-ray spectroscopy»

Physics 1924

Presentation Speech by Professor A. Gullstrand, Chairman of the Nobel Committee for Physics of the Royal Swedish Academy of Sciences

Your Majesty, Your Royal Highnesses, Ladies and Gentlemen.

The Royal Academy of Sciences has this year awarded the Nobel Prize for Physics for 1924 to Karl Manne Georg Siegbahn, Professor at the University of Uppsala, for his discoveries and researches in X-ray spectroscopy.

When the Prize for Physics was awarded to Röntgen at the First Nobel Festival, the conception of a spectrum of X-rays could not be set up, or at least could not be supported by experimental evidence. In fact, the domain of the work for which a prize has now been awarded did not yet exist. The assumption that X-radiation, like the radiation long known under the names of light and heat, consisted of transverse electric oscillations, it is true, was advanced by eminent scientists at a comparatively early date; but every attempt to demonstrate any of the phenomena characteristic of such oscillations – such as refraction, polarization or diffraction and interference – yielded results that were negative, or at least not free from ambiguity. The only means of distinguishing different kinds of X-rays was, and remained until later, the penetrative power or what is known as the degree of hardness, which was accessible for physical measurement.

But in the hands of a skilful investigator even this means was sufficient for the discovery of the characteristic X-radiation of the elements. Barkla in Edinburgh found that a series of elements, independently of the chemical composition in which they were used, emitted, in a certain experiment, X-rays of a degree of hardness which was characteristic of the element in question. As he proceeded from element to element with increasing atomic weight, the penetrative power of the characteristic radiation became greater, in other words the X-rays became harder and harder. If the atomic weight was sufficiently high, there appeared a new and much softer characteristic radiation, which in the same way became more and more penetrating the higher the atomic weight possessed by the element investigated. Barkla called these two radiations, by means of which the different elements could thus be distinguished from one another, their K- and L-radiation. These fundamental discoveries, as was soon to be seen, belong already to the domain of X-ray spectroscopy.

After Barkla had also found a kind of polarization of X-rays, it became more and more probable – though this phenomenon did not appear in the same way as the polarization of light – that the two forms of radiation were after all of the same nature, and enough progress had been made to render it possible to estimate the order of magnitude of the wavelength of the X-radiation, if that radiation really were a wave motion.

A spectrum in which every place corresponds to a definite wavelength is obtained by decomposing composite light. If all wavelengths are represented in this light, the spectrum is continuous; if not, the spectrum consists of lines or bands. The decomposition into a spectrum is effected either by refraction in a prism or by diffraction and interference in a grating. As gratings, there are generally used parallel grooves, very close together in a reflecting metal surface, but also gratings that let the light through, decompose it, in which case a spectrum may result both by the passage of the light and by its reflection. The closer together the grooves lie, the more effective is the decomposition and the shorter are the wavelengths that can be investigated. Metal gratings have been employed with great success for the investigation of wavelengths of that order of magnitude that occurs in light; but there seemed to be no prospect of measuring by such means the wavelengths, several thousand times smaller, which, it was estimated, should characterize X-radiation. If, on the other hand, as was assumed in crystallography, a regular arrangement of the atoms or the molecules in a space lattice was the basis of the shapes of the natural crystals, then, according to estimates, the distances of the points of the lattice ought to be exactly of that order of magnitude that was required for the decomposition of X-radiation in a spectrum. If this radiation were essentially a wave motion, therefore, a crystal ought to be a suitable grating for the spectral decomposition of the radiation, whether the X-rays had passed through the crystal or had been reflected in it. But it was only von Laue who drew from this the conclusion that an inquiry ought to be made as to whether such a diffraction and interference could be shown photographically when the X-rays passed through crystals. The experiment showed that this was the case. This epoch-making discovery, which not only bore upon the nature of X-radiation and the reality of the space lattice assumed in crystallography, but also placed a new means of research into the hands of Science, was rewarded with the Nobel Prize for 1914, though its distribution was postponed till the following year.

The new phenomenon could be employed for two different purposes, both for investigations of the crystal lattices and for spectral investigation of the X-radiation itself. It was only natural that precedence was given to the investigations first named, as a fruitful spectroscopical investigation of X-rays presupposed a certain knowledge of the lattice used. Inasmuch as this is a three-dimensional grating, its effect is in essential respects unlike the effect of the previously known line and cross gratings. It was by a stroke, brilliant in its simplicity, that the Englishman W. L. Bragg succeeded in replacing von Laue's comparatively complicated theory of the effect of the crystal lattice by an extremely manageable formula, which could not only be employed to interpret von Laue's photographs obtained by X-rays passing through the crystals, but also enabled his father, W. H. Bragg, to design a real X-ray spectrometer, which was based, like the majority of subsequent designs, on the reflection of radiation. With these means father and son cooperated in investigating the often very complicated structure of the lattices in a number of crystals; and their services were rewarded with the Nobel Prize for Physics of 1915.

The second path through the newly discovered region of X-ray spectroscopy, namely the investigation of X-radiation in the different elements, was trodden with the greatest success by the young scientist Moseley, who was also an Englishman. As the penetrative power of X-radiation increases with the decrease of the wavelength, it was now evident that Barkla's K- and L-rays must represent more or less limited X-ray spectra, which in passing over to elements with a higher atomic weight are displaced in the direction of shorter wavelengths. Now, Moseley investigated these rays by a photographic method and found the former to consist of two, the latter of four, spectral lines. He further discovered the simple mathematical law by means of which the frequencies determined by the position of the lines – and consequently the corresponding wavelengths – can be obtained by what is known as the atomic number, i.e. the number of the element in a series in which all the elements are arranged with a generally increasing atomic weight. As the atomic number has proved to distinguish the elements better than the atomic weight, it has now attained the very greatest importance for atomic physics of the present day. Moseley fell at the Dardanelles before he could be awarded the prize, but his researches had directed attention to the merits of Barkla, who consequently in 1918 was proposed for the Nobel Prize, which was awarded to him without delay.

Siegbahn has won his place in this noble row of eminent investigators by the work for which the Prize has now been awarded to him. It had already become clear that the X-radiation must arise in the inner parts of the atoms, and that consequently exact X-ray spectroscopical investigations form the only means for an experimental research of those parts. Clearly perceiving this fact, Siegbahn has in the course of ten years' assiduous and systematic labour devised a series of improvements and new designs dealing with almost every detail of the various apparatus and so constantly increased the exactitude of his measurements. The method has generally been photographical, and the crystal lattices have been used not only for reflection but also, in the case of shorter wavelengths, for diffraction of rays passing through the crystals. The high level to which he has brought X-ray spectroscopy can perhaps best be defined by the statement that the exactitude with which wavelengths can now be measured by his methods is a thousand times greater than that attained by Moseley. It was only to be expected that these much more accurate means would in his hand be used for a series of new discoveries. Thus to begin with, he has found a large number of new lines in the K- and L-series. Moreover he has made the experimental discovery of a new characteristic X-radiation, the M-series; and another such radiation, the N-series, has been discovered under his guidance. The fact that the existence of these radiations had already been surmised by Barkla in no wise diminishes the scientific value of their discovery and exact measurement.

In order to obtain an idea as to what has been gained by the researches of Siegbahn and his collaborators, it is sufficient to compare Moseley's results, two K- lines and four L- lines, with Siegbahn's statement ten years later. The K- series has been recently subjected to a fresh investigation for 42 elements. For 27 of these all the four main lines have been determined. For the lighter elements there are also special tables of eight fainter lines. The L- series has 28 lines and has been investigated for some 50 elements. The new M- series with 24 lines has been examined for 16 elements, and the N- series, which is also new, has been demonstrated for three of the heaviest elements, whereby five lines belonging to that series have been measured for uranium and thorium.

Siegbahn's work attains the character that is required for the award of the Nobel Prize not only because his methods of measurement provide an implement of hitherto undreamt-of exactitude, apt to further new scientific advances, or because he himself has used them to make a number of new discoveries, but above all owing to the importance for atomic physics that his methods of measurement and discoveries have.

It is obvious to everybody that it will always remain one of the chief goals of physics to gain knowledge of the laws that regulate the energy relations within the atom and the exchange of energy between the atoms and the various forms of radiations. But that goal lay far away as long as no other radiations were known than the electromagnetic oscillations that appear in the form of light, dark heat radiation, or ultraviolet rays, and the analogous oscillations with wavelengths of a higher order of magnitude which are brought about directly by electricity, and which play such a great part in our days. So long as science was restricted to these means of research, there was no such thing as atomic physics. Scientists worked on the assumption that the oscillations were emitted by what are known as dipoles, consisting of two points, one charged with positive electricity and the other with negative electricity, which were bound to one another by an attractive force.

Then came the discovery of the corpuscular radiations, first the cathode rays which, in a sufficiently strong vacuum, proceed from the negative pole of a suitable source of electric current to the positive pole, and which consist of free negative electric units of charge, known as electrons, and then the discovery of radioactive radiation, which, together with an electron radiation and an X-radiation of very short wavelength, contains positively charged corpuscles, known as alpha particles. With these means of research, it soon became evident that the notion of oscillating dipoles could not give a satisfactory picture of the structure of the atom.

Planck, however, even before a better picture had been obtained, had come to the conclusion that, if the electromagnetic theory is correct, it is impossible to obtain a theory of heat radiation agreeing with the facts without introducing the assumption that each dipole can exist only in a discontinuous series of different states of oscillation. The product of the frequency and a hitherto unknown constant, forms a value of energy, known as a quantum, and the dipoles can have no other values of energy than those which consist of an integral number of such quanta. The great importance due to this famous Planck's constant was only made clear through the later development of atomic physics.

A logical consequence of Planck's theory is that a transition from one state to another can only take place in such a way that an integral number of energy quanta is emitted or absorbed. An exchange of energy between matter and radiation, therefore – that is to say an emission or absorption of radiation – can be effected only by the transmission of an integral number of energy quanta. It was not Planck, however, but Einstein, that drew this conclusion, which involves the law of the photoelectric effect – a law that now, especially thanks to Millikan's work, has been verified in a brilliant manner. It is through Einstein's law that the Planck's constant and the whole-quanta theory have attained their greatest importance.

After the electrons had been discovered, and after it had been found that their mass is in round numbers only a two-thousandth part of that of an atom of hydrogen – while the positive unit charge never appears with a mass of such a small order of magnitude – atom models were devised in accordance with this fact. An observation that Rutherford made in the investigation of the paths of alpha particles shot out from radioactive substances, showed that the positively charged parts of an atom must be very small in proportion to the whole atom. According to his view, therefore, the atom consisted of a positive nucleus, surrounded by electrons moving in orbits, in the same way as the sun is surrounded by its planets. Rutherfords' atom model is the proto-type of the one we now have, both in the matter of the distribution of electric charges and also in a much more important respect: it is in conflict with the electromagnetic theory of light.

The fact that this contradiction already existed and apparently could not be removed, provides perhaps a psychological explanation of the fact that someone hit upon the idea of propounding a theory like the one now accepted. It was the young Dane Bohr who carried things to a conclusion and laid down amongst his fundamental postulates that the electrons – in conflict with the current theory – do not radiate energy through their orbital motion. The electrons can only move in so-called stationary orbits, and energy is emitted or absorbed by the passing of an electron from one orbit to another. In accordance with Einstein's law, the exchange of energy between atom and radiation in such cases is always a quantum, forming the product of the frequency of the radiation with the Planck's constant, and the various stationary qualities that the atoms may possess are thus distinguished from one another by amounts of energy that form an integral number of Planck's quanta. This theory, which in the course of its development and accomplishment in the hands of a large number of investigators has attained a high degree of perfection, is supported experimentally by the fact that it is in accordance with important evidence concerning line spectra and the decomposition of spectral lines under the influence of magnetic and electric forces. For the merits thus indicated, both Planck and Einstein on the one hand, and also Bohr on the other, have been awarded the Nobel Prize for Physics.

As the chemical properties of the elements vary periodically with increasing atomic weight, while the characteristic X-radiation shifts continuously from element to element throughout the whole series, regardless of the chemical composition in which the element is used in exciting the radiation, it can be concluded already from Barkla's researches that the X-radiation must arise in the inner parts of the atom. Moseley's researches show again that the atomic number discovered by him in Bohr's atomic theory must give the number of free positive unit charges in the nucleus of the atom, that is to say also the number of electrons that move in the orbits when the atom is electrically neutral. In an element that can emit both K- and L-rays, the former radiation has much shorter wavelengths and consequently greater frequencies than the latter. As the energy quanta are proportional to the frequencies, therefore, the K radiation involves a larger change in the energy of the atom than the L radiation; and in the atomic theory this is as much as to say that an orbit into which an electron falls on emission of a K-line must lie nearer the nucleus than an orbit to which an electron falls on emission of an L-line. In this way it was inferred that there is a K-level nearest the nucleus, outside that an L-level, and after that an M-level and an N-level, all these four being experimentally determined. Further out hypothetical O- and P-levels have been assumed in the atomic scheme.

It is only through a consideration of these results that the importance of the discovery of the M- and N-series is fully realized. The value of Siegbahn's exact measurements and discoveries of new lines is best illustrated by the fact that they have formed the foundation of the work of a number of investigators, through which it has become evident that there are three different L-levels of energy, five M-levels, seven N-levels, and so on. The results of his measurements, in fact, form an immense material which is as yet far from being fully worked out, and which for a long time to come will probably remain the touchstone for future modifications or revolutions in atomic physics.

To this account of the most outstanding features of Siegbahn's work it will suffice to add that, partly alone and partly in collaboration with his pupils, he has made a number of other discoveries in the same subject. These include, for instance, an apparatus with which it is possible, by means of two X-ray exposures each lasting two hours, to make a qualitative analysis of an unknown substance and thereby find out all the elements in the substance extending from sodium with the atomic number 11 to uranium with the atomic number 92. And finally, also the refraction of X-rays in a prism, hitherto sought for with no less zeal than futility, has been demonstrated in his laboratory.

Professor Siegbahn. Once before, a Swede, to the honour of his country, has won world-wide fame through exact determinations of wavelengths. It was Anders Jonas Ångström, who investigated the spectrum of light, and whose name survives as the denomination of the unit with which wavelengths are measured in this range of radiation. I now give expression to the pride of the Academy of Sciences in the fact, that once again a Swede, to the honour of his country, has gained a similar world-wide fame, and to her conviction that your work will always be inscribed in the history of the microcosm of the atom. It is a profound joy to us all that you have won this prize, which I now invite you to receive from the hands of His Majesty the King.

M A N N E   S I E G B A H N

The X-ray spectra and the structure of the atoms

Nobel Lecture, December 11, 1925

We all know that the discovery of X-rays provided the medical sciences with a new and invaluable working tool; and we must all be equally aware that recent developments in the study of X-rays have opened up new paths of investigation in various fields of the natural sciences. One can already point to a whole range of major problems which the use of X-rays has made it possible to solve.

It is obvious that the fact that X-rays are such an important tool for workers in various fields of science forms a very cogent reason for undertaking a thorough investigation of their nature.

It is also clear that, seen from this viewpoint, any investigation of X-radiation must be planned on a broad basis, and cannot be directed solely towards the more or less specialized problems affecting different branches of science.

The study of X-rays is not, however, motivated only by their application in the various sciences such as we have just mentioned. X-rays provide us in addition with an insight into the phenomena within the bounds of the atom. All the information on what goes on in this field of physical phenomena is, so to speak, transmitted in the language of the X-rays; it is a language which we must master if we are to be able to understand and interpret this information properly.

The phrases of the language, in this instance, are made up of electromagnetic waves, and the features of these which we are able to recognize, record, and interpret are in the first place the *wavelength* and *intensity* of this radiation. Experience has taught us that if we concentrate our attention on a particular atom, then a system of waves is emitted from this atom having an entirely fixed composition with respect to the wavelengths involved. These wavelengths are also, in practice, entirely independent of such external circumstances as the chemical or physical forces acting upon the atom concerned. The system of waves is governed solely by the field of force of the atom being studied.

The first task which faces us, if we seek to unlock the mystery of the atom in this way, will therefore be to find some way of measuring and ana-lysing the wave systems emitted by the atoms of the 92 different elements.

I should like, here, to comment on one point. The problem I have just mentioned might well have been insoluble because of utter complexity in the wave system. We have only to remember how, in the field of ordinary optics, certain spectra are composed of tens of thousands of different wave-lengths, and continue to defy all attempts at a preliminary classification. Where the X-radiation from the atom is concerned, however, Nature has been rather more accommodating. Not only are the wave systems peculiar to each type of atom moderately complicated, but also the wave systems belonging to the different atoms show considerable general agreement. This agreement is not, as in normal spectroscopy, confined to the vertical groups of Mendeleev's table, but extends to all elements.

It is noteworthy, therefore, that the general type in which X-ray spectra occur has a far-reaching analogy with precisely the type in the normal spec-tral range which is to be found in the first vertical group in Mendeleev's table, i.e. the alkali spectra.

In order to be able to demonstrate this, I shall have to say a few words on the subject of obtaining an energy diagram from the observed wave system.

Let us assume that at a given moment a certain atom is in such state that its total energy has the value E_1. At that moment a rearrangement occurs within the atom which has the effect of reducing the total energy to E_0. In the course of this process of rearrangement the quantity of energy liberated is therefore:

$$E_1 - E_0$$

We may assume, with Bohr, that this quantity of energy appears in the form of a wave, making up part of the wave system which is characteristic for the atom in question. Its wavelength we may term λ with a corresponding fre-quency ν, and we may define ν as the reciprocal value of λ, thus:

$$\nu = \frac{1}{\lambda}$$

According to the Einstein-Bohr formula there is thus a relationship between the frequency ν_1 for the wave and the energy liberated from the atom:

$$\nu_1 = \frac{E_1 - E_0}{h}$$

where h is a universal constant (Planck's constant).

We can therefore imagine that the energy of the atom during a rearrangement of this nature, is then changed from E_2 to E_0, during which a wave of frequency ν_2 is emitted. Thereby is

$$\nu_2 = \frac{E_2 - E_0}{h}$$

The series can be continued further:

$$\nu_3 = \frac{E_3 - E_0}{h} \text{, and so on.}$$

By measuring the wavelengths it is possible experimentally to determine a series of ν-values: ν_1, ν_2, ν_3, ... It would, however, require a special and not always simple analysis of the wavelengths available in order to select and bring together those frequency values which belong to one and the same series. The first person to succeed, within the field of normal spectroscopy,

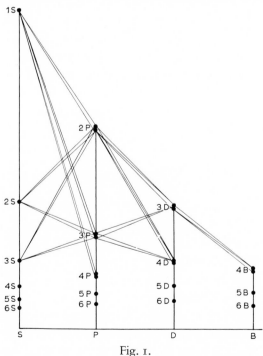

Fig. 1.

in solving this difficult, but for future research fundamental, problem was the Swedish scientist J. R. Rydberg.

Rydberg, namely, found a general formula for the relationship between v-values forming part of the same series, and he made use of this formula to collect the different series for each separate element from the range of wavelengths available.

For the alkali spectra, in particular, Rydberg found three different series, which he termed the principal series, the sharp, and the diffuse secondary series. These three series have since been supplemented, through new measurements, by a further series commonly known as the Bergman series.

If we now apply the Einstein-Bohr formula we can, by using the known v-values, disentangle four series of energy values determined with high exactitude relative to each other. These four energy-level series are usually graphically represented as shown in Fig. 1. For each point, the height above the horizontal base line is a measure of the amount of energy characteristic of the state in question. These four series, each shown on a vertical line, are usually termed the s-, p-, d-, and b-series. From the energy series we come according to the formula

$$v_\mathrm{I} = \frac{E_1 - E_0}{h}$$

back to the frequency series (shown in Fig. 1 by the inclined lines).

What is characteristic for the optical spectra belonging to the first vertical group of Mendeleev's table, i.e. for the alkali spectra, is the fact that of the four energy series, the s-series consists of simple energy levels, while the three remaining series, that is to say the p-, d-, and b-series, are made up of double levels, as will be seen from Fig. 1 which represents the energy and frequency diagram for potassium.

If we now switch from the optical spectra to X-ray spectra, an examination of the combined results of measurements indicates that the X-ray spectra for all elements can be represented by an energy diagram of exactly the same kind as was previously found for the alkali spectra. This diagram is shown in Fig. 2. Apart from the energy levels corresponding to the s-, p-, d-, and b-series (the vertical lines), there are the observed transitions, spectral lines represented by lines linking the two energy levels which correspond to the initial and final state of the atom when the spectral line in question is emitted. It follows from this that the main series in normal optics matches the K-series in the X-ray spectra. The L-series, on the other hand, is put together from the two secondary series in optics and a few other lines of the principal-series type.

The main reason for giving the energy diagram for X-ray spectra in this form is, that by doing so the rules of combination remain identical with those which apply to alkali spectra. In both cases, for instance, transitions occur only between two adjacent vertical series. There are, moreover, no transitions occurring within one and the same vertical series.

There were, additionally, a few very approximative estimates of the intensity of some of the X-ray lines, which seemed to suggest that the analogy not only applied to the rules of combination, but that in the case of intensity conditions as well there existed a certain agreement. If such is the case, then this provides particularly strong support for the diagram we have assumed.

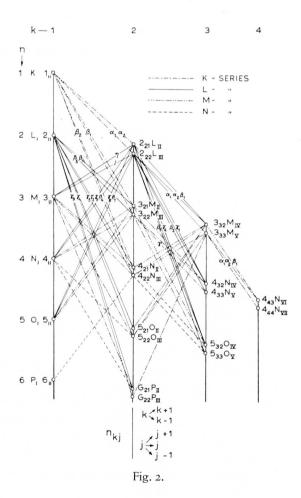

Fig. 2.

In passing judgment on this latter question we can now take into account the results of a study recently carried out by lecturer Axel Jonsson at the Uppsala Institute of Physics. Measurements made hitherto have referred to the X-ray spectra of tungsten and platinum, and they show, with one or two very minor exceptions, a very fine agreement with the intensity conditions in the optical alkali spectra. In some respects, otherwise, this result goes further and deeper than what is the case in the optical field, and the measurements can also be used to get a better insight in the mechanism of radiation itself than has been possible up till now.

If we bring together on the one hand the measurements of wavelength and on the other those of intensity, then we have in them both strong support for the justification of the diagram shown.

What then is the further, deeper reason for the X-ray spectra exhibiting such a far-reaching analogy with the alkali spectra in particular? In fact, the answer is not so difficult to give. An alkali atom consists of an internally completed electron structure of the same type as that of the inert atom next to it, but has in addition a loosely bound valency electron. The optical spectrum is emitted when this loosely bound valency electron moves from one quantum orbit to another. For the X-ray spectra, too, we must assume that light emission takes place when an electron, but in this instance one belonging to the inner electron system of the atom, moves from one quantum orbit to another while the state of all the remaining electrons is not altered to any significant extent.

Quite irrespective of whether the energy diagram should be given this or some other form, X-ray spectroscopy measurements provide us with a quantitative and thorough knowledge of the energy content and energy relationships within each particular atom. Any further work on the structure of the atom must rest upon this firm, empirical foundation.

An energy diagram as complete as that shown in Fig. 2 is, however, only found for the heaviest elements. If we go further down the Mendeleev table towards the lighter elements, one level after the other will stepwise disappear until, when we reach helium and hydrogen, there is only a single energy level. This successive disappearance of the levels is seen in Fig. 3, which shows the diagrams for the inert gases. At the same time the figure shows how the number of X-ray spectrum lines successively decreases, so that for argon, for example, we only find four L-lines apart from the K-series, while there are only two K-lines for neon.

This way of representing the energy diagram for various elements also gives us a good guidance when we have to extrapolate data from the field of X-ray spectroscopy to that of normal optical spectroscopy. It is then clear that only those spectrum systems in the optical field which allow a represen-tation in the form of an alkali diagram can be considered as a continuation of X-ray spectra. The interpretations of line systems in the optical field as a continuation of known X-ray series which are proposed in some cases is contrary to this first, logical requirement.

Otherwise, the comparison of the diagrams indicates that the chances of rediscovering the actual X-ray series in the optical field are greatest for the heaviest elements, where a large number of levels with small differences in energy occur.

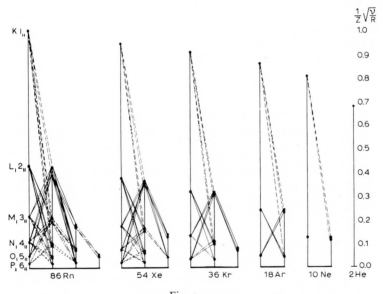

Fig. 3.

We may now ask ourselves whether this diagram of levels is merely a con-venient and clear way of representing the results of observations, or whether the diagram, in this or some similar form, has a deeper significance. Thanks to the fact that we can in many cases determine with considerable accuracy the absolute energy value for a number of levels in the diagram, we are, by means of measurements of wavelength in the line spectrum, in a position to state the absolute energy values for all the levels. This diagram, which has now been given for the majority of the elements, thus supplies fundamental information on the energy state of the atom of each element. These are primary natural constants which are obtained in this manner with the help of X-ray spectroscopy. If we cast our minds back to the work that has, over the years, been devoted to other atomic constants, such as the determination of the atomic weight of the elements, and if we further consider that the atomic weight of most elements is no more than an average value from discontinuously varying group values, and that this is not true of the energy diagram of the elements, then I dare to feel that the efforts which have been directed to finding this energy diagram for the atoms has been fully justified.

This has also, I should like to say, closed the first chapter in the history of X-ray spectroscopy. This work has, however, given rise to new problems which have now to be tackled. Recently, in a lecture to the Swedish Society of Chemists, I drew attention to preliminary studies which are being made in one of these new fields – the matter of the chemical properties of the atoms having an effect upon the phenomenon of X-radiation.

I would like to close this lecture with a short report on a few recent results in another field of study which stems from the X-ray spectroscopy measurement we have been discussing. The very first accurate measurements of X-ray wavelengths using the new precision methods showed us that the accepted law of Bragg was not entirely exact. These experiments, originally carried out by Dr. W. Stenström, were interpreted by him as indicating that X-rays were diffracted when they passed through the surface of the crystal being used as a grating. With the further increases in the accuracy of measurement which have been attained since then, it has become possible employing this method to make extremely accurate quantitative measurements of the refraction of the X-rays in various crystals. The method has also been used in a modified form by a number of American workers. In a letter to the British journal *Nature* about a year ago, E. Hjalmar and I reported on a number of results which seemed to indicate that the refraction in a crystal underwent a discontinuous change when the frequency of the radiation passed the characteristic frequency of the type of atoms making up the crystal. That is to say, we suggested that the experiment must be considered as depending upon an anomalous dispersion.

The analogous phenomenon which has long been known in ordinary optics, where it has been the subject of careful study, has proved to be of fundamental importance for an understanding of the mechanism of radiation itself. It therefore seems to me to be of particular interest to try to find, in the field of X-radiation, some more direct method of obtaining this effect, and perhaps of making quantitative measurements. To this end civil engineer A.

Larsson at the Uppsala Institute of Physics has been making a number of experimental studies using the following method which will give a direct indication of any anomalous dispersion.

A suitably chosen line spectrum is recorded photographically, once with a copper-sulphate crystal and again with a calcium-sulphate crystal. If the spectrum selected is such that it contains spectrum lines on either side of the characteristic radiation frequency of the copper, any anomalous dispersion would betray itself as an irregular shift of the spectrum lines on the plate made with the copper-sulphate crystal compared to the position of the lines on exposure with the other crystal. The results of the exact measurements on the two plates have shown that such is the case. I should add, in conclusion, that the experiment was so arranged as completely to eliminate the differing absorption of radiation on either side of the characteristic frequency of copper.

The demonstration of anomalous dispersion in X-radiation has opened up a new path for further work, a path which seems likely to lead us to new data on one of the most urgent problems of atomic physics today – that of the distribution of electrons within the atom. Only continued experimental work can show how close this path will bring us to our goal.

Biography

Karl Manne Georg Siegbahn was born on the 3rd of December, 1886, at Örebro in Sweden. His father was Nils Reinhold Georg Siegbahn, a station-master of the State Railways, and his mother was Emma Sofia Mathilda Zetterberg.

After receiving a high-school education he entered the University of Lund in 1906, where he obtained his doctor's degree, in 1911, on the thesis « Magnetische Feldmessung ». From 1907 to 1911 he served as Assistant to Professor J. R. Rydberg in the Physics Institute of the University, afterwards he was appointed lecturer and (in 1915) Deputy Professor of Physics. On the death of Rydberg, he was appointed Professor (1920). In 1923 he became Professor of Physics at the University of Uppsala. In 1937 came his appointment as Research Professor of Experimental Physics, at the Royal Swedish Academy of Sciences. When the Physics Department of the Nobel Institute of the Academy came into being, that same year, Siegbahn was made its first Director.

Siegbahn's early work (1908–1912) was concerned with problems of electricity and magnetism.

From 1912 to 1937 his research work was mainly devoted to X-ray spectroscopy. He developed new methods, and designed instruments for this purpose. His improvements and new constructions of air pumps and X-ray tubes enabled a considerable increase of the radiation intensity, and the numerous spectrographs and crystal or linear gratings which he constructed, have resulted in a highly increased accuracy of his measurements. In this way, a large number of new series within the characteristic X-radiations of elements could be discovered. The new precision technique thus developed by Siegbahn led to a practically complete knowledge of the energy and radiation conditions in the electron shells of the atoms, while at the same time a solid empirical foundation was created for the quantum-theoretical interpretation of attendant phenomena. Siegbahn's findings in this field have been summarized by him in his book *Spektroskopie der Röntgenstrahlen*, 1923 (rev. ed., 1931; ed. in English, 1924), a classic in scientific literature. As a measure of the high precision achieved by Siegbahn's spectrographs (which are held at a constant temperature and read, in tenths of seconds, by means of two microscopes mounted diametrically opposite one another on a precision goniometer) may be mentioned the fact that his energy-level values, arrived at thirty years ago, still serve for many purposes.

The research activity in the Institute under Siegbahn's leadership was directed towards problems of nuclear physics. For this purpose a cyclotron was constructed capable of accelerating deuterons of up to 5 to 6 MeV (1939), which was soon to make place for a larger one for deuteron energies of up to 30 MeV. In addition to this, a high-tension generator for 400,000 volts was built, as a provisional measure, during the War (transformed into a plant for 1.5 million volts in 1962). For the purpose of studying the energy and radiation of the different radioactive isotopes an electromagnetic separator has been constructed at the Institute, and several new types of β-spectrographs for various purposes have been designed and built. With these technical resources, and after suitable methods had been developed, a number of important projects for research were taken up. The radiation processes of unstable atomic nuclei and nuclear reactions of various kinds have been studied and exact measurements made of the magnetic properties of atomic nuclei. Other projects tackled by Siegbahn and his staff include the construction of an electron microscope of a new pattern and an automatically working ruling-engine for scratching well-defined gratings (with up to 1,800 lines per mm), especially for X-rays and the extreme ultraviolet field. A large number of young scientists, including many from foreign countries, have taken part in the progressively developed research work to study the atomic nucleus and its radioactive properties.

Siegbahn travelled a great deal and visited practically all important centres of scientific activity in Europe (1908–1922), Canada and the United States (1924–1925), where he, on invitation of the Rockefeller Foundation, gave lectures at the Universities of Columbia, Yale, Harvard, Cornell, Chicago, Berkeley, Pasadena, Montreal, and several other universities. After World War II, he visited the main nuclear research institutes in the U.S.A. during the years 1946 and 1953 (Berkeley, Pasadena, Los Angelos, St. Louis, Chicago, M.I.T. Boston, Brookhaven, Columbia, etc.).

As member of the Commission Internationale des Poids et Mesures (1937) he took part in annual meetings of this Commission in Paris; he was elected honorary member of this Commission when he left his membership (1956). Siegbahn was President of the International Union of Physics, during the period 1938–1947. Other honours, in addition to the Nobel Prize in Physics (1924) awarded to Professor Siegbahn included the Hughes Medal (1934) and the Rumford Medal (1940) from the Royal Society, London; the Duddel Medal from the Physical Society, London (1948). He is honorary doctor in Freiburg (1931), Bukarest (1942), Oslo (1946), Paris (1952) and the Technical Faculty in Stockholm (1957). He is Member of the Royal Society, London and Edinburgh, of the Académie des Sciences, Paris, and of several other academies.

Professor Siegbahn married Karin Högbom in 1914. They have two sons: Bo (b. 1915), at present (1964) Ambassador at Marocco; and Kai (b. 1918), since 1954 Professor of Physics at the University of Uppsala, on the same Chair that his father held during 1923–1937.

Physics 1925

JAMES FRANCK

GUSTAV HERTZ

«for their discovery of the laws governing the impact of an electron upon an atom»

Physics 1925

Presentation Speech by Professor C.W. Oseen, member of the Nobel Committee for Physics of the Royal Swedish Academy of Sciences

Your Majesty, Your Royal Highnesses, Ladies and Gentlemen.

The Physics Nobel Prize for the year 1925 has been awarded to Professor James Franck and Professor Gustav Hertz for their discovery of the laws governing the impact of an electron upon an atom.

The newest and most flourishing branch of the great tree of physical research is atomic physics. When Niels Bohr founded this new science in 1913, the material at his disposal consisted of data concerning the radiation of glowing bodies, which had been accumulated over several decades. One of the earliest findings in the field of spectroscopy was that the light emitted by a glowing gas when observed through a spectroscope, splits up into a large number of different lines, called spectral lines. The fact that simple relationships exist between the wavelengths of these spectral lines, was first discovered by Balmer in 1885 for the hydrogen spectrum, and demonstrated later by Rydberg for a large number of elements. Two questions relating to theoretical physics arose as a result of these discoveries: How is it possible for a single element to produce a large number of different spectral lines? And what is the fundamental reason behind the relationships that exist between the wavelengths of the spectral lines of a single element? A large number of attempts were made to answer these two questions, on the basis of the physics which we are now accustomed to call classical physics. All were in vain. It was only through a radical break with classical physics that Bohr was able to resolve the spectroscopic puzzles in 1913. Bohr's basic hypotheses can be formulated as follows:

Each atom can exist in an unlimited number of different states, the so-called stationary states. Each of these stationary states is characterized by a given energy level. The difference between two such energy levels, divided by Planck's constant h, is the oscillation frequency of a spectral line that can be emitted by the atom. In addition to these basic hypotheses, Bohr also put forward a number of specific hypotheses, with the aid of which it was possible to calculate the spectral lines of the hydrogen atom and the helium ion. The extraordinarily good agreement with experience obtained in this way,

explains why after 1913 almost a whole generation of theoretical and experimental physicists devoted itself to atomic physics and its application in
spectroscopy.

Bohr's more specific assumptions have had the same fate as that which
sooner or later overtakes most physical hypotheses: science outgrew them.
They have become too narrow in relation to all the facts which we now
know. For a year now attempts have been made to solve the puzzle of the
atom in other ways. But the new theory which is now in process of being
established, is yet not a completely new theory. On the contrary, it can be
termed a further development of Bohr's theory, because among other things
in it Bohr's basic assumptions remain completely unchanged. In this over-
throwing of old ideas, when all that has been gained in the field of atomic
physics seemed to be at stake, there is nobody who would have thought it
advisable to proceed from the assumption that the atom can exist in different
states, each of which is characterized by a given energy level, and that these
energy levels govern the spectral lines emitted by the atoms in the way
described. The fact that Bohr's hypotheses of 1913 have succeeded in establishing this, is because they are no longer mere hypotheses but experimentally proved facts. The methods of verifying these hypotheses are the work
of James Franck and Gustav Hertz, for which they have been awarded the
Physics Nobel Prize for 1925.

Franck and Hertz have opened up a new chapter in physics, viz., the theory of collisions of electrons on the one hand, and of atoms, ions, molecules
or groups of molecules on the other. This should not be interpreted as
meaning that Franck and Hertz were the first to ask what happens when an
electron collides with an atom or a molecule, or that they were the orig-
inators of the general method which paved the way for their discoveries and
which consists of the study of the passage of a stream of electrons through
a gas. The pioneer in this field is Lenard. But Franck and Hertz have developed and refined Lenard's method so that it has become a tool for studying
the structure of atoms, ions, molecules and groups of molecules. By means
of this method and not least through the work of Franck and Hertz themselves, a great deal of material has been obtained concerning collisions between electrons and matter of different types. Although this material is important, even more important at the present time is the general finding that
Bohr's hypotheses concerning the different states of the atom and the connexion between these states and radiation, have been shown to agree completely with reality.

Professor Franck. Professor Hertz. Through clear thinking and pain-staking experimental work in a field which is continuously being flooded by different hypotheses, you have provided a firm footing for future research. In gratitude for your work and with sincere good wishes I request you to receive the Physics Nobel Prize for 1925 from the hands of our King.

JAMES FRANCK

Transformations of kinetic energy of free electrons into excitation energy of atoms by impacts

Nobel Lecture, December 11, 1926

Ladies and gentlemen!

The exceptional distinction conferred upon our work on electron impacts by the Royal Swedish Academy of Sciences requires that my friend Hertz and I have the honour of reporting to you on current problems within this province:

The division of the material between us left me with the task of presenting, in a historical setting, the development of these projects which have led to an association with Bohr's atomic theory.

Investigations of collision processes between electrons, atoms and molecules have already got well under way. Practically all investigations into the discharge of electricity through gases can be considered under this heading. An enormous amount of knowledge, decisive for the whole development of modern physics, has been gained, but it is just in this gathering that I feel it is unnecessary for me to make any special comment, since the lists of the men whom the Swedish Academy of Sciences have deemed worthy of the Nobel Prize contain a large number of names of research workers who have made their most significant discoveries in these fields.

Attracted by the complex problems of gas discharges and inspired particularly by the investigations of my distinguished teacher E. Warburg, our interest turned in this direction. A starting-point was provided by the observation that in inert gases (and as found later, also in metal vapour) no negative ions were formed by the attachment of free electrons to an atom. The electrons remained rather as free ones, even if they were moving slowly in a dense gas of this type, which can be inferred from their mobility in an electric field. Even the slightest pollution with normal gases produced, at once, a material attachment of the electrons and thus the appearance of normal negative ions.

As a result, one can perhaps divide gases somewhat more clearly than has been the case up to now from the observations described in the literature, into one class with, and one class without, an electron affinity. It was to be expected that the motion of electrons in gases of the latter kind would obey laws of a particularly simple kind. These gases have exhibited special behaviour during investigations of other kinds into gas discharges. For instance, according to Ramsay and Collie, they have a specially low dielectric strength, and this was, further, extremely dependent upon the degree of purity of the gas (see, for example, Warburg's experiments). The important theory of the dielectric strength of gases, founded by Townsend, the equations of which even today, when used formally, still form the basic foundation of this field failed in these cases. The reason for this seemed likely to be that Townsend's hypothesis on the kind of collisions between slow electrons and atoms, particularly inert-gas atoms, differed from the reality, and it seemed promising to arrive at a kinetic theory of electrons in gases by a systematic examination of the elementary processes occurring when collisions took place between slow electrons and atoms and molecules. We had the experiences and techniques to support us, which men like J. J. Thomson, Stark, Townsend, and in particular, however, Lenard, had created, and also had their concept of the free path-lengths of electrons and the ionization energy, etc., to make use of.

The free path-lengths in the light inert gases were examined first. By «free path» in this connection is to be understood that path which, on the average, is that which an electron traces between two collisions with atoms along a straight track. The distance is measurable as soon as the number of atoms per unit volume is sufficiently small, this being attained by taking a low gas pressure. The method of measurement itself differed but slightly from that developed by Lenard. It is unnecessary to go into closer detail since the results gave the same order of values for the free path-length as Lenard obtained for slow electrons in other gases. The value is of that order which is obtained by calculation if the formulas of the kinetic gas theory are used for the free path-length, taking for the impact radius of the electron a value which is very small compared with the gas-kinetic atom radii. With this assumption, the electrons behave, to a first approximation, like a gaseous impurity in the inert gas, not reacting chemically with it – an impurity, however, which has the special quality of consisting of electrically charged particles and having a vanishingly small impact radius. As a result of significant experiences, we know, today, from the work of Ramsauer and others on the free path-lengths of electrons in heavy inert gases that the picture we had formed at that time was a very rough one, and that for collisions of slow electrons the laws of quantum theory are of far more significance than the mechanical diameter, but as a first approximation for the establishment of the kinetics it suffices. Further, it also sufficed, as it turned out, to gain an understanding of the energy conversion on the occurrence of a collision between the slow electrons and the atoms of the inert gases and metal vapours. Since the mass of the electron is 1800 times smaller than that of the lightest atom we know, the hydrogen atom, the transfer of momentum from the light electron to the heavy atom during customary gas-kinetic collisions, i.e. collisions such as between two elastic balls, must be exceptionally small according to the laws of momentum. A slow electron with a given amount of kinetic energy, meeting an atom at rest, ought to be reflected without practically any energy loss, much the same as a rubber ball against a heavy wall. These elastic collisions can now be pursued by measurements.

I will pass over the detection of the single reflection and mention in more detail a simple experimental arrangement which, by means of an accumulation of collisions, enables us to measure the energy loss which is otherwise too small to measure in one elementary process. The mode of action might well be clear from a schematic layout (Fig. 1).

Fig. 1.

G indicates the electron source. It consists of a tungsten wire, heated to a bright-red glow by an electric current. That such a glowing wire is a source of electrons can, I think, be taken as read in this age of radio. A few centimetres away is a wire-screen electrode N. If we now charge the screen positively with respect to the glowing wire, by means of an accumulator, the electrons emitted by the wire towards the screen will be accelerated. The kinetic energy which the electrons must gain through this acceleration can easily be found for the case where no gas exists between G and N, that is, when the electrons fall through the field of force freely without collisions. We have the relationship:

$$\tfrac{1}{2} mv^2 = e \cdot V$$

Here, $\frac{1}{2}mv^2$ is the kinetic energy of each electron, e is its electrical elementary charge, and V is the applied potential difference. If the latter is measured in volts, then, for instance, the kinetic energy of an electron which has fallen through 10 volts is approximately 10^{-11} ergs. We have become accustomed to speak of x-volt electrons, and to simply denote the acceleration voltage (x volts) as a measure of energy. Thus in our arrangement the electrons fall upon the screen with an energy of x volts (the potential difference between G and N). Some of the electrons are caught by the screen, some fly through the mesh. The latter, assuming no field between N and P which would throw the electrons back, all reach the electrode P and produce a negative current which flows to earth through a galvanometer. By introducing an electric field between N and P the energy distribution of those electrons passing through the screen can be determined. If, for example, we take only 4-volt beams, which pass perpendicularly through the screen, then the electron current measured at the galvanometer as a function of a decelerating potential difference applied between N and P, must be constant, until P becomes 4 volts more negative than N. At this point the current must become suddenly zero since henceforth all electrons will be so repelled from P that they return to N. If now we introduce an inert gas such as helium or a metal vapour between the three electrodes and choose such a pressure as will ensure that the electrons between G and N will make many impacts upon atoms, whilst passing freely through the space between N and P, we can determine, by plotting the energy distribution of the electrons arriving at P, whether the electrons have lost energy by impacts on the atoms. In discussing the resulting current-voltage curve it should be noted that the electrons no longer pass through the screen mesh perpendicularly, but are scattered in all directions due to reflection from the atoms. As a result of this, there is an easily calculable change in shape of the curve, and this holds, too, for uniform kinetic energy of the electrons. From a consideration of the resulting curves it was found that for not too high pressures, particularly for monatomic gases of high atomic weight, the kinetic energy of slow electrons was the same as for those in vacuum under the same acceleration voltage. The gas complicates the trajectory of the electrons in the same way that a ball's trajectory is affected by rolling down a sloping board bedecked with a large number of nails, but the energy (because of the large mass of the atom compared with that of the electron) is practically the same as for conditions of free fall. Only for high pressures, that is, with the occurrence of many thousands of collisions, can the energy loss corresponding to elastic collision be demonstrated.* A calculation of the number of collisions was later carried out by Hertz. Taking this as a basis and evaluating the curves measured for higher pressures accordingly, it emerges that, for example, energy is transferred to a helium atom amounting to $1.2-3.0 \times 10^{-4}$ of the energy of the electron prior to the collision, whilst the calculated value for the mass ratio under conditions of pure mechanical elastic impact is 2.9×10^{-4}. We may therefore, with close approximation to reality, speak of elastic collisions.

For polyatomic gases a significantly greater average energy loss was determined. Using the methods available at that time, it was not possible to distinguish whether this latter effect was contingent upon attachment of the electrons to the molecule, that is, the formation of negative ions, or whether a transfer of the kinetic energy of the striking electrons into vibrational and rotational degrees of freedom of the molecules was taking place. An investigation just carried out in my institute by Mr. Harries shows that the latter elementary process, even though at a low level, does occur, and is important in the explanation of the energy losses.

Can the principles of action found for slow electrons in the case of elastic collisions hold good for higher electron velocities? Apparently not, for the elementary knowledge of gas discharges teaches us that with faster electrons, i.e. with cathode rays, the impacted atoms are excited to luminescence or become ionized. Here, energy of the impacting electrons must be transferred into internal energy of the impacted atoms, the electrons must henceforth collide inelastically and give up greater amounts of energy. The determination of the least amount of energy which an electron must possess in order to ionize an atom was therefore of interest. Measured in volts, this energy is called the ionization voltage. Calculations of this value of energy by Townsend were available for some gases and these were based upon the validity of his assumptions about the course of the elementary action on collision. I mentioned already the reasons for doubting the correctness of these indirectly determined values. A direct method had been given by Lenard, but it gave the same ionization voltage for all gases. Other writers had obtained the same results within the range of measurement. We therefore repeated Lenard's investigations, using the improved pumping techniques which had become available in the meantime, and obtained characteristic, marked differences in values for the various gases. The method used by

---

* It is better to use here the experimental arrangements indicated later by Compton and Benade, Hertz, and others.

Lenard was as follows. Electrons, from a glowing wire, for example, were accelerated by a suitable electric field and allowed to pass through a screen grid into a space in which they suffered collisions with atoms. By means of a strong screening field these particular electrons were prevented from reaching an electrode to which was connected a measuring instrument. Atoms ionized by the impact resulted in the newly formed positive ions being accelerated through the screening field, which repelled the electrons, towards the negatively charged electrode. A positive current was thus obtained as soon as the energy of the electrons was sufficient for ionization to take place. I will talk later about the fact that a positive charge appears if the impacted atoms are excited to emit ultraviolet light, and that, as shown later, the charges measured at that time are to be attributed to this process and not to ionization, as we formerly supposed.

In any case, as already discussed, inelastic collisions were to be expected between electrons and atoms for the characteristic critical voltages appertaining to each kind of atom. And it proved easy to demonstrate this fact with the same apparatus as was used for the work on elastic collisions. Measurement of the energy distribution of the electrons, on increasing the accelerating voltage above the critical value, showed that electrons endowed with the critical translation energy could give up their entire kinetic energy on collision, and that electrons whose energy exceeded the critical by a fraction, likewise gave up the same significant amount of energy, the rest being retained as kinetic energy. A simple modification of the electric circuit diagram of our apparatus produced a significantly sharper measurement of the critical voltage and a visual proof of the discontinuously occurring release of energy from the electrons on collision. The measurement method consisted of measurements of the number of those electrons (possessing markedly different energies from zero after many collisions) as a function of the accelerating voltage.

The graph (Fig. 2) shows the results of measurements of electron current in mercury vapour. In this case, all electrons whose energy is greater than the energy of $\frac{1}{2}$-volt beams were measured. It can be seen that in Hg vapour this partial electron current increases with increasing acceleration, similar to the characteristic of « glow-electron » current in vacuum, until the critical energy stage is reached when the current falls suddenly to almost zero. Since the electrons cannot lose more or less than the critical amount of energy, the cycle begins anew with further increase of voltage. The number of electrons whose velocity is greater than $\frac{1}{2}$ volt, again climbs up until the critical value is

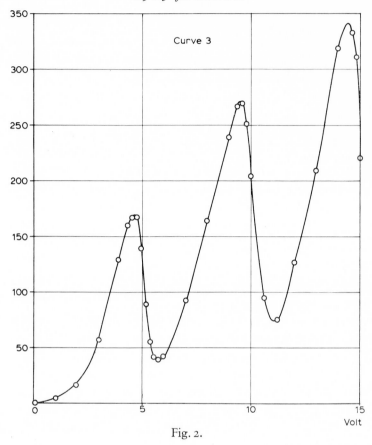

Fig. 2.

reached, the current again falls away. The process repeats itself periodically as soon as the accelerating voltage overreaches a multiple of the critical voltage. The distance between the succeeding maxima gives an exact value of the critical voltage. This is 4.9 V for mercury vapour.

As already mentioned we took this value to be the ionization voltage (the same applied to He which was determined by the same method and was about 20 V). Nevertheless, the quanta-like character of the energy transfer could not help but remind us – who practically from the start could witness from nearby the developments of Planck's quantum theory – to the use of the theory made by Einstein to explain the facts of the photoelectric effect! Since here, light energy is converted into the kinetic energy of electrons, could not perhaps, in our case, kinetic energy from electrons be converted into light energy? If that were the case, it should be easy to prove in the case of mercury; for the equation $\frac{1}{2} mv^2 = h\nu$ referred to a line of 2,537 Å which is easily accessible in the ultraviolet region. This line is the longest wavelength absorption line of Hg vapour. It is often cited as Hg–resonance line since R.W. Wood has carried out with it his important experiments on resonance fluorescence. If the conjectured conversion of kinetic energy into light on impact should take place, then on bombardment with 4.9 eV electrons, the line 2,537 Å, and only this line out of the complete line spectrum of mercury, should appear.

Fig. 3 shows the result of the experiment. Actually, only the 2,537 Å line appears in the spectrogram next to a continuous spectrum in the long-wave region emitted by the red-glowing filament. (The second spectrogram shows the arc spectrum of mercury for comparison.) The first works of Niels Bohr on his atomic theory appeared half a year before the completion of this work. Let us compare, in a few words, the basic hypothesis of this theory with our results.

According to Bohr an atom can absorb as internal energy only discrete quantities of energy, namely those quantities which transfer the atom from one stationary state to another stationary state. If following on energy supply an excited state results from a transfer to a stationary state of higher energy, then the energy so taken up will be radiated in quanta fashion according to the $h\nu$ relationship. The frequency of the absorption line having the longest wavelength, the resonance line, multiplied by Planck's constant, gives the energy required to reach the first state of excitation. These basic concepts agree in very particular with our results. The elastic collisions at low electron velocities show that for these impacts no energy is taken up as inner energy, and the first critical energy step results in just that amount of energy required for the excitation of the longest wave absorption line of Hg. Subse-

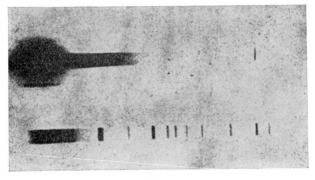

Fig. 3.

quently it appeared to me to be completely incomprehensible that we had failed to recognize the fundamental significance of Bohr's theory, so much so, that
we never even mentioned it once in the relevant paper. It was unfortunate
that we could not rectify our error (due in part to external circumstances)
ourselves by clearing up the still existing uncertainties experimentally. The
proof that only monochromatic light was radiated at the first excitation
step, as Bohr's theory required, and that the gas is not simultaneously ionized (as we were also obliged to think for reasons other than those mentioned) came about instead during the war period through suggestions from
Bohr himself and from van der Bijl. The appearance of positive charge at
the first excitation step in Lenard's arrangement was explained by them on
the basis of a photoelectric effect at the collector electrode, an hypothesis
which was substantiated by Davis and Goucher.

Time does not allow me to describe how our further difficulties were
clarified in the sense of Bohr's theory. And in regard to further development,
too, I would like to devote only a few words, particularly since my friend
Hertz's lecture covers it more closely. The actual ionization voltage of mercury was for the first time determined by Tate as being 10.3 volts, a value
which agreed exceptionally well with that resulting, according to Bohr,
from the limit of the absorption series. A great number of important, ele-
gantly carried out, determinations of the first excitation level and the ionization voltage of many kinds of atoms was made during the war years and
also in the following years, above all by American scientists; research workers such as Foote and Mohler, K. T. Compton and others are to be thanked
for extensive clarification in this field.

Without going into details of the experimental arrangements, I should
like to mention that it later proved successful, by the choice of suitable experimental conditions, to demonstrate also, from the current-voltage curves,
the stepwise excitation of a great number of quantum transitions, lying between the first excitation level and ionization. A curve plotted for mercury
vapour might well serve again as an example. It shows the quantum-like
appearance of higher excitation levels by kinks in the curve (Fig. 4). It is
noteworthy that, in addition, transitions which under the influence of light
according to Bohr's correspondence principle do not appear, manifest themselves clearly. When, as is the case with mercury, and still more decidedly
so with helium, the first transition is such that it cannot be achieved by
light, we have excited atoms in a so-called metastable state. The discovery
of a metastable state by means of the electron-impact method was first suc-

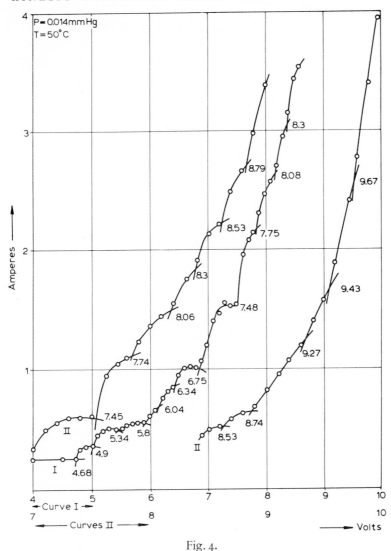

Fig. 4.

cessful with helium. Since helium is a gas in which the absorption series lies in the far ultraviolet−it was later found optically by Lyman−and on the other side, helium, apart from hydrogen, is the most simply constructed atom, the approximate determination of the energy levels of helium and perhaps too, the appearance, in particular, of the metastable level has proved useful for the development of Bohr's theory.

Much more could be said, but I think I have given you the main outline as far as is possible within the framework of a short survey, and must therefore draw to a close. The desire to describe, historically, our part in the development of the investigations leading to the establishment of the quantum transfer of energy to the atom by impacting electrons has forced me to take up your time with the description of many a false trail and roundabout path which we took in a field in which the direct path has now been opened by Bohr's theory. Only later, as we came to have confidence in his leadership, did all difficulties disappear. We know only too well that we owe the wide recognition that our work has received to contact with the great concepts and ideas of M. Planck and particularly of N. Bohr.

Biography

James Franck was born on August 26, 1882, in Hamburg, Germany. After attending the Wilhelm Gymnasium there, he studied mainly chemistry for a year at the University of Heidelberg, and then studied physics at the University of Berlin, where his principal tutors were Emil Warburg and Paul Drude. He received his Ph.D. at Berlin in 1906 under Warburg, and after a short period as an assistant in Frankfurt-am-Main, he returned to Berlin to become assistant to Heinrich Rubens. In 1911, he obtained the « venia legendi» for physics to lecture at the University of Berlin, and remained there until 1918 (with time out for the war in which he was awarded the Iron Cross, first class) as a member of the physics faculty having achieved the rank of associate professor.

After World War I, he was appointed member and Head of the Physics Division in the Kaiser Wilhelm Institute for Physical Chemistry at Berlin-Dahlem, which was at that time under the chairmanship of Fritz Haber. In 1920, Franck became Professor of Experimental Physics and Director of the Second Institute for Experimental Physics at the University of Göttingen. During the period 1920–1933, when Göttingen became an important center for quantum physics, Franck was closely cooperating with Max Born, who then headed the Institute for Theoretical Physics. It was in Göttingen that Franck revealed himself as a highly gifted tutor, gathering around him and inspiring a circle of students and collaborators (among them: Blackett, Condon, Kopfermann, Kroebel, Maier-Leibnitz, Oppenheimer, and Rabinovich, to mention some of them), who in later years were to be renowned in their own fields.

After the Nazi regime assumed power in Germany, Franck and his family moved to Baltimore, U.S.A., where he had been invited to lecture as Speyer Professor at Johns Hopkins University. He then went to Copenhagen, Denmark, as a guest professor for a year. In 1935, he returned to the United States as Professor of Physics at Johns Hopkins University, leaving there in 1938 to accept a professorship in physical chemistry at the University of Chicago. During World War II Franck served as Director of the Chemistry

Division of The Metallurgical Laboratory at the University of Chicago, which was the center of the Manhattan District's Project.

In 1947, at the age of 65, Franck was named professor emeritus at the University of Chicago, but he continued to work at the University as Head of the Photosynthesis Research Group until 1956.

While in Berlin Professor Franck's main field of investigation was the kinetics of electrons, atoms, and molecules. His initial researches dealt with the conduction of electricity through gases (the mobility of ions in gases). Later, together with Hertz, he investigated the behaviour of free electrons in various gases–in particular the inelastic impacts of electrons upon atoms–work which ultimately led to the experimental proof of some of the basic concepts of Bohr's atomic theory, and for which they were awarded the Nobel Prize, for 1925. Franck's other investigations, many of which were carried out with collaborators and students, were also dedicated to problems of atomic physics – those on the exchange of energy of excited atoms (impacts of the second type, photochemical researches), and optical problems connected with elementary processes during chemical reactions.

During his period at Göttingen most of his studies were dedicated to the fluorescence of gases and vapours. In 1925, he proposed a mechanism to explain his observations of the photochemical dissociation of iodine molecules. Electronic transitions from a normal to a higher vibrational state occur so rapidly, he suggested, that the position and momenta of the nuclei undergo no appreciable change in the process. This proposed mechanism was later expanded by E. U. Condon to a theory permitting the prediction of most-favoured vibrational transitions in a band system, and the concept has since been known as the Franck-Condon principle.

Mention should be made of Professor Franck's courage in following what was morally right. He was one of the first who openly demonstrated against the issue of racial laws in Germany, and he resigned from the University of Göttingen in 1933 as a personal protest against the Nazi regime under Adolf Hitler. Later, in his second homeland, his moral courage was again evident when in 1945 (two months before Hiroshima) he joined with a group of atomic scientists in preparing the so-called « Franck Report » to the War Department, urging an open demonstration of the atomic bomb in some uninhabited locality as an alternative to the military decision to use the weapon without warning in the war against Japan. This report, although failing to attain its main objective, still stands as a monument to the rejection by scientists of the use of science in works of destruction.

In addition to the Nobel Prize, Professor Franck received the 1951 Max Planck Medal of the German Physical Society, and he was honoured, in 1953, by the university town of Göttingen, which named him an honorary citizen. In 1955, he received the Rumford Medal of the American Academy of Arts and Sciences for his work on photosynthesis, a subject with which he had become increasingly preoccupied during his years in the United States. In 1964, Professor Franck was elected as a Foreign Member of the Royal Society, London, for his contribution to the understanding of exchanges of energy in electron collisions, to the interpretation of molecular spectra, and to problems of photosynthesis.

Franck was first married (1911) to Ingrid Josefson, of Göteborg, Sweden, and had two daughters, Dagmar and Lisa. Some years after the death of his first wife, he was married (1946) to Hertha Sponer, Professor of Physics at Duke University in Durham, North Carolina (U.S.A.).

Professor Franck died in Germany on May 21, 1964, while visiting in Göttingen.

GUSTAV HERTZ

The results of the electron-impact tests in the light of Bohr's theory of atoms

Nobel Lecture, December 11, 1926

The significance of investigations on the ionization of atoms by electron impact is due to the fact that they have provided a direct experimental proof of the basic assumptions of Bohr's theory of atoms. This lecture will summarize the most important results, and show that they agree in every detail, so far as can be observed at present, with what we should expect on the basis of Bohr's theory.

The fact that atoms are capable of exchanging energy with electromagnetic radiation, led the classical physicists to conclude that atoms must contain moving electrical charges. The oscillations of these charges produce the emission of light radiation, while light absorption was ascribed to forced oscillations of these charges owing to the electrical field of the light waves. On the basis of Lorentz's theory of the normal Zeeman effect, of the magnetic splitting of the spectral lines, it was concluded that these moving charges must be the electrons to which we are acquainted in cathode rays. If only one or several spectral lines were associated with each type of atom, then it might be assumed that the atom contained, for each spectral line, an electron of corresponding characteristic frequency. In reality, however, the number of spectral lines emitted by each atom is infinitely large. The spectral lines are certainly not randomly distributed, on the contrary there exists a certain relationship between their frequencies, but this relationship is such that it is impossible on the basic of classical physics to explain it in terms of the characteristic frequencies of a system of electrons. Here Bohr stepped in with his atomic theory. He applied Planck's quantum theory to the problem of atomic structure and light emission, and thereby greatly extended this theory. It is well-known that Planck, in evolving the law of heat radiation was in contradiction to classical physics. He had come to the conclusion that the processes of emission and absorption of light did not obey the laws of classical mechanics and electrodynamics. In Planck's quantum theory it is assumed that emission and absorption of monochromatic radiation can occur only in an electrical oscillator of the same frequency, moreover that in such processes the energy must be emitted or absorbed in discrete quantities only. According to Planck, the magnitude of such a quantum is proportional to the frequency of the radiation. The proportionality factor is Planck's constant $h = 6.55 \times 10^{-27}$ erg sec, which is fundamental to the entire later development. Bohr realized that the simple picture of emission and absorption by an oscillating electron and hence the connection between the frequency of the light wave and that of the oscillating electron, was inadequate in explaining the laws governing line spectra. But he retained from Planck's theory the basic relationship between the radiation frequency and the magnitude of the emitted and absorbed energy quanta, and based his atomic theory on the following fundamental assumptions:

(1) For every atom there is an infinite number of discrete stationary states, which are characterized by given internal energy levels in which the atom can exist without emitting radiation.

(2) Emission and absorption of radiation are always connected with a transition of the atom from one stationary state to another, emission involving transition to a state of lower energy, and absorption involving transition to a state of higher energy.

(3) The frequency of the radiation emitted or absorbed respectively during such a transition is given by the equation

$$hv = E_1 - E_2$$

where h is Planck's constant and E_1 and E_2 denote the energy of the atom in the two stationary states.

These basic assumptions were supplemented by special theories concerning the nature of the motion of the electrons in the atom, and here Bohr adopted Rutherford's theory that the atom consists of a positive nucleus and of a number of electrons, the total charge of the electrons being equal to the charge of the nucleus. By means of equations also containing Planck's constant, the possible states of motion are determined. These can be considered to be stationary states of the atom. The laws of the motion of the electrons in the atom constituted a major part of Bohr's theory, and in particular have enabled us to calculate the Rydberg constant on the basis of thermal and electrical data, and explain the Periodic System of the elements; however, we need not deal with them in detail here. One fact only is of importance with regard to the electron-impact tests, namely that the set of stationary states of an atom associated with a series spectrum, corresponds to a gradual decrease in binding energy of one of the electrons of an atom. Moreover, the successive stationary states differ by progressively smaller amounts of binding energy of the electron, and converge towards the state of total separation of the electron from the atom.

As an example of series spectra we will now take the simplest case, the spectrum of the hydrogen atom. The frequencies of all the lines in this spectrum can be obtained with great accuracy from the formula

$$\nu = R\left(\frac{1}{m^2} - \frac{1}{n^2}\right)$$

where m and n can represent any integers. Every line is associated with a given value of m, while n ranges over the series of integers from $m + 1$ to ∞. In this way the lines form series; thus, for example, for $m = 2$ we get the well-known Balmer series which is shown diagrammatically in Fig. 1. The characteristic arrangement of the lines, with an accumulation of lines when approaching a given limiting frequency, the so-called series limit, is found in all spectral line series.

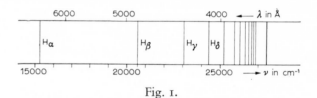

Fig. 1.

In the above formula the frequency of a given spectral line is equated to the difference between two quantities, each of which can assume an infinite series of discrete values. The interpretation of these quantities in the sense of Bohr's theory follows directly from the basic assumptions of this theory: apart from a numerical factor, they are equal to the energy of the atom in its various stationary states. Closer consideration shows that here the energy has to be given a minus sign, i.e. a lower energy is associated with a smaller value of m or n. Thus, the lines of a series correspond to transitions from a series of initial states of higher energy to one final state.

Fig. 2 illustrates diagrammatically the origination of the series associated with the first four stationary states of the hydrogen atom.

In the other elements the situation is in varying degrees more complicated than in the case of hydrogen. All series spectra however have one property in common with that of hydrogen; this is the property represented by the Ritz combination principle, which states that the frequencies of the individu-

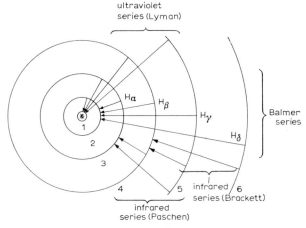

Fig. 2.

al spectral lines are always represented as differences between one or more series of discrete numerical values. These numerical values, the so-called terms, replace the quantities R/n^2 in the case of hydrogen. They differ from these quantities since the formulae representing their values are more complicated, but they agree with these quantities in so far as the differences between the successive terms become smaller and smaller and the term values converge towards zero as the current number n increases.

As an example, Fig. 3 represents diagrammatically the spectrum of mercury. The individual terms are shown by short horizontal lines with the current number at the side of them, and they are arranged in increasing order with the highest term at the top, so that the value of a term can be determined from its distance from the straight line running across the top of the figure. The terms are also presented in the figure in such a way that for a given series they always appear in a column, so that it can be seen how the terms of such a series come closer and closer together as the current number increases, finally converging towards zero. We need not discuss here the reasons for this particular arrangement of the terms. What is important, is that the frequency of every spectral line is equal to the difference between two terms. Thus, a certain combination of two terms is associated with each line. In Fig. 3 some of the lines of the mercury spectrum are indicated by a straight line connecting the two terms with which the line in question is associated. It should be noted that the length of these straight connecting lines is of no physical importance, the frequency of the line depends solely on the difference between the two terms, i.e. the difference between their heights in

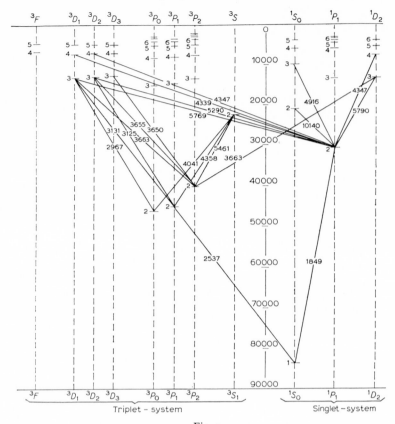

Fig. 3.

Fig. 3. Incidently, the scale included in Fig. 3 gives the terms not in frequencies but in the unit of wave numbers (reciprocal of the wavelength) commonly used in spectroscopy.

In exactly the same way as in the above case of hydrogen, we now come to the interpretation of this diagram by the Bohr theory.

A comparison of the relation between the frequency of a spectral line and the corresponding two terms namely:

$$\nu = T_1 - T_2$$

on the one hand and the Bohr frequency condition namely:

$$h\nu = E_1 - E_2$$

on the other hand, leads to the following equation:

$$T_n = -\frac{E_n}{h}$$

Thus, according to Bohr, the spectral terms denote the energy levels of the atom in the various stationary states, divided by Planck's constant and pre-fixed by a minus sign. The reason why the energy levels are negative here, is simply due to the omission of an arbitrary constant which has always to be added to the energy; here it is omitted because we are simply determining the energy differences. Since in our Fig. 3 the terms are arranged in vertical columns with the highest term at the top, the corresponding energy levels rise from the bottom to the top; hence the term diagram gives a direct indication of the energy levels at which the atom can exist in its stationary states. The minimum level energy is associated with the stationary state of the atom from which further transitions to states of still lower energy are impossible. The term associated with this energy level is called the ground term of the spectrum, and corresponds to the normal state of the atom. In contrast with this normal state, the states richer in energy are called excited states. To lift the atom from its ground state into a given excited state a certain work is required, and this is called the excitation energy. The magnitude of the excitation energy can be found directly from the term diagram, because it must be equal to the energy difference between the ground state and the relevant excited state. If we call the ground term T_0, we obtain the excitation energy to produce the excited state associated with a term T namely:

$$A = h\,(T_0 - T)$$

As a special case we will now consider the excitation energy for producing the state associated with the term $T = 0$. This is the term on which all the term series converge with increasing current numbers. According to Bohr's theory, this term corresponds to the state of the atom in which an electron is completely removed, i.e. the state of the positive ion. The associated excitation energy is the work required to remove an electron, the so-called ionization energy. Thus Bohr's theory requires that the ionization energy of an atom and the ground term of its series spectrum should be simply inter-related by:

$$A_{ioniz} = hT_0$$

The possibility to check this relationship experimentally by means of an electron-impact test follows from Bohr's theory. The identity of the energy difference between the terms of the series spectrum and of the energy of the atom in its various stationary states, leads to the conclusion that the amounts of energy transmitted during collisions between electrons and atoms can be measured directly, and that phenomena which occur when given amounts of energy are imparted to the atom, can be observed. What can we expect on the basis of Bohr's theory, when electrons of a given velocity collide with atoms? If energy is imparted to the atom during such a collision, the result can only be that the atom will be lifted from its ground state to a stationary state of higher energy.

Hence, only given amounts of energy can be transferred to the atom, and each of the possible energy amounts is equal to the excitation energy of a given excited state of the atom. Hence, according to what we have said above, each possible energy amount should be calculable from the associated series term. Among the excited states of an atom, there is always one state for which the excitation energy is a minimum. Thus, the excitation energy associated with this state represents the minimum amount of energy that can be imparted to the atom as a result of an electron impact. So long as the energy of the colliding electron is smaller than this minimum excitation energy, no energy will be transferred to the atom by this collision, which will be a purely elastic one, and the electron will then lose only the extraordinarily small amount of energy which owing to the conservation of momentum takes the form of kinetic energy of the atom. But as soon as the energy of the electron exceeds the minimum excitation energy, some energy will be transmitted from the electron to the atom by the collision, and the atom will be brought into its first excited state. If the energy of the electron rises further, so that it progressively equals and exceeds the excitation energy of higher excited states, the electron will lift the atom into these higher states by the collision, while the energy quantum transmitted will always be equal to the excitation energy of the excited state. If the energy of the electron finally equals the ionization energy, an electron will be removed from the atom by the collision, so that the atom will be left as a positive ion.

In the experimental investigation of these processes a given energy is usually imparted to the electrons by accelerating them by a given voltage. The energy of an electron after the collision is studied by determining the retarding potential which it can still overcome. Therefore, the excitation energy of a given state corresponds to the potential difference through which an electron with zero initial velocity has to fall in order to make its energy equal to the excitation energy of the atom. This excitation potential is thus equal to the excitation energy divided by the charge of the electron. The ionization potential is associated with the ionization energy in the same way. The main object of the electron-impact experiments was the measurement of the excitation and of the ionization potentials. The methods used can be divided into three main groups. Those of the first group are similar to the Lenard method we used in our first tests. They are characterized by the fact that the occurrence of non-elastic collisions of given excitation potentials is studied by investigating electrically the resulting phenomena. The phenomena concerned here are the photoelectric release of electrons by the ultraviolet light produced as a result of excitation collisions, and the positive charging of collector electrodes by positive ions in the case of impacts of electrons with energies above the ionizing potential. The improvement made to this method by Davis and Goucher, which made it possible to distinguish between these two phenomena, was of fundamental importance. This consisted of introducing a second wire gauze within a short distance from the collector plate. To this gauze a small positive or negative potential respectively as compared with the collector plate was applied. When this potential was positive, then the test equipment operated exactly as in the original Lenard method, i.e. the photo-electrons released at the plate were carried away from the plate, while the positive ions produced as a result of ionizing collisions were drawn on to the collector plate. On the other hand, if a negative potential was applied to the wire gauze, the positive charging up of the plate was prevented, since the photo-electrons were returned to the plate by the electrical field. Instead, negative charging of the plate occurred by the photo-electrons released at the wire gauze. Another way of improving the Lenard method consists in arranging the effective collisions between the electrons and the gas molecules in a field-free space, again by introducing a second wire gauze, so that all the collisions occur at a uniform electron velocity. There, the inelastic collisions occur from a given excitation potential onwards far more sharply. In this way it was possible to determine, not only the lowest excitation potentials but also the higher ones, from kinks in the curve representing the photo-electric current released on the plate as a function of the accelerating potential of the electrons.

The methods of the second group follow closely those which we used first in the case of mercury vapour, where we did not study the phenomena caused by the electron impact, but the primary electrons themselves, in order to find out whether or not they lost energy during the collision. In its original form this method is particularly suitable for measuring the first excitation potential of metal vapours. Like the Lenard method, this method was modified in such a way that the electric collisions occurred in a field-free space, i.e. at a uniform electron velocity. Here too it was possible to measure the higher excitation potentials. A special version of this method, which has been found particularly useful in the case of the inert gases, consists of measuring the number of electrons with zero velocity after the collisions. This can be the case only when the energy of the electrons before the collision is exactly equal to the excitation energy of a given stationary state. Hence, a sharply defined peak in the measured curves is obtained for every excitation potential.

Whereas in the first two groups of experimental methods the excitation and ionization potentials were determined by electrical measurements, in the third group of methods we carried out a spectroscopic examination of the light emitted as a result of collisions between electrons and molecules, or so far mostly of collisions between electrons and atoms. The method of observation is that which we used to determine the quantum excitation of the mercury resonance line, and it was refined in exactly the same way as the methods described earlier, by making the collisions take place in a field-free space. Since this method has been used mainly to determine the successive appearance of the individual lines of a spectrum at the corresponding excitations potentials, and not to carry out accurate measurements of excitation potentials, we shall not discuss the results obtained thereby until we have dealt with those obtained with the other methods.

By comparing the values of the excitation and ionization potentials found experimentally, with the values calculated from the series terms, we will now show that extremely good agreement has been obtained in all the cases studied so far. The position is simplest in the case of the alkali metals. Fig. 4 illustrates the series diagram of sodium graphically; the spectra of the other metals of this group are of a similar type. The ground term is the term denoted by $1S$; proceeding from this term to the states of higher energy, we first find two different terms, the energies of which differ very little from each other and which are denoted by 2^2P_1 and 2^2P_2. The transitions of the atom from the stationary states associated with these terms, to the ground state, are connected with the emission of the so-called resonance lines; in the case of sodium these are the two components of the well-known yellow sodium line. They are called resonance lines because an atom that has been excited through absorption of radiation of the frequency of these lines must,

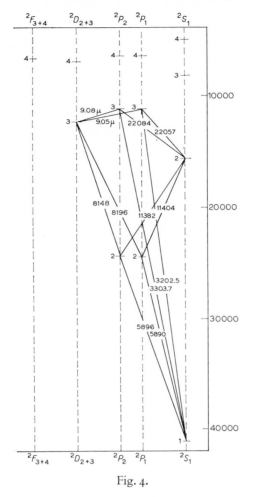

Fig. 4.

on returning to the ground state, emit as radiation of the same frequency, all the energy which it gained by absorption. Hence in relation to the radiation of this frequency, the atom behaves as an electrical oscillator of this characteristic frequency. The first excitation potential V_{exc} of the alkali metals is found, not only as in all the other cases from the difference between the ground term and the next term above it, but, on the basis of Bohr's frequency condition, very simply from the frequency ν_{res} of the resonance line, viz.:

$$V_{exc} \cdot e = h\nu_{res}$$

where e is the charge of the electron. It will be seen from Fig. 4 that for electron impacts leading to this first excitation potential, emission of the resonance lines must take place; hence, the name of resonance potential has been given to this excitation potential of the resonance lines. It should be noted, however, that it is only in the case of the alkali metals that the resonance potential is identical with the first excitation potential. Table 1 compares the spectroscopic data, the data calculated therefrom on the basis of Bohr's theory, and the resonance and ionization potentials observed in electron-impact tests, for the alkali metals. The agreement between the calculated and observed values shows that the conclusions from Bohr's theory are completely verified by the electron-impact tests.

In the case of the metals of the second column of the Periodic Table the spectrum is rather more complicated, because it is made up of two systems, the singlet and the triplet system, as can be seen for example in the diagram of the mercury spectrum shown in Fig. 3. Each of these systems contains a resonance line, in the case of mercury these are the lines 1849 and 2537 Å drawn in the diagram. Here, however, the first excitation potential is not equal to the excitation potential of a resonance line, because there is still another stationary state at a slightly lower energy level than that to which

Table 1.

	Z		ν	λ in Å	Volts	
					Spectroscopic	Electrical
Li	3	$1S$	43484.45		5.368	
		$1S-2P_2$ \} $1S-2P_1$ \}	14903.09	6708.2	1.840	
Na	11	$1S$	41448.59		5.116	5.13[1] 5.18[2]
		$1S-2P_2$	16955.88	5895.9 \}		
		$1S-2P_1$	16973.52	5889.9 \}	2.093	2.12[1] 2.13[2]
K	19	$1S$	35005.88		4.321	4.1[1] 4.41[2]
		$1S-2P_2$	12985.05	7699.1	1.603 \}	1.55[1,2]
		$1S-2P_1$	13042.95	7664.9	1.610 \}	1.63[4]
Rb	37	$1S$	33684.80		4.159	4.1[3]
		$1S-2P_2$	12579.01	7947.6	1.553 \}	1.6[3]
		$1S-2P_1$	12816.72	7800.2	1.582 \}	
Cs	55	$1S$	31406.70		3.877	3.9[3]
		$1S-2P_2$	11178.4	8943.6	1.380 \}	1.48[3]
		$1S-2P_1$	11732.5	8521.2	1.448 \}	

[1] I. T. Tate and P. D. Foote; [2] A. Campetti; [3] P. D. Foote, O. Rognley, and F. L. Mohler; [4] R. C. Williamson.

the atom is excited by absorption of the longer-wave resonance line. Such a state is called metastable by Franck, because an atom which has reached such a state cannot return to the normal state spontaneously through emission. In the case of mercury, where this initial excitation potential is located 0.22 V below the resonance potential, the separation of the two terms can be proved experimentally. In the other metals of this column of the Periodic Table the difference is only a few hundredths of a volt, so that the two terms cannot be distinguished by the electron–impact method. Table 2, which is similar to Table 1, compares the experimental values with the values obtained from the series terms, for the metals of the second column of the Periodic Table.

In addition to metal vapours, the inert gases are suitable for investigation by the electron-impact method, because they too are monatomic and have no electron affinity. Compared with metal vapours, it is of the great advantage that the inert gases can be examined at room temperature, and this is very important for accurate measurements. Since their excitation potentials are greater than those of all other gases, they are highly sensitive to impurities. Another drawback, especially in the case of the heavy inert gases, is due to the fact that the yield of the excitation collisions is far smaller than that of the metal vapours. Hence, the methods that can be used with metal vapours are more or less unsatisfactory in the case of the inert gases. For example, the method of determining the absolute value of the first initial excitation potential from the distance between successive peaks, cannot be used here. This makes it very difficult to find the absolute values of the excitation potentials. The velocity of the impacting electrons does generally not correspond accurately to the applied accelerating potential. Instead, owing to the initial velocity of the electrons, the potential drop along the hot filament, and any Volta potential difference between the hot filament and the other metal parts of the test equipment, a correction has to be made, amounting to a few tenths of a volt. If, as in the case of the metal vapours, the initial excitation potential can be determined by a method in which this error is eliminated, then the correction is known immediately for the other excitation potentials as well. If this is impossible, then an uncertainty arises; this in fact proved to be very troublesome in the first measurement of the excitation potential of helium. It was only after the excitation potentials of helium had been determined accurately by spectroscopic means, that this gas could be used to calibrate the apparatus, i.e. to determine the correction required. In this way, especially after the introduction of the above-mentioned method, it became possible to measure accurately the excitation and ionization potentials of the other inert gases.

Already our first measurements had indicated that the initial excitation potential of helium was about 20 V (at the time we erroneously believed that this was the ionization potential). Later and more accurate measurements by Franck and Knipping confirmed this result, they also showed that the true ionization potential is 4.8 V higher than this. Fig. 5 gives the diagram of the helium spectrum as it was known at the time when these measurement were made. The spectrum consists of two series systems, the terms of which do

Table 2.

Z			ν	λ in Å	Volts	
					Calculated	Observed
Be	4	1^1S				
		1^1S—2^3P_1				
		1^1S—2^1P				
Mg	12	1^1S	61663.0		7.61	7.75[1] 8.0[2]
		1^1S—2^3P_1	21869.5	4571.33	2.70	2.65[1] 2.65[2]
		1^1S—2^1P	35050.3	2852.2	4.32	... 4.42[2]
Ca	20	1^1S	49304.8		6.08	6.01[3]
		1^1S—2^3P_1	15210.1	6572.8	1.88	1.90[3]
		1^1S—2^1P	23652.4	4226.7	2.92	2.85[3]
Sr	38	1^1S	45924.31		5.67	
		1^1S—2^3P_1	14502.9	6892.8	1.79	
		1^1S—2^1P	21697.66	4607.5	2.68	
Ba	56	1^1S	42029.5		5.19	
		1^1S—2^3P_1	12636.6	7911	1.56	
		1^1S—2^1P	18060.2	5535.5	2.23	
Zn	30	1^1S	75758.6		9.35	9.5[4] 9.3[2]
		1^1S—2^3P_1	32500.7	3076.0	4.02	4.1[4] 4.18[2]
		1^1S—2^1P	46743.6	2139.3	5.77	5.65[2]
Cd	48	1^1S	72532.8		8.95	9.0[2] 8.92[5]
		1^1S—2^3P_1	30655.2	3261.2	3.78	3.95[2] 3.88[5]
		1^1S—2^1P	43691.2	2288.8	5.39	5.35[2]
Hg	80	1^1S	84181.5		10.39	10.2[2] 10[6] 10.1[7] 10.8[8] 10.3[9] 10.4[10]
		1^1S—2^3P_1	39412.6	2536.5	4.86	4.9[2]
		1^1S—2^1P	54068.7	1849.5	6.67	6.7[2]

[1] P. D. Foote and F. L. Mohler; [2] F. L. Mohler, P. D. Foote, and W. F. Meggers; [3] F. L. Mohler, P. D. Foote, and H. F. Stimson; [4,5] I. T. Tate and P.D.Foote; [6] F.M. Bishop; [7] C. G. Found; [8] G. Stead and B. S. Gossling; [9] I. T. Tate; [10] B. Davis and F. S. Goucher.

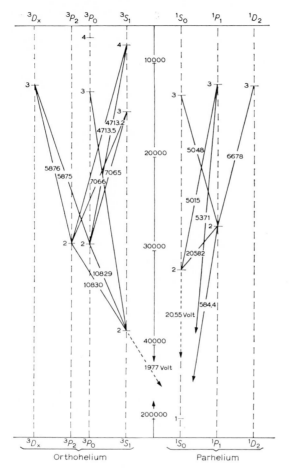

Fig. 5.

not combine with each other. This means that there are two systems of stationary states, having the property that by light emission the atom will always pass from an excited state in one of the two systems, to a state of the very same system. A comparison with the measured values of the excitation and ionization potentials shows immediately that the lowest term of this diagram is not by any means the ground term, though it is the term corresponding to the normal state of the helium atom. This term is not equal to the ionization energy divided by h, but it is equal to the difference between the initial excitation energy and the ionization energy, divided by h. Hence the diagram of helium has to be supplemented by another term, the ground term, which lies about 20 V below the term with the lowest energy of those previously known. The existence of this term was soon demonstrated by Lyman's spectroscopic measurements of the helium spectrum in the extreme ultraviolet region, when its magnitude was also determined accurately. The resulting values of the critical potentials are: for the initial excitation potential 19.77 V, for the ionizing potential 24.5 V. Franck recognized as metastable the first excited state of helium on the basis of Paschen's observation of resonance fluorescence in electrically excited helium, and thus was the first to demonstrate the existence of atoms in the metastable state.

The other inert gases are also very interesting as regards to the verification of Bohr's theory by means of electron-impact tests. Their excitation and ionization potentials were measured at a time when the spectra in the short-wave ultraviolet region which were required for the spectroscopic determination of these critical potentials, were still unknown. Table 3 illustrates the close agreement between the values of the initial excitation potentials and the ionization potentials measured by the electron-impact method, and the values obtained later from measurements in the short-wave spectrum. Because the time here is not available we have to refrain here from discussing other interesting features of the results.

In the third group of tests, i.e. those in which the radiation produced by electron-collisions was studied in relation to the energy of the colliding electrons by spectroscopic methods, the results appeared for some time to contradict Bohr's theory. In fact, our results concerning the mercury resonance line showed that the impact of electrons with energies immediately above the resonance potential excited the mercury atom to emit this line without the appearance of the other lines, and this was confirmed by a study of the corresponding lines of other metals of the second column of the Periodic

Table 3.

	First excitation potential– measured (volts)	Excitation potential of long-wave resonance line– calculated (volts)	Ionizing potential– measured (volts)	Ionizing potential– calculated (volts)
Neon	16.6	16.60	21.5	21.47
Argon	11.5	11.57	15.4	15.7
Krypton	9.9	9.99	13.3	still unknown
Xenon	8.3	8.40	11.5	

Table. These investigations, which were carried out mainly by American workers, also showed that the behaviour of the second resonance line was exactly the same. It will be seen directly from the diagram of the mercury spectrum in Fig. 3 (cf. also Table 2), that this line must also appear, as soon as by an increase of the accelerating potential above the excitation potential of the longer-wave resonance line, the excitation potential of the shorter-wave resonance line is reached. The emitted spectrum now contains only the two resonance lines. In Fig. 6, which shows photographs of the magnesium spectrum obtained from excitation by the impact of electrons of various velocities (taken from a work by Foote, Meggers, and Mohler), these two stages

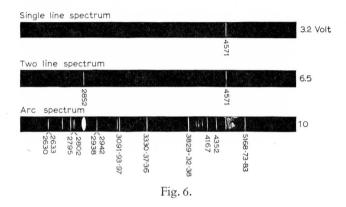

Fig. 6.

are clearly visible. According to Bohr it was be expected that on further rise in the velocity of the impacting electrons the other spectral lines would appear in succession at the excitation potentials calculated from the series diagram. Surprisingly, the tests first gave a different result, namely that the higher-series lines all seemed to appear simultaneously once the ionizing potential was exceeded. But it is the behaviour of these higher-series lines which is of greatest importance for the experimental verification of Bohr's theory. In the case of the resonance lines, which correspond to transitions of the atom from an excited state to the normal state of the atom, the excitation potential is determined by the simple relation $V \cdot e = h\nu$; in relation to the emission of a resonance line, the atom thus behaves like a Planck oscillator having the frequency of this line. It is in fact characteristic for Bohr's theory that in the case of the higher-series lines the excitation potential must be calculated, not from the frequency of the line on the basis of the $h\nu$-relation, but from the series terms in the manner described in detail above. When the tests were

further refined, mainly by eliminating the interference of space charges, the
higher-series lines were also found to behave in the manner predicted according to Bohr's theory. As examples to illustrate this behaviour we present
in Figs. 7 and 8 photographs of the spectra of mercury and helium which
were excited by the impact of slow electrons of various velocities. The
wavelengths of the individual lines are given, together with (in brackets) the
excitation potentials in volts, calculated from the series terms.

   Summarizing therefore, it can be stated that all the results so far attained
with the electron-impact method agree very closely with Bohr's theory and
in particular that they verify experimentally Bohr's interpretation of the
series terms as a measure of the energy of the atom in its various stationary
states. We can hope that further applications of this method of investigation
will provide more material for testing recent developments of the theory. So

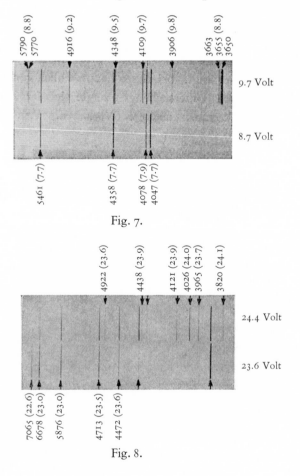

Fig. 7.

Fig. 8.

far the tests are concerned almost exclusively with the amount of energy transmitted by electron-impact. The next important task consists in the measurement of the yield of non-elastic electron-collisions, i.e. of the probability that in a collision between an electron of sufficient velocity and an atom, energy will in fact be transferred. Exploratory tests in this field have already been made, but no definitive conclusions have yet been reached. Naturally such tests will also lead to a closer investigation of the elastic collisions, and to a study of problems of the mean free path, which have become particularly interesting as a result of Ramsauer's measurements, and of many other problems, so that there is ample scope for further experimental work in this field.

Biography

Gustav Ludwig Hertz was born in Hamburg on July 22nd, 1887, the son of a lawyer, Dr. Gustav Hertz, and his wife Auguste, *née* Arning. He attended the Johanneum School in Hamburg before commencing his university education at Göttingen in 1906; he subsequently studied at the Universities of Munich and Berlin, graduating in 1911. He was appointed Research Assistant at the Physics Institute of Berlin University in 1913 but, with the onset of World War I, he was mobilized in 1914 and severely wounded in action in 1915. Hertz returned to Berlin as Privatdozent in 1917. From 1920 to 1925 he worked in the physics laboratory of the Philips Incandescent Lamp Factory at Eindhoven.

In 1925, he was elected Resident Professor and Director of the Physics Institute of the University of Halle, and in 1928 he returned to Berlin as Director of the Physics Institute in the Charlottenburg Technological University. Hertz resigned from this post for political reasons in 1935 to return to industry as director of a research laboratory of the Siemens Company. From 1945 tot 1954 he worked as the head of a research laboratory in the Soviet Union, when he was appointed Professor and Director of the Physics Institute at the Karl Marx University in Leipzig. He was made emeritus in 1961, and since then he has lived in retirement, first in Leipzig and later in Berlin.

Hertz's early researches, for his thesis, involved studies on the infrared absorption of carbon dioxide in relation to pressure and partial pressure. Together with J. Franck he began his studies on electron impact in 1913 and before his mobilization, he spent much patient work on the study and measurement of ionization potentials in various gases. He later demonstrated the quantitative relations between the series of spectral lines and the energy losses of electrons in collision with atoms corresponding to the stationary energy states of the atoms. His results were in perfect agreement with Bohr's theory of atomic structure, which included the application of Planck's quantum theory.

On his return to Berlin in 1928, it was his first task to rebuild the Physics Institute and re-establish the School, and he worked tirelessly towards this end. There he was responsible for a method of separating the isotopes of neon by means of a diffusion cascade.

Hertz has published many papers, alone, with Franck, and with Kloppers, on the quantitative exchange of energy between electrons and atoms, and on the measurement of ionization potentials. He also is the author of some papers concerning the separation of isotopes.

Gustav Hertz is Member of the German Academy of Sciences in Berlin, and Corresponding Member of the Göttingen Academy of Sciences; he is also Honorary Member of the Hungarian Academy of Sciences, Member of the Czechoslovakian Academy of Sciences, and Foreign Member of the Academy of Sciences U.S.S.R. He is recipient of the Max Planck Medal of the German Physical Society.

Professor Hertz was married in 1919, with Ellen *neé* Dihlmann, who died in 1941. They had two sons, both physicists: Dr. Hellmuth Hertz, Professor at the Technical College in Lund, and Dr. Johannes Hertz, working at the Institute for Optics and Spectroscopy of the German Academy of Sciences in Berlin.

Since 1943, Professor Hertz is married with Charlotte, *neé* Jollasse.

Physics 1926

JEAN BAPTISTE PERRIN

«for his work on the discontinuous structure of matter, and especially for his discovery of sedimentation equilibrium»

Physics 1926

Presentation Speech by Professor C.W.Oseen, member of the Nobel Committee for Physics of the Royal Swedish Academy of Sciences

Your Majesty, Your Royal Hignesses, Ladies and Gentlemen.

Nature can be physically explained in two ways. When a group of phenomena is to be understood, we can seek to deduce, on the basis of observations, general laws from which it will be possible to infer concrete phenomena. Or we can proceed from a hypothesis on the structure of matter and seek to explain the phenomena from that. These two methods have been exployed so long as physical research has been carried out.

An example will allow me to show the difference between the phenomenological and the atomistic description of Nature. We all know that air is less dense at the top of a mountain than at ground level. This phenomenon is explained completely by the laws which govern a heavy gas, and there is no reason for not considering the gas as a continuous medium. The problem is herewith solved so far as the phenomenological description is concerned. But for the supporters of the molecular theories the results obtained in this way constitute only a superficial description of the phenomena. For him, a gas evokes the image of a multitude of molecules moving in all directions. Only an explanation which reduces the phenomenon to the laws of molecular movements can be satisfactory to him.

The object of the researches of Professor Jean Perrin which have gained for him the Nobel Prize in Physics for 1926 was to put a definite end to the long struggle regarding the real existence of molecules.

The idea which Professor Perrin pursued in the early stages of his researches was this. If it follows from the laws governing the movements of molecules that in spite of its weight air is not compressed against the surface of the earth, but that it extends–while becoming rarefied, it is true–well above the highest mountains, in that case, and seeing that the movements of molecules obey the same laws as every other minute body, there must be something analogous for every system of small bodies. If a large quantity of sufficiently small and light particles is distributed in a liquid, not all of them should yet settle at the bottom even if they are heavier than the liquid, but they should distribute themselves at different levels according to a law similar to that for the air. Perrin, now, had to realize this experiment.

He had for this purpose to prepare a system of very small particles, all of which, moreover, should have the same weight and the same size. He succeeded herein by using gamboge, a preparation obtained from a vegetable sap and which can be handled like soap. By rubbing the gamboge between his hands under water, Perrin obtained an emulsion which under the microscope proved to consist of a swarm of spherical particles of different size. He then succeeded in obtaining from it an emulsion of particles of the desired dimension and all of equal size. This was by no means an easy operation which is proved by the fact that after several months of accurate and careful work Perrin was able to obtain from one kilogram of gamboge only some decigrams of particles of the desired size. It then became possible to undertake the experiment. The result was as expected. By means of his gamboge emulsion Perrin was able to determine one of the most important physical constants, Avogadro's number, that is to say the number of molecules of a substance in so many grams as indicated by the molecular weight, or to take a special case, the number of molecules in two grams of hydrogen. The value obtained corresponded, within the limits of error, to that given by the kinetic theory of gases. Vast work to verify this, has not shaken the soundness of the method.

It may perhaps be said that in the work which we have just summarized Perrin has offered indirect evidence for the existence of molecules. Here, follows a direct evidence. Microscopic particles in a liquid are never at rest. They are in perpetual movement, even under conditions of perfect external equilibrium, constant temperature, etc. The only irrefutable explanation for this phenomenon ascribes the movements of the particles to shocks produced on them by the molecules of the liquid themselves. A mathematical theory of this phenomenon has been given by Einstein. The first experimental proof of this theory was given by a German physicist, Seddig. After him, the problem was taken up by two scientists simultaneously. One of them was Perrin; the other Svedberg. I have to speak of Perrin only. His measurements on the Brownian movement showed that Einstein's theory was in perfect agreement with reality. Through these measurements a new determination of Avogadro's number was obtained.

The molecular impacts produce not only a forward movement of the particles distributed in a liquid, but also a rotational movement. The theory of this rotation was developed by Einstein. Measurements in relation herewith were carried out by Perrin. In these measurements he has found another method for determining Avogadro's number.

What then is the result of these researches? How many molecules are there in two grams of hydrogen? The three methods have given the following answers to this question: 68.2×10^{22}; 68.8×10^{22}; 65×10^{22}.

Professor Perrin. For more than thirty years you have worked with your head and your hands in the service of atomistic ideas. Please, accept our congratulations on the result that you have achieved. Allow me also to express the happiness which we experience in greeting you as a representative of the glorious sciences of France. I ask you to receive from the hands of our King the Nobel Prize in Physics for 1926.

JEAN PERRIN

Discontinuous structure of matter

Nobel Lecture, December 11, 1926

Since I have the great honour to have to summarize here the work which has enabled me to receive the high international distinction awarded by the Swedish Academy of Sciences, I shall speak of the «discontinuous structure of matter».

Introduction

A fluid such as air or water seems to us at first glance to be perfectly homogeneous and continuous; we can put more water or less water into this glass, and the experiment seems to suggest to us that the amount of water contained in it can vary by an infinitely small amount, which is the same as saying that water is «indefinitely divisible». Similarly, a sphere of glass or of quartz, a crystal of alum, are received by our senses as being perfectly continuous, and particularly when we see this alum crystal growing in a supersaturated solution, each of the planes bounding the crystal moves parallel to itself in a continuous manner.

However, this can be taken for granted only up to the degree of subtlety reached by the resolving power of our senses which, for example, would certainly be unable to distinguish between two positions of the crystal face one millionth of a millimetre apart. Beyond the things which our senses separate in this manner, our imagination remains free, and ever since ancient times, just as the philosophers who started from the « full » or the « void », has hesitated between two hypotheses.

For the former, matter remains continuous: « full », not only (as is reasonable and probable) a little beyond this domain on our scale where our senses make it appear as such, but indefinitely.

For the latter, who were the first atomists, all matter consists of minute grains separated by empty gaps; not any hypothesis has been formulated for the structure of these grains themselves, *atoms*, which were considered as indestructible constituent elements of the Universe.

Lastly, and doubtless always, but particularly at the end of the last century, certain scholars considered that since the appearances on our scale were finally the only important ones for us, there was no point in seeking what might exist in an inaccessible domain. I find it very difficult to understand this point of view since what is inaccessible today may becomes accessible tomorrow (as has happened by the invention of the microscope), and also because coherent assumptions on what is still invisible may increase our understanding of the visible.

Indeed, increasingly numerous and strong reasons have come to support a growing probability, and it can finally be said the certainty, in favour of the hypothesis of the atomists.

There is, first of all, the familiar observation of solutions; we all say, for example, that sugar and water are present in sugar water, although it is impossible to distinguish the different parts in it. And similarly, we *recognize* quite simply bromine in chloroform. This can be understood if the bromine and the chloroform are formed respectively by very small particles in continuous movement which can intermingle with one another without losing their individuality. Those elementary constituent particles, those *molecules*, are probably of the same kind, like articles made in series, for each *pure substance* (defined by its resistance to the fractionation test) or even more surely for each definite *chemical species* (experiment proves that it is never necessary to consider a continuous sequence of chemical species), and we come to formulate the molecular hypothesis by saying that for a sufficient magnification any fluid appears to us as formed by molecules in continuous movement which impinge ceaselessly upon one another, and of which there are as many distinct varieties as chemical species can be recognized in the fluid under consideration.

These molecules which exist in the mixtures are not indestructible since they must disappear (or appear) when a chemical reaction causes the chemical species which they constitute to disappear (or appear); when a mixture of hydrogen and oxygen explodes to give water, the molecules of hydrogen and oxygen certainly have to disappear at the same time as the water molecules appear. But we know that the decomposition of chemical species, when carried out as far as possible, has led to the experimental definition of a small number of *simple bodies* which can always be recovered, without any change in their nature, and without loss or gain of mass, from combinations in which they have been introduced. It is then very difficult not to assume that, for example, one and the same substance « exists » in all the chemical species from which the simple substance hydrogen can be regained and which passes, disguised but indestructible, through our various reactions. Dalton supposed, and this is the essential point of the atomic hypothesis, that this substance is formed by a definite variety of particles which are all identical and which cannot be cut into pieces in the reactions which we can produce, and which for this reason are called *atoms*. There are, therefore, one or several atoms of hydrogen in each molecule of a hydrogenated chemical species.

The fundamental laws of chemistry which are well known to you and which are laws of discontinuity (discontinuity between chemical species, and discontinuous variation according to the «multiple proportions» in the composition of species made from the same simple bodies) then become immediately clear: they are imposed solely by the condition that the molecule constituting a compound contains a necessarily whole number of atoms of each of the simple bodies combined in this compound. And I do not need to tell you that if one admits that «analogous» bodies (alkali halides, for example) must have analogous formulae, simple chemical analysis will give for the elements of the same «family» the ratios of the weights of the atoms, or «atomic weights», of these elements.

But in order to pass from one family to another, from hydrogen to oxygen for example, it was necessary to have the gas laws and Avogadro's hypothesis or law which I recall because my researches are based on it: when one of those cases occurs where the ratios of the weights of the molecules of the two compounds are known, it is found that masses proportional to these masses (which must, therefore, contain the same number of molecules) occupy equal volumes in the gaseous state under the same conditions of temperature and pressure. This means that as far as these substances are concerned, equal numbers of heavy or light molecules develop equal pressures at the same temperature and in equal volumes. Since the mass of a molecule, and not its nature, must affect the impact of the molecule upon the wall, I see here a justification (not yet agreed, I must say) of the following proposition known as Avogadro's postulate, or hypothesis:

When gaseous masses, at the same temperature and pressure, occupy equal volumes, they all contain the same number of molecules.

These «equimolecular» masses are determined for the various chemical species, as soon as one of them has been chosen. They are called *gram-molecules* when the masses in the gaseous state occupy, at the same temperature and pressure, the same volume as 32 grams of oxygen. The number N of the molecules constituting any gram-molecule is *Avogadro's number*. For each simple substance the gram-molecule of a compound contains as many *gram-atoms* as the molecule contains atoms of this simple substance, and the gram-atom is the product of the mass of the atom and Avogadro's number N.

In short, if molecules and atoms exist, their relative weights are known to us, and their absolute weights would be known at the same time as Avogadro's number.

You also know how—particularly for understanding substitutions—it was assumed that the atoms of a molecule are held together by *valences* of which each unites only two atoms, a kind of bolt holding rigidly together two bars or protuberances which pre-exist on the two atoms. A new detail is thus introduced here to the concept of the atom, but once this new hypothesis is accepted, the structural formulae can be determined for an enormous number of compounds, and with such success in regard to forecasting the properties that it could be said that the hundreds of thousands of structural formulae set up by the organic chemists constitute just as many arguments in favour of the atomic theory.

These brilliant successes tell us, otherwise, nothing about the absolute weights of the atoms. If they all became at the same time a thousand times smaller, a milliard times smaller, infinitesimal in the mathematical sense of the word, with matter becoming again continuous at each reduction, our chemical laws and our formulae would be unchanged, and the idea of the atom, then driven back infinitely far beyound all experimental reach, would lose its interest and its reality.

It will be noted that the laws of *crystallography*, which are laws of discontinuity just as the fundamental laws of chemistry, lead to similar considerations in regard to the dimensions of an elementary cell which is repeated periodically along the three dimensions of a parallelepipedic lattice and should constitute the crystal which is homogeneous in appearance on our scale. Only in this way can one understand how the symmetries of crystals are soley those of reticular systems (for example, never symmetry axes of the order of 5), and explain at the same time the law of rational indices (a kind of laws of multiple proportions which describe what discontinuities separate the possible faces), a law which requires the three dimensions of the elementary parallelepiped to be in definite ratios. Here again the grain of matter could become infinitely small without the laws having to be changed.

In short, in order really to establish the Atomic Theory, it was necessary to obtain the weights and dimensions of the atoms and not only their ratios.

A remarkably successful attempt to do this was made about fifty years ago by the physicists who created the *kinetic theory of gases* by assuming that gases are made of elastic molecules which are on the average fairly widely separated from one another so that, between two collisions, each molecule can move in a straight line, the duration of the collision being negligible in relation to that of the *free path*.

Furthermore, if it is agreed that the pressure of a gas on a wall is solely due to the impacts of the molecules upon this wall, and if we write that this (known) pressure must consequently be numerically equal to the impulse exerted perpendicularly on the wall by the molecules impinging against unit surface in unit time, an equation is obtained which shows the *mean velocity* of the gas molecules.

It is also known that if, in a gas, a rigid plane is made to slide parallel to a fixed plane at a distance D and with a constant velocity V, each intermediate layer at a distance d from the fixed plane is involved with a velocity equal to $V(d/D)$, and that the fixed and moving planes are drawn in opposite directions by forces (per unit surface) equal to the product of the velocity gradient V/D and a fixed factor for each gas, the latter measuring the *viscosity* of this gas (at the temperature of the experiment). This is readily understood from the kinetic theory: the unit surface of the fixed plane is drawn in the direction of the movement by a force numerically equal to the total excess impulse received in this direction, this excess being proportional to the number of impinging molecules (in other words, both to the density and to the mean molecular velocity which we can determine), and proportional to the mean excess impulse of each impinging molecule; this individual mean excess is itself proportional to the distance of the layer in which the molecule was at the time of the previous impact, and consequently to the *mean free path*. In this way it is seen how Maxwell was able to deduce this *mean free path* from the experimental determination of the viscosity.

Now, as Clausius observed, the molecules are all the smaller as the mean free path (now known) becomes greater (if the molecules were reduced to points, they would never collide with one another). And it is seen, therefore, that if the free path is known, it is possible to calculate the *total surface* of the molecules which form a given mass of gas. The *total volume* of these same molecules is probably little different from the volume occupied by this mass if it were solidified. Finally, from two obvious equations we derive both the number and the diameter of the molecules which constitute, let us say, a gram-molecule of the gas.

Depending on the gas, the diameters found in this way are graded between 2 and 5 ten-millionths of a millimetre; and the values found for Avogadro's number are between 40×10^{22} and 120×10^{22}. The uncertainty is largely 100 per cent, both because of the inaccuracy of certain measurements and especially because the calculations have been simplified by making assumptions which can only be approximate. But the order of magnitude is achieved: an atom vanishes in our substance almost as the latter would vanish in the sun.

The sequence of reasonings which I have just summarized deserves our profound admiration; however, they were not sufficient to carry conviction owing to the uncertainty which in spite of everything existed not only in the simplifying assumptions (sphericalness of the molecules, for example), but in the very hypotheses on which the reasoning is based. This conviction will without doubt come to life if entirely different paths lead us to the same values for the molecular sizes.

The Brownian movement

Let us consider a liquid in equilibrium: the water contained in this glass, for example. It appears to us homogeneous and continuous, and immobile in all its parts. If we place in it a denser object, it falls, and we know quite well that once it has arrived at the bottom of the glass, it stays there and is unlikely to ascend again « by itself ».

We could have observed this water before it reached equilibrium, and to see how it reached it, at the moment when we filled this glass; then we should have been able to find (by observing the visible indicator dust which was specially mixed with the water) that the movement of the various parts of the water which were coordinated at first in parallel movements, became more and more uncoordinated by scattering in all directions between smaller and smaller parts until the whole appeared completely immobile (nothing prevents us as yet from assuming that this scattering will continue without limit).

It is very remarkable that these so familiar ideas become false on the scale of the observations which we can make under a microscope: each microscopic particle placed in water (or any other liquid), instead of falling in a regular manner exhibits a continuous and perfectly irregular agitation. It goes to and fro whilst turning about, it rises, falls, rises again, without tending in any way towards repose, and maintaining indefinitely the same mean state of agitation. This phenomenon which was predicted by Lucretius, suspected by Buffon, and established with certainty by Brown, constitutes the *Brownian movement.*

The nature of the grains is not important, but the smaller a grain is, the more violently does it become agitated. There is also complete independence between the movements of two grains, even if they are very close together, which excludes the hypothesis of collective convection produced by the impacts or temperature differences. We are, finally, forced to think that each grain only follows the portion of liquid surrounding it, in the same way that an indicating buoy indicates and analyses the movement all the better if it is smaller: a float follows the movement of the sea more faithfully than a battleship.

We obtain from this an essential property of what is called a liquid in equilibrium: *its repose is only an illusion due to the imperfection of our senses, and what we call equilibrium is a certain well-defined permanent system of a perfectly irregular agitation.* This is an experimental fact in which no hypothesis plays any part.

Since this agitation remains on an average constant (it would be possible to make this « impression» accurate by measurements), the movement possessed by a part of the liquid does not scatter without limit in all directions between smaller and smaller parts, in spite of what observations made on our scale suggest to us; this spreading does not go beyond a certain limit for which, at each moment, just as much movement is coordinated as becomes uncoordinated.

This is explainable if the liquid consists of elastic grains, and I do not see how it can be understood if the structure is continuous. Moreover, it is seen that the agitation for a given observable particle must increase with the size of the molecules: the magnitude of the Brownian movement, therefore, will probably enable us to calculate the molecular sizes.*

In short, the Brownian movement (an experimental fact) leads us to the hypothesis of the molecules; and we then understand quite well how each particle that is situated in a liquid and is being bombarded ceaselessly by neighbouring molecules, receives shocks which on the whole have all the less

---

* Similarly, the fact that there exists a definite isothermal radiation for each temperature, and that even a temperature is definable without the energy present in the form of radiation continuously gliding towards colours of increasingly smaller wavelengths, requires a structure to be discontinuous (Planck).

change of coming to equilibrium as the particle becomes smaller, with the result that this particle must be tossed to and fro irregularly.

This applies to absolutely whatever kind of particle. If it has been possible to bring into suspension in a liquid a large number of particles all of the same nature, we say that an *emulsion* has been produced. This emulsion is stable if the particles in suspension do not stick together when the hazards of the Brownian movement bring them into contact, and if they re-enter the liquid when these hazards bring them against the walls or to the surface. From this two-fold point of view such a *stable emulsion* is comparable to a *solution*. It is precisely by pursuing this analogy that I have been able to obtain a simple determination of the molecular sizes.

Extension of the gas laws to emulsions

I must, first of all, recall how the gas laws and particularly Avogadro's law came to be regarded, thanks to Van 't Hoff, as applicable to dilute solutions.

The pressure exerted by a gas on the walls limiting its expansion becomes, for a dissolved substance, the *osmotic pressure* exerted on *semi-permeable* walls which allow the solvent to pass, but hold back this dissolved substance. Such is a membrane of copper ferrocyanide which separates sugared water from pure water.

Now, the measurements of Pfeffer show that in fact the equilibrium exists only if there is a certain excess pressure from the side on which the sugar is, and Van 't Hoff has pointed out that the value of this excess pressure or osmotic pressure is precisely that of the pressure which would be exerted, in accordance with Avogadro's law, on the wall of the container containing the sugared water if the sugar present could occupy the entire container alone and in the gaseous state. It is then probable that the same would occur with every dissolved substance, but we do not need to recall the thermodynamic reasoning with which Van 't Hoff justified this generalization nor to make other measurements of the osmotic pressure: Arrhenius has indeed shown that every substance which, in solution, confirms the well-known Raoult laws through its freezing temperature and its vapour pressure, necessarily exerts through this very fact the pressure predicted by Van 't Hoff on every wall which halts it without halting the solvent. In short, the Raoult laws which were established by a very large number of measurements, are logically equivalent to the law of Van't Hoff which consists in the extension of Avogadro's law to solutions, and we can now say:

Equal numbers of molecules, regardless of the kind, in the gaseous state or dissolved, exert – at the same temperature and in equal volumes – equal pressures on the walls detaining them.

This law applies equally to heavy or light molecules, in such manner that, for example, the molecule of quinine which contains more than one hundred atoms, has neither a greater nor a lesser effect when it impinges against the wall than the light molecule of hydrogen which contains two atoms.

I have thought that it was perhaps valid for stable emulsions with visible grains, in such manner that each of these grains which is agitated by the Brownian movement, counts as a molecule when it collides with a wall.

Let us assume then that we can measure the osmotic pressure which equal grains exert, through their Brownian movement, against a unit of a wall which holds them up and allows water to pass (let us say blotting paper). Let us also assume that we can count these grains in the immediate vicinity of the wall unit, that is to say that we know the «abundance» of the grains per unit volume near this wall unit. This number n also measures the abundance of molecules in any gas (let us say hydrogen) which would exert the same pressure on the walls of the container in which it would be enclosed. If, for example, the osmotic pressure measured is the hundred-millionth of a barye, we shall know that a cubic centimetre of hydrogen under normal conditions (pressure equal to a million baryes) contains 100 million million times n molecules ($10^{14} n$). And the gram-molecule (22,412 c.c. in the gaseous state under normal conditions) will contain 22,412 times more molecules: this number will be *Avogadro's number*.

This is very simple; but how to measure the stupendously weak osmotic pressure that an emulsion exerts?

This will, in fact, not be necessary nor, as we have just explained, will it be nesessary to measure the osmotic pressure of a solution to make sure that this solution obeys the gas laws. And it will be sufficient for us to find an experimentally accessible property for emulsions which would be logically equivalent to the gas laws.

I found such a property (1908) by extending to emulsions the fact that is qualitatively well known to you, that in a vertical column of a gas in equilibrium the density decreases as the altitude increases.

Law of the vertical distribution of an emulsion

We all know that air is more rarefied at the top of a mountain than at sea level and, generally speaking, the pressure of air has to diminish as one goes higher since this pressure has then to carry only a smaller part of the atmosphere which applies its weight against the earth.

If we specify this slightly vague reasoning in the Laplace manner, we shall say that each horizontal slice of a gas in equilibrium in a large vertical pump would remain in equilibrium if it were imprisoned between two rigid pistons (which would no longer allow exchange of molecules between this slice and the neighbouring slices of the gas) and these pistons would exert respectively the pressures existing at the lower face and at the upper face of the slice; with the result that, per unit surface, the difference of these pressures is equal to the weight of the gas supported. That is to say that if the thickness dh of the slice is sufficiently small so that the abundance of molecules near the upper face differs little from the abundance n near the lower face, the pressure difference dp between the two faces will be equal to $n\,\pi\,dh$, where π denotes the weight of a molecule.

This very simple equation expresses two important facts: first of all, as the abundance n of molecules is proportional to the pressure p at each given temperature, we see that for a column of a given gas (for a given π)and of uniform temperature, the relative reduction of the pressure dp/p, or also the relative reduction of the abundance dn/n which can be said to measure the rarefaction, always has the same value for the same difference in level dh, whatever this level may be. For example, each time that you climb a flight of stairs, the pressure in the air (or the abundance of molecules) is reduced by one forty-thousandth of its value. Adding these effects for each step, we see that at whatever level we were originally, each time we ascend by the same height, the pressure (or the density) in air at a uniform temperature will be divided by the same number; for example, in oxygen at 0° the rarefaction will be doubled for each rise of 5 kilometres.

The other fact which emerges immediately from our equation relates to the weight π of the molecule; for the same value of level dh, the rarefaction dp/p (or dn/n) varies in inverse ratio with the weight of the molecule. Adding here again the effects for each step, we see that in two different gases at the same temperature, the rises producing the same rarefaction are in inverse ratio to the molecular weights. For example, as we know that the oxygen molecule (if it exists, and in accordance with the laws summarized above) must weigh 16 times more than the hydrogen molecule, it is necessary to rise 16 times higher in hydrogen than in oxygen, i.e. 80 kilometres, for the rarefaction to be doubled.

You can appreciate the influence of the altitude, and of the molecular weight, on the rarefaction by looking at this schematic picture where I have drawn three gigantic vertical test tubes (the highest is 300 kilometers) containing equal numbers of hydrogen molecules, helium molecules, and oxygen molecules. At a uniform temperature the molecules would be distributed as shown in the drawing, being more numerous near the bottom as they increase in weight.

Let us now admit that Avogadro's law applies to emulsions as it does to gases.

We assume, therefore, that we have a stable emulsion made of equal grains which is left to itself at a constant temperature, being only under the influence of its own weight. We can repeat the previous reasoning with the only change that the intergranular space, instead of being void, is now a liquid which exerts on each grain, in an opposite direction to its weight, a push in accordance with Archimedes' principle. Consequently, the effective weight π of the grain to which this reasoning is applied, is its actual weight reduced by this push.

If now our generalization is justified, once the emulsion is in equilibrium it will produce *a miniature atmosphere of visible molecules* where equal rises will be accompanied by equal rarefactions. But if, for example, the rise in the emulsion to double the rarefaction is a milliard times less than in oxygen, it means that the effective weight of the grain is a milliard times greater than that of the oxygen molecule. It will, therefore, be sufficient to determine the effective weight of the visible grain (which forms links between the magnitudes on our scale and the molecular magnitudes) in order to obtain by a simple ratio the weight of any molecule, and consequently Avogadro's number.

It is in this sense that I carried out my experiments which I was able to do successfully.

I first prepared stable emulsions made from solid (vitreous) spheres of various resins in suspension in a liquid (generally water). This was done by dissolving the resin in alcohol and adding to this limpid solution a large amount of water. The resin is quite insoluble in the water and is then precipitated as microscopic spherules of all sizes. By means of prolonged centrifuging similar to those in which the red blood corpuscles are separated from the blood serum, it is possible to collect these grains as a consistent deposit which splits up again as a stable emulsion of distinct spherules when it is agitated in the pure water after the supernatant alcohol solution has been removed.

It was then necessary, starting with an emulsion where the grains are of very different size, to succeed in separating these grains according to size in order to have *uniform* emulsions (consisting of equal grains). The process which I used can be compared with fractional distillation: just as, in a distillation, the fractions which come off first are richer in the most volatile constituents, so in a centrifuging of a *pure* emulsion (spherules of the same substance), the parts which settle out first are richer in coarse grains, and this is a method of separating the grains according to size by proceeding according to rules which it would be unnecessary to elaborate here. It is also necessary to be patient: I treated in my most careful fractionation one kilogram of gamboge and obtained after several months of daily operations a fraction containing several decigrams of grains with a diameter of approximately three-quarters of a thousandth of a millimetre which was appreciably equal to what I had wanted to obtain.

If a droplet of a very dilute emulsion made with such equal grains is allowed to evaporate on the slide under a microscope, the grains are seen, when the evaporation is almost complete (and doubtless as a result of capillary action), to run and join together in regular lines just as cannon-balls in a horizontal row of a pile of cannon-balls.

You can see this on the photograph which is now projected. And you will understand how it is possible simultaneously to obtain a successful centrifuging and to measure the mean diameter of the grain of the emulsion. (Other processes are, moreover, possible.)

On the other hand, there is no difficulty in determining the density of the glass constituting the spherules (several processes: the most correct consists in suspending the grains in a solution which is just so dense that the centrifuging cannot separate the grains).

We then know everything necessary for calculating the effective weight of the grain of the emulsion.

On the other hand, we shall have studied the equilibrium distribution of the emulsion under the action of gravity. For this we imprison a drop of the emulsion in a well-closed dish (evaporation must be impossible) arranged for microscopic observation. The distribution of the grains is at first uniform, but it is found that the grains accumulate progressively in the lower layers until a limiting distribution is reached with reversible settling or expansion depending on whether the temperature is lowered or raised. There are two possible methods of observation, as shown in the drawing projected here. In one method (the horizontal microscope) the rarefaction of the emulsion is obtained immediately from the height, and the resemblance to a miniature atmosphere is extremely striking, precise measurements being possible from instantaneous photographs. But it is then difficult to give the emulsion a height lower than, shall we say, one millimetre, and the time needed for establishing a permanent state becomes long (several days) which involves complications and difficulties.

In the other method of observation the microscope is vertical, and the emulsion imprisoned between the slide and the cover-glass has now a thickness only of the order of a tenth of a millimetre. We take an objective of high magnifying power and weak focal depth so that a very thin horizontal layer of the emulsion (of the order of 2 microns) is clearly seen, and an instantaneous photograph is taken. We thus have the abundance at a certain level (as an aviator could take the density of air at every level). The abundances at different levels are then compared at our leisure.

The success is complete. Before insisting that it is so, I can show a cinematographic film on which you will see for yourselves the equilibrium distribution of an emulsion formed from spherules which are agitated by the Brownian movement.

The observations and the countings which this film summarizes for you prove that the laws of ideal gases apply to dilute emulsions. This generalization was predicted as a consequence of the molecular hypothesis by such simple reasoning that its verification definitely constitutes a very strong argument in favour of the existence of molecules. In particular, it was necessary – it can be verified effectively, and it is very remarkable – that the various emulsions studied lead, within the limit of the possible errors, to the same value for Avogadro's number. In fact, I changed (with the valuable assistance of Bjerrum, Dabrovski, and Bruhat) the mass of the grains (from 1 to 50), their nature (gamboge, mastic), their density (1.20 to 1.06), the nature of the intergranular liquid (water, strongly sugared water, glycerol in the upper layers of which the grains of mastic, being lighter, accumulated) and lastly the temperature (from $-9°$ to $+60°$). My most careful measurements made with an emulsion the rarefaction of which doubled with each rise of 6 microns, gave a value for N of 68×10^{22}.

The accuracy of such determinations, so far of several hundredths, can certainly be improved; the same does not apply to values obtained from the kinetic theory of gases, because here perfecting the measurements would not diminish the uncertainties inherent in the simplifying assumptions which were introduced to facilitate the calculations.

Non-diluted emulsions

Proceeding then further in tracing the similarities between liquids and emulsions, I was able to show (1913) that a non-diluted emulsion is comparable to a compressed liquid of which the molecules would be visible.

For this purpose it was necessary to determine the osmotic pressure as a function of the concentration when the gas laws cease to be applicable. Let us, therefore, consider a vertical column of emulsion which extends upwards practically without limit. At each level the osmotic pressure can be regarded as supporting the whole of the grains above it, and we shall, therefore, know it by counting all these grains. The emulsion will be imprisoned between two vertical plate glasses only several microns apart so that all the grains can be taken by an instantaneous photograph. The concentration of the grains at each level is, on the other hand, fixed by the known number of grains present in a small known volume near this level. In short, we shall in this way know the pressure corresponding to a known concentration: this will give experimentally the law of compressibility which can then be compared with Van der Waals' law.

René Costantin made these measurements under my direction and confirmed that Van der Waals' law applies to emulsions which are already too concentrated to conform to the gas laws. The resulting value for Avogadro's number is 62×10^{22}.

Even Van der Waals' law is no longer suitable for concentrations above 3 per cent, but the compressibility remains measurable, consequently the law of compressibility remains known empirically.

This enables – and this idea was due entirely to René Costantin who died for France in 1915 – a theory of Smoluchovski to be checked on the density fluctuations which the molecular agitation should produce in a liquid in equilibrium. According to this theory, the *fluctuation* $(n'-n)/n$ in a volume containing accidentally n' molecules whilst it should contain only n if the distribution were uniform, has a mean value which can be calculated if the compressibility of the liquid is known, and which includes Avogadro's number.

For our emulsions of equal grains, considered as fluids with visible molecules, the measurements of osmotic compressibility, carried out as far as a content of 7 per cent, have confirmed Smoluchovski's theory by giving approximately 60×10^{22} for Avogadro's number.

Measurements of the Brownian movement

The equilibrium distribution of an emulsion is due to the Brownian movement, and the more rapidly as this movement is more active. But this rapidity is not important for the final distribution. In fact, as we have just seen, I also studied the distribution first on the permanent state without making any measurement on the Brownian movement. But by means of such measurements it is possible, though in a less obvious manner, to demonstrate the discontinuous structure of matter and to obtain a determination of Avogadro's number.

It is due to Einstein and Smoluchovski that we have a kinetic theory of the Brownian movement which lends itself to verification.

Without being disturbed by the intricate path described by a grain within a given time, these physicists characterize the agitation by the rectilinear segment joining the point of departure with the point of arrival, the segment being on an average greater as the agitation is livelier. This segment will be the *displacement* of the grain during the time considered.

If we then admit that the Brownian movement is *perfectly irregular* at right angles to the vertical, we prove that the mean horizontal displacement of a grain is doubled when the duration of the displacement is quadrupled, and is tenfold if that duration becomes a hundredfold, and so forth. This means that the mean square of the horizontal displacement is proportional to the duration t of this displacement. This can easily be verified.

Now, this mean square is equal to twice the mean square $\overline{X^2}$ of the projection of the displacement on an arbitrary horizontal axis. Consequently, the mean value of the quotient $\overline{X^2}/t$ for a given grain remains constant. Obviously, since it increases as the grain is more agitated, this mean quotient characterizes *the activity of the Brownian movement*.

Having said this, there must be a *diffusion* for the grains of an emulsion just as for the molecules of a solution; Einstein shows that the coefficient of diffusion should be equal to the half of the number which measures the activity of the agitation.

On the other hand, the steady state in a vertical column of emulsion is produced and maintained by the interplay of two opposing actions, gravity and the Brownian movement; this can be expressed by writing that at each level the flow through diffusion towards the poor regions is equal to that which gravity produces towards the rich regions.

In order to calculate the flow by diffusion it must be admitted, as we have done, that grains or molecules are equivalent to each other in regard to the osmotic pressures; in order to calculate the flow produced by gravity, in the case of spherules of radius a, it must be admitted, though at first it appeared uncertain, that the (very weak) mean velocity of fall of a grain animated by a very active Brownian movement can still be calculated by « Stokes' law » which applies to the uniform fall in a viscous liquid of a large sphere which is practically not animated by a Brownian movement. In fact, I have since shown experimentally that this is so.

Having admitted this hypothesis, Einstein finds that the diffusion coefficient $\frac{1}{2}\overline{X^2}/t$ is equal to $(RT/N)(6\pi az)^{-1}$ (R being the gas constant, T the absolute temperature, and z the viscosity).

So far we have thought of the *translational* Brownian movement only. Now a grain rotates at the same time as it is displaced. Einstein was able to show that if $\overline{A^2}$ denotes the mean square in a time t of the component of the angle of rotation around an axis, the agitation coefficient of rotation $\overline{A^2}/t$ is fixed for the same grain and should be equal to (RT/N) $(4\pi a^3 z)^{-1}$. His reasoning implies equality between *the mean energy of translation* and *the mean energy of rotation* which was predicted by Boltzmann and which we shall make more probable if we succeed in confirming this equation.

These theories can be judged by experiment if we know how to *prepare spherules of a measurable radius*. I was, therefore, in a position to attempt this check as soon as I knew, thanks to Langevin, of the work of Einstein.

I must say that, right at the beginning, Einstein and Smoluchovski had pointed out that the order of magnitude of the Brownian movement seemed to correspond to their predictions. And this approximate agreement gave already much force to the kinetic theory of the phenomenon, at least in broad outline.

It was impossible to say anything more precise so long as spherules of known size had not been prepared. Having such grains, I was able to check Einstein's formulae by seeing whether they led always to the same value for Avogadro's number and whether it was appreciably equal to the value already found.

This is obtained for the displacements by noting on the camera lucida (magnification known) the horizontal projections of the same grain at the beginning and at the end of an interval of time equal to the duration chosen, in such a manner as to measure a large number of displacements, for example, in one minute.

In several series of measurements I varied, with the aid of several collaborators, the size of the grains (in the ratio of 1 to 70,000)as well as the nature of the liquid (water, solutions of sugar or urea, glycerol) and its viscosity (in the ratio of 1 to 125). They gave values between 55×10^{22} and 72×10^{22}, with differences which could be explained by experimental errors. The agreement is such that it is impossible to doubt the correctness of the kinetic theory of the translational Brownian movement.

It must otherwise be observed that although it is didactically of comparable difficulty to the kinetic theory of the viscosity of gases, Einstein's theory does not introduce simplifying approximations and, like the measurement of height distribution, lends itself to a precise determination of Avogadro's number.

My most careful measurements which gave me N equal to 69×10^{22} had been made on grains which, for reasons which are no longer of interest, had their initial position at 6μ from the bottom of the preparation. In the course of the verifications which I had asked René Costantin to make on preparations which were only several microns thick, he found that the vicinity of a wall slowed down the Brownian movement. The measurements made at a distance from the walls gave a value for N of 64×10^{22}.

With regard to the *rotational* Brownian movement, Einstein's formula predicts a mean rotation of approximately 8° per hundredth of a second for spheres of 1μ diameter, a rotation which is too rapid to be perceived and which–with greater reason–escapes measurement. And, in fact, this rotation had not been made the subject of any experimental study, at least not quantitatively. (Einstein did not suppose that his formula could be verified.)

I overcame the difficulty by preparing large spherules of mastic. I arrived at them by making pure water pass slowly under an alcohol solution of resin. A passage zone is produced where the grains form which then have generally a diameter of some twelve microns. They are limpid spheres, like glass balls. They frequently seem to be perfect, and then their rotation is not observable. But they also frequently contain small vacuoles, *guide marks by means of which the rotational Brownian movement is easily perceived.*

But the weight of these large grains keeps them very close to the bottom which disturbs their Brownian movement. I, therefore, tried to give the intergranular liquid the density of the grains by dissolving suitable substances in it. A complication soon arose in that at the amount necessary for keeping the grains suspended between the two waters, almost all these substances agglutinated the grains into *bunches of grapes*, showing thus in the nicest way possible the phenomenon of *coagulation* which is not easy to obtain on ordinary suspensions or colloidal solutions (of ultramicroscopic grains). Coagulation failed to occur in a single substance, urea.

In water containing 27 per cent urea I was, therefore, able to follow the agitation of the grains and to measure their rotation. For this I noted at equal intervals of time the successive positions of certain vacuoles from which it was then possible, at one's leisure, to find again the orientation of the sphere at each of these moments and to calculate its rotation from one moment to the next. The calculations were made on approximately 200 (fairly rough) angle measurements on spheres having a diameter of 13 μ, and gave me for N the value of 65×10^{22}. This agreement with the previous determinations is all the more striking as even the order of magnitude of the phenomenon was not known (1910).

The molecular reality

Briefly, and in spite of the variety of experimental conditions and techniques, the study of the emulsions gave me for Avogadro's number:

68×10^{22} by means of the distribution of emulsions analogous to gases;
62×10^{22} by means of that of emulsions analogous to liquids;
60×10^{22} by means of the fluctuations in concentrated emulsions;
64×10^{22} by means of the translational Brownian movement;
65×10^{22} by means of the rotational Brownian movement;

or, as a crude average, *64×10^{22}*.

I can recall here that on the other hand, considering gases as consisting of molecules which diffract light (Rayleigh, Smoluchovski, Einstein) it was possible to obtain (somewhat after my first experiments) Avogadro's number by means of measurements relating to the *critical opalescence* (Keesom: 75×10^{22}), the *blueness of the sky* (Bauer and L. Brillouin, then Fowler:

65×10^{22}), and relating in a particularly precise manner to light that was laterally diffused by gases (Cabannes: 65×10^{22}; 1921).

The theory of black-body radiation, where the reasoning is allied to that of the kinetic theory, gives again the same value (64×10^{22}).

Along other lines, the measurements of the electric charges of charged microscopic dust, which should be whole multiples of the elementary charge of ions, led–by stages with Townsend, J. J. Thomson, Harold A. Wilson, Ehrenhaft, and finally Millikan (1909)–to the same result (61×10^{22}).

Lastly, radioactivity which enables the atoms forming a given mass of helium to be counted one by one, has given in a totally different manner proofs of the discontinuity of matter by imposing once again the same value (62×10^{22} to 70×10^{22}) on Avogadro's number.

Such a collection of agreements between the various pieces of evidence according to which the molecular structure is translated to the scale of our observations, creates a certitude at least equal to that which we attribute to the principles of thermodynamics. The *objective reality of molecules and atoms* which was doubted twenty years ago, can today be accepted as a *principle* the consequences of which can always be proved.

Nevertheless, however sure this new principle may be, it would still be a great step forward in our knowledge of matter, and for all that a certitude of a different order, if we could perceive directly these molecules the existence of which has been demonstrated.

Without having arrived there, I have at least been able to observe a phenomenon where the discontinuous structure of matter can be seen directly.

Monomolecular films

I encountered this phenomenon (1913) by observing under the microscope small laminae of «soapy water», and in such simple conditions that it is surprising it was not discovered earlier.

You know the properties of *thin laminae*: each ray reflected from such a lamina is formed by the superposition of a ray reflected from the front side of the lamina on a ray reflected from the rear side. For each elementary colour these rays add together or subtract from one another according to a classical formula, depending on whether they are in phase or out of phase; in particular, there is extinction when the thickness of the lamina is an even multiple of one quarter of the wavelength, and there is maximum reflection when it is an odd multiple.

If, therefore, white light strikes a lamina which has a thickness increasing continuously from zero, the reflected light is at first non-existent (black lamina), then weak (grey lamina), then lively and still almost white, becoming successively straw yellow, orange yellow, red, violet, blue (tints of the first order), then again (but with different tints) yellow, red, violet, blue, green (second order); and so on, the reflected colour becoming continuously more complex and more off-white up to the «white of a higher order» (the spectrum is furrowed with black grooves the number of which increases with the thickness of the lamina). All these tints will be present at the same time on a lamina which has not a uniform thickness and which will be black or grey in its thinnest region, straw yellow in a thicker region, red in an even thicker region, and so forth.

It is the same with ordinary soap bubbles, with their magnificent colours. The gradation of these colours seems to us perfectly continuous, from the lowest part of the bubble where the wall is thicker, to its upper part, which thinning progressively, becomes white and then grey, after passing through the «first-order» tints. At that moment, just before the bubble bursts, this thin region begins to show one or several *black spots*, quite round, which contrast strongly with the neighbouring grey tone (I mistook them for holes when I was a child) and the very sharp edge of which marks a strong discontinuity in the thickness. In fact, they are not completely black, but reflect so little light that their thickness is certainly small in relation to the wavelengths of white light. In an enclosed space that is free from dust, these black spots may extend over areas of the order of one square decimetre, and remain for several months (Dewar).

A more careful examination has long since shown that in the first black spot may form even blacker circles, therefore thinner ones, again with a sharp periphery. In measurements which were at the time very remarkable, although not very accurate, Reinold and Rücker, and then Johonnott had shown that the darkest spot could have a thickness of 6 mμ (milli-microns), and the other roughly twice this. No interpretation had been given: it was simply thought that the surface tension which is variable below a certain thickness, became equal again for the thickness of the two black spots to what it is for large thicknesses. In the light of subsequent observations we shall understand that the black spot represents a kind of carpet formed by two layers or perhaps even by a single layer of molecules held together parallel with one another.

Without indicating here the intermediate stages which I passed through, let us say straightaway that, by observing in the microscope in bright light a small horizontal lamina of a given soapy water (approximately 5 per cent pure alkali oleate), I have seen the discontinuities multiplying of which the black spots were the first example.

The observation is made as for a metal surface: the light emitted through a lateral aperture in the tube of the microscope and reflected towards the objective, passes it and is reflected on the thin lamina, returning to the eye through the objective and the eye-piece to give a clear image of the lamina.

We then see, first of all, the colours in continuous gradation of the ordinary laminae of soapy water; then the lamina quivers; liquid gathers together in globules; at the same time, uniform bands, with flat tints separated from one another by arcs of a circle, appear in the whole lamina which becomes a kind of mosaic. These arcs terminate at the globules around which they radiate like stars. Once this stratification is organized, a very slow evolution takes place by displacement of the contours and the globules, giving (according to circumstances over which I had no control) more or less importance to one band or the other or a series of bands which is the reason for the extraordinary variety of stepped laminae which are observed. Very frequently kinds of flat bulges are seen protruding from the globules or from the non-stratified peripheral liquid and spreading over bands which have already formed.

We thus observe, in order of increasing thickness, black bands which do not seem to differ from the « black spots » which we just mentioned; then grey, white, yellow, red, blue bands; and then bands having second-order tints, and so on, up to higher-order white. Each band has a uniform colour standing out clearly and discontinuously against adjacent bands. The richness of the colours can be extreme as you see from the colour photographs (Lumière autochrome plates) which are here projected. The richness pertaining partly to a transitional tint – e.g. some purple – represented by an insignificant region on a lamina of ordinary soap, may extend here as a flat tint over an important area.

These bands are definitely liquids; this is shown by the existence of exactly circular contours (when solidification occurs, the areas become like dried skins with a dentated contour), by the mobility of these contours which change by blowing without breaking the lamina, by the existence finally of a « two-dimensional » Brownian movement which is found (for droplets, or for small flat discs, pieces detached from the bands), on grey or coloured bands (the Brownian movement is all the less lively when these bands are thicker which is natural in view of the fact that the frictions then become more important).

Let me add that I have also been able to obtain such stepped laminae with alkali oleate in glycerol, and also with alkali colophonates and resinates in water.

Having examined a large number of stratified laminae, it occurred to me, before I made any measurement, that the difference in thickness between two adjacent bands cannot fall below a certain value and that this elementary minimum difference, a kind of « step of a staircase », is included a whole number of times in each band. Similarly, if we throw playing-cards on the table, the thickness at each point is that of a whole number of cards, without all possible thicknesses being necessarily present, since two or three cards may remain stuck together. The stratified liquid strips would, therefore, be formed by the piling up of identical sheets, more or less overlapping each other, their liquid state imposing on the free contours the form of arcs of a circle (which are fixed at their extremities on globules or on the non-stratified periphery, according to conditions so far unknown).

The measurements confirmed this impression. From 1913 onwards I found a value ranging between 4.2 and 5.5 mμ. And since then, precise photometric determinations made under my direction in 1921 by P. V. Wells, who otherwise had to overcome serious experimental difficulties, have fully established what we can call a law of multiple thicknesses.

We first of all applied simply the classical relationship between the thickness of the lamina and the intensity of the reflected light, using monochromatic lighting.

On the first-order band 120 measurements were made, giving thicknesses grouped according to the law of chances around 4.4 mμ. It is certainly the best measurement made so far of the thickness of the « black spot » for which Johonnott gave 6 mμ. The extreme thinness of this band, the faintness of the reflected light, and the difficulties due to parasitic lights make this determination particularly interesting.

The set of the measurements for the first fifteen bands give similarly thicknesses which are, within several hundredths, of the successive multiples of 4.5 mμ.

As this elementary thickness is not known with a precision greater than 4 per cent, it seems impossible to verify the law above a certain thickness. For example, at this accuracy any thickness greater than 120 mμ would be a multiple of 4.5 mμ. But if the law exists, the thickness should always vary in the same way between two adjacent areas; or again the « step of the stairs » should remain the same, and this can be verified.

This is, in fact, what Wells saw, operating this time in white light and using a method which René Marcelin had suggested to me in 1914, by obtaining tints identical to those of the lamina by means of a quartz compensator of variable thickness which was placed between crossed nicols. (The difference between the thicknesses of quartz which gave the tints of the two adjacent liquid bands, determines the difference in thickness of these bands.) He obtained in this way 4.2 mμ near the first-order violet and 4.3 near the second-order violet.

In short, the « step of the staircase » has the same value near the first, the fiftieth or the hundredth band, i.e. approximately 4.4 mμ; and we can be sure that:

In a stratified liquid lamina the thickness of each band is a whole multiple of the same elementary thickness;
in other words, it is very probable that:

The bands of the stratified laminae are formed by the overlapping, in any number, of identical fundamental « sheets ».

This is how a « discontinuous and periodic structure » of matter is perceived quite directly, at least in a certain group of cases.

Similar experiments, suggested precisely by these observations of stratified laminae of soapy water, were made on mica at the beginning of 1914 by René Marcelin (who died for France in 1914). We know that if we pour selenium on to mica, and if we try to tear off this mica, thin laminae of mica remain adhering to the selenium. These laminae exhibit bright colourations which are divided into completely flat tints separated by clear rectilinear contours which mark discontinuities of thickness. The minimum difference of thickness measured with the Michel Lévy comparator was found to be equal to 0.7 mμ which would, therefore, be the thickness of a monomolecular layer in the crystal. But the measuring accuracy becomes low for such a small thickness.

Let us return to the stratified laminae of soapy water for which the size of the discontinuities is such that we have readily accessible the elementary sheet the periodic repetition of which forms the bands. We shall want to know what this elementary sheet is. I see in it a monomolecular film of hydrated bioleate.

We know, in fact (Rayleigh, A. Marcelin, Langmuir) that water on which float globules of oleic acid, is covered between these globules with a veil of oleic acid 1.9 mμ thick. According to its known density, this veil can be formed only by a single layer of molecules arranged perpendicularly to the surface and probably glued to the water by their (hygroscopic) acid groups. The surface of a soapy water is greasy (low surface tension, arrest of the movements of camphor); it is, therefore, covered at least by a similar layer of oleic acid or oleate, as can be shown by analysing a known quantity of soapy water drawn in the form of laminae having a known total surface area (Jean Perrin, Mouquin). The black spot corresponding to the maximum possible thinning would, therefore, be a kind of sandwich containing a layer of water molecules against each side of which, and glued to it by their acid groups, parallel molecules of oleic acid or oleate are arranged, the whole forming an anisotropic lamina or liquid crystalline sheet. The piling-up of such sheets, easily sliding over each other—with weak cohesion forces existing between them—would give the successive bands.

In remarkable agreement with this conception is the fact that the molecular length as calculated for oleic acid from X-ray diffraction measurements recently made in the laboratories of Bragg and Friedel agrees with the thickness of our fundamental sheet.

I do not think that there is any more to be said, at the moment, on the direct visibility of molecules.

The discontinuous structure of the atom

Even whilst evidence continued to accumulate on the still disputed atomic reality, a start was made to penetrate the interior structure of these atoms, a research in which Rutherford and Bohr obtained marvellous results, as we know. And I must summarize here my contribution to this research.

It was known that when an electric discharge passes in a glass tube through a sufficiently rarefied gas, the part facing the cathode is illuminated by a fluorescence on which the shadow of any obstacle placed in front of the cathode is outlined; and that the *cathode rays* definable in this way, are deflected by the magnetic field, describing a circular trajectory when they are thrown at right angles to a uniform field (Hittorf). Crookes had had the intuition that these rays were trajectories of negative particles emitted by the cathode and violently repelled by it (1886), but he did not succeed in establishing this electrification. And this emission theory was abandoned when Hertz on the one hand failed in his attempts to manifest the negative electricity of the rays, and on the other hand showed that they were able to pass through glass foil or aluminium foil several microns thick. It was assumed since then that the *cathode rays* were immaterial and had a wave-like nature similar to light. This opinion was held principally by Lenard (1894) who showed that these rays can leave the tube where they are formed, through a «window» made of a fairly thick foil to support the atmospheric pressure, and that they can be studied in this way in any gas or in an absolute vacuum.

It seemed to me, however, that the electrified projectiles imagined by Crookes *might differ sufficiently, in size and in velocity, from ordinary molecules, to pass through walls which were impermeable to these molecules,* and seeking to apply without complication the very definition of the electric charge, I made cathode rays penetrate into a «Faraday cylinder» contained inside a protective chamber. As soon as the rays (which can, first, be drawn aside by a magnetic field which is just strong enough to do so) enter the cylinder, the latter presents phenomena which give precisely the definition of a negative electric charge, and which enable it to be measured (1895). This experiment was successful even when the protective chamber was entirely closed, the rays penetrating it through a thin metal foil. Almost at the same time I showed (1896) that cathode rays are deflected by an electric field, and that there is a method here for measuring the drop in potential which had until then been unknown and from which they obtained their energy.

These experiments were at once repeated, and confirmed, by Lenard himself (whose theory they ruined), by Wiechert, by Wien, and by J. J. Thomson.

I had begun to make measurements which were intended to give the velocity (obviously variable according to the circumstances) of the cathode projectiles and the e/m ratio of its charge to its mass, supplementing the measurement of the drop in potential with that of the magnetic field capable of producing a given deflection. I was anticipated here by J. J. Thomson who in the very paper in which he published the confirmation of my experiments showed that once the electrification of the rays had been demonstrated, it was easy to obtain the velocity and the charge of the projectiles from the action of the electrical field and the magnetic field. He found that the e/m ratio, independently of all the circumstances, is approximately 2,000 times greater than it is for hydrogen in electrolysis, and consequently he had the honour of proving that the cathode projectile is much lighter than the hydrogen atom (1897). The experimental idea of the *electron* as a universal sub-atomic constituent was therefore reached, and my experiments had played a certain part in this growth of our knowledge of the manner in which matter is discontinuous.

The problem of the structure of the atom was immediately raised as it ceased to be the ultimate unit of matter. J. J. Thomson assumed that whilst the atom as a whole was neutral, it consisted of a homogeneous sphere of positive electricity inside which the electrons were held in such positions that the attractions and repulsions were in equilibrium.

I was, I believe, the first to assume that the atom had a structure reminding to that of the solar system where the « planetary » electrons circulate around a positive « Sun », the attraction by the centre being counterbalanced by the force of inertia (1901). But I never tried or even saw any means of verifying this conception. Rutherford (who had doubtless arrived at it independently, but who also had the delicacy to refer to the short phrase dropped during a lecture in which I had stated it) understood that the essential difference between his conception and that of J. J. Thomson was that there existed near the positive and quasi-punctual Sun, enormous electrical fields as compared with those which would exist inside or outside a homogeneous positive sphere having the same charge, but embracing the whole atom.

The result was that if a positive charge which is itself quasi-punctual, is sufficiently fast to be able to pass near such a nucleus, it will be strongly deflected just as a comet can be deflected when it comes from the infinite and passes near the Sun. It was in this way (1911), that Rutherford discovered and explained that certain α rays (rays described by helium atoms projected by radioactive substances) undergo very strong deflections when they pass through a thin film, producing on a phosphorescent screen, really far from the mean impact of the bundle of rays, scintillations which mark their individual arrivals. All these deflections are explained quantitatively on condition that the *nucleus* is credited with a charge such that the number of planetary electrons is equal to the « rank number » of the atom in Mendeleev's series. In this way each atom consists of an unimaginably small positive nucleus where almost the entire mass of the atom is concentrated and around which the planetary electrons, the presence of which determines the physical and chemical properties of the corresponding element, revolve at relatively colossal distances.

The nucleus itself, lastly, has been revealed as being discontinuous and composed of hydrogen nuclei, or *protons*, which are possibly «cemented» by nuclear electrons.

As Prout had predicted, each atom can, in fact, be regarded as resulting from the condensation on a whole number of hydrogen atoms (the deviating elements having proved to be mixtures of *isotopes*, which confirm the law separately); the small differences which exist are explained (by applying Einstein's law of the mass of energy) by the large variations of internal energy which may accompany these condensations (Langevin). And I have pointed out (1920) that the loss of energy which must then accompany the condensation of hydrogen into helium suffices alone to account for approximately one hundred milliard years of solar radiation at the present rate (the first theory to allow the understanding of the stupendous antiquity of climatic conditions only slightly different from the present conditions: the Helmholtz-Kelvin theory explained only a maximum of 50 million years, a grossly insufficient figure as far as geology is concerned).

This led me to think that the atoms of hydrogen, and then of helium (the only ones revealed by spectrum analysis in the non-resolvable nebulae) condense progressively, in the course of stellar evolution, into heavier and heavier atoms, radioactive disintegration being the exception and atomic integration being the rule.

However, Rutherford succeeded in proving, in admirable experiments (1922), that when a nucleus of nitrogen, aluminium, or phosphorus is struck forcefully by an α projectile (sufficiently fast to «hit» it in spite of the electrical repulsion), a proton is expelled (α ray) with an energy which may exceed that of the α projectile, and Rutherford interpreted this *transmutation* as being the effect of an explosive disintegration (similar to that of a shell which is exploded by an impact). I maintained, on the contrary (1923), that there was then an integration, that the helium nucleus at first combines with the nucleus that it has hit, to form a radioactive atom (of a species as yet unknown) which soon expels a proton, and that there finally remains an atom which is three units heavier than the atom that has been hit. This has since been confirmed by Blackett (1925) in the very laboratory of Rutherford: three converging rays are counted (by the method of C.T.R. Wilson) when a Rutherford transmutation occurs, instead of the four which would exist if the striking projectile retained its individuality after the impact.

But this refers rather to the evolution of Matter than to its discontinuity; if I were to say any more, I should be departing from the subject on which I came here to speak.

Biography

Jean Baptiste Perrin was born in Lille, September 30, 1870, where he was educated at the École Normal Supérieure, becoming an assistant in physics during 1894–1897, when he began his researches on cathode rays and X-rays. He received the degree of «docteur ès sciences» in 1897 for a thesis on cathode and Röntgen rays and was appointed, in the same year, to a readership in physical chemistry at the Sorbonne, University of Paris. He became Professor here in 1910; a post which he held till 1940, when the Germans invaded his country.

His earliest work was on the nature of cathode rays, and their nature was proved by him to be that of negatively charged particles. He also studied the effect of the action of X-rays on the conductivity of gases. In addition, he worked on fluorescence, the disintegration of radium, and the emission and transmission of sound. The work for which he is best known is the study of colloids and, in particular, the so-called Brownian movement. His results in this field were able to confirm Einstein's theoretical studies in which it was shown that colloidal particles should obey the gas laws, and hence to calculate Avogadro's number N, the number of molecules per grammolecule of a gas. The value thus calculated agreed excellently with other values obtained by entirely different methods in connection with other phenomena, such as that found by him as a result of his study of the sedimentation equilibrium in suspensions containing microscopic gamboge 'particles of uniform size. In this way the discontinuity of matter was proved by him beyond doubt: an achievement rewarded with the 1926 Nobel Prize.

Perrin was the author of many books and scientific papers. His book *Les Atomes*, published in 1913, sold 30,000 copies up to 1936. His principal papers were: «Rayons cathodiques et rayons X» (Cathode rays and X-rays), *Ann. Phys.*, 1897; *Les Principes* (The principles), Gauthier-Villars, 1901; «Électrisation de contact» (Contact electrificaton), *J. Chim. Phys.*, 1904–1905; «Réalité moléculaire» (Molecular reality), *Ann. Phys.*, 1909; «Matière et Lumière» (Matter and light), *Ann. Phys.*, 1919; «Lumière et Réaction chimique» (Light and chemical reaction), *Conseil Solvay de Chimie*, 1925.

Many honours were conferred on him for his scientific work; the Joule Prize of the Royal Society in 1896, the Vallauri Prize of Bologna in 1912 and, in 1914, the La Caze Prize of the Paris Academy of Sciences.

He held honorary doctorates of the Universities of Brussels, Liege, Ghent, Calcutta, New York, Princeton, Manchester, and Oxford. He was twice appointed a member of the Solvay Committee at Brussels in 1911 and in 1921. He held memberships of the Royal Society (London) and of the Academies of Sciences of Belgium, Sweden, Turin, Prague, Rumania, and China. In 1923 he was elected to the French Academy of Sciences. He became a Commander of the Legion of Honour in 1926, and was also made Commander of the British Empire and of the Order of Leopold (Belgium).

Perrin was the creator of the Centre National de la Recherche Scientifique, an organization offering to most promising French scientists–whose scientific talents would otherwise be lost–a career outside the University. It was due to this institute that Frédéric Joliot could carry out his magnificent investigations. In addition to this, he founded the Palais de la Découverte (Palace of discovery); he was also responsible for the establishment of the Institut d'Astrophysique, in Paris, and for the construction of the large Observatoire de Haute Provence; without his prestige and his power of persuasion the Institut de Biologie Physico-Chimique would never have come into being.

Perrin was an officer in the engineer corps during the 1914–1918 War. When the Germans invaded his country in 1940 he escaped to the U.S.A., where he died on the 17th of April, 1942. After the War, in 1948, his remains were transferred to his fatherland by the battleship Jeanne d'Arc, and buried in the Panthéon.

Physics 1927

ARTHUR HOLLY COMPTON

«for his discovery of the effect named after him»

CHARLES THOMSON REES WILSON

«for his method of making the paths of electrically charged particles visible by condensation of vapour»

Physics 1927

Presentation Speech by Professor K. M. G. Siegbahn, member of the Nobel Committee for Physics of the Royal Swedish Academy of Sciences

Your Majesty, Your Royal Highnesses, Ladies and Gentlemen.

The Royal Academy of Sciences has awarded this year's Nobel Prize in Physics to Professor Arthur Holly Compton of the University of Chicago for the discovery of the phenomenon named after him the Compton effect, and to Professor Charles Thomson Rees Wilson of the University of Cambridge for his discovery of the expansion method of rendering visible the tracks of electrically charged particles.

Professor Compton has won his prize by work in the field of X-radiation. Soon after Röntgen's discovery it became known that matter exposed to X-rays emits radiations of different character. Besides an emission of electrons, corresponding to the photoelectric effect known also in the optical region of radiation, there is also a secondary X-radiation. Even before the methods of X-ray spectrometry were known, these secondary X-rays were proved by the investigation of their absorption to be of a twofold nature. It was Barkla who, through his fundamental researches, proved that the secondary X-radiation consists partly in a scattering of X-rays, which he thought to have the same penetrability as the original radiation, and partly in a specific X-radiation which was characteristic of the chemical atom and which was more easily absorbed.

When X-rays fell upon matter with small atomic weight, as for example graphite, Barkla was not able to detect the mentioned characteristic X-radiation, but only a scattering; and consequently the secondary rays ought to have the same properties as the original X-rays. Barkla, however, in the course of his investigations of the absorption, had already been able to show that in this case also the secondary X-rays – at least partly – are more easily absorbed than the original radiation and therefore have a greater wavelength. Barkla thought this to be a new characteristic X-radiation.

This is the point where Compton comes in and affects the development of science. He made exact spectrometrical investigations of the secondary X-radiation from matter with small atomic weight: in other words, he undertook to investigate exactly the scattered X-radiation. After some preliminary work, he found an experimental method that gave results which were as exact as they were astonishing.

Using homogeneous X-rays – corresponding optically to monochromatic illumination, that is to say, to the use of a source of light that emits only one single spectral line – he found that the scattered radiation consists of two lines, one exactly the same as that of the source of rays, the other with a somewhat greater wavelength. This is the first evident manifestation of the Compton effect. Its reality was at first disputed, but of late years it has been well established and verified.

The change in wavelength soon proved to be independent of the nature of the matter used for scattering, while it varies with the angle between the incident and the scattered rays. Hence the phenomenon cannot be explained as a new characteristic radiation of the same nature as that hitherto known; and Compton deduced a new kind of corpuscular theory, with which all experimental results showed perfect agreement within the limits of experimental error.

According to this theory, a quantum of radiation is re-emitted in a definite direction by a single electron, which in so doing must recoil in a direction forming an acute angle with that of the incident radiation. In its mathematical dress this theory leads to an augmentation of the wavelength that is independent of the wavelength of the incident radiation and implies a velocity of the recoil electron that varies between zero and about 80% of the velocity of light, when the angle between the incident and the scattered radiation varies between zero and 180°.

Thus this theory predicts recoil electrons with a velocity generally much smaller than that of the above-mentioned electrons which correspond to the photoelectric effect. It was a triumph for both parties when these recoil electrons were discovered by Wilson's experimental method both by Wilson himself and, independently, by another investigator. Hereby the second chief phenomenon of the Compton effect was experimentally verified, and all observations proved to agree with what had been predicted in Compton's theory.

Quite apart from the improvements and additions that have been made to this theory by other investigators, the Compton effect has, through the latest evolutions of the atomic theory, got rid of the original explanation based upon a corpuscular theory. The new wave mechanics, in fact, lead as a logical consequence to the mathematical basis of Compton's theory. Thus the effect has gained an acceptable connection with other observations in the sphere of radiation. It is now so important that, in the future, no atomic theory can be accepted that does not explain it and lead to the laws established by its discoverer.

Finally, the fact deserves to be emphasized that the Compton effect has proved to be of decisive influence upon the absorption of short-wave electromagnetic – especially radioactive – radiation and of the newly discovered cosmic rays.

Professor Compton.   Your discovery of the phenomenon known as the Compton effect has already proved so important that the Royal Academy of Sciences has awarded you a Nobel Prize, which I now ask you to receive from the hands of His Majesty.

Professor Wilson has been awarded his prize for the discovery of a purely experimental method, which dates back from as long ago as 1911. It is based upon the formation of clouds, which develop when sufficiently moist air is suddenly expanded. The refrigeration caused by the expansion brings the temperature to sink below the dew-point, and the vapour is condensed into small drops, which form together visible clouds. In the first stage of condensation a droplet is always formed round a nucleus. The fact that an electrically charged particle acts as a nucleus in the formation of drops could, after the discovery of the corpuscular radiations, be concluded from an experiment that Helmholtz had, long before, made when he found that a stream of vapour loses its transparency in the vicinity of electrically charged objects.

After it had become known that electricity is conducted through gases by means of ions, and that ions are formed – or, in other words, gases are ionized – under the influence of X-rays or radioactive substances, the way lay open for Wilson to follow photographically the formation of droplets around electrically charged particles. Alpha and beta particles emitted by radioactive substances ionize the gases, and their tracks are marked by a formation of droplets. A suitable photograph of these droplets then gives a picture of the tracks of the ionizing particles.

The problem is a little more complicated when the nature and the details of the ionization caused by X-rays have to be analysed; and the perfect method for such investigations was not described until in a paper of 1923. The extremely delicate regulation of small-time intervals which is necessary in such researches is attained by the use of three pendulums of adjustable period, which are all released simultaneously. The pendulum which comes down first, opens a communication with a vacuum, and the resulting suction is used, by a mechanical device, to produce a sudden expansion of the gas that is being examined. The second pendulum releases an electric spark, which passes through an X-ray tube, oscillatory sparks being excluded; and thus the anticathode is brought to send an X-radiation of extremely short duration through the gas before the lenses of a stereoscopic camera. The third pendulum releases another electric spark, which passes through mercury vapour and momentarily illuminates the clouds. By means of sliding weights on the different pendulums, just as on an ordinary metronome, Wilson was able to bring it about that the X-rays were sent through the gas at the moment when the expansion was complete, and the illuminating spark just as long afterwards as was needed for a sufficient formation of droplets round the ions, but before the droplets had time to be dislocated by currents in the gas, which might have deformed the tracks visible on the photographic pictures.

Wilson's method attracted attention at first mainly as an elegant and popular method of demonstration. The formation of droplets by α-particles is so dense that the resulting cloud photographs show continuous white lines: and everybody was glad to recognize on these lines the sharp bendings which correspond to the sudden change of direction previously known. Along the β-rays, on the other hand, are seen isolated droplets, and their tracks show a multitude of different types according to differences in initial velocity. For the investigation of such rays with a comparatively small velocity, the most suitable method is the excitation by the momentary X-radiation described above. Here there has been collected a very large photographic material, from which probably not all possible conclusions have yet been drawn, and to which Wilson has devoted assiduous work.

Of late years, new and scientifically important results have been attained which could not have been gained by other methods. The consequence of this is that the discovery, although it was made so long ago, satisfies the provisions for the award of the Nobel Prize. It would not be of much use to describe these results on this occasion, as the understanding of them presupposes full knowledge of the structure of the atom. I will merely call to mind that in 1923 Wilson gave the experimental proof of the existence of the recoil electron tracks that had been postulated by Compton for his explanation of the change in wavelength of scattered X-rays, and that his method has rendered possible the closer examination of these tracks.

Professor Wilson. Although a long time has elapsed since you discovered your elegant expansion method, the high value of your discovery has been greatly augmented both through your own assiduous investigations and through results obtained by others. The Academy is happy that an article in the Statutes allows it in such cases to reward even discoveries of comparatively old date; and I now ask you to receive the prize that you have won from the hands of His Majesty.

Arthur H. Compton

X-rays as a branch of optics

Nobel Lecture, December 12, 1927

One of the most fascinating aspects of recent physics research has been the gradual extension of familiar laws of optics to the very high frequencies of X-rays, until at the present there is hardly a phenomenon in the realm of light whose parallel is not found in the realm of X-rays. Reflection, refraction, diffuse scattering, polarization, diffraction, emission and absorption spectra, photoelectric effect, all of the essential characteristics of light have been found also to be characteristic of X-rays. At the same time it has been found that some of these phenomena undergo a gradual change as we proceed to the extreme frequencies of X-rays, and as a result of these interesting changes in the laws of optics we have gained new information regarding the nature of light.

It has not always been recognized that X-rays is a branch of optics. As a result of the early studies of Röntgen and his followers it was concluded that X-rays could not be reflected or refracted, that they were not polarized on transversing crystals, and that they showed no signs of diffraction on passing through narrow slits. In fact, about the only property which they were found to possess in common with light was that of propagation in straight lines. Many will recall also the heated debate between Barkla and Bragg, as late as 1910, one defending the idea that X-rays are waves like light, the other that they consist of streams of little bullets called «neutrons». It is a debate on which the last word has not yet been said!

The refraction and reflection of X-rays

We should consider the phenomena of refraction and reflection as one problem, since it is a well-known law of optics that reflection can occur only from a boundary surface between two media of different indices of refraction. If one is found, the other must be present.

In his original examination of the properties of X-rays, Röntgen[1] tried unsuccessfully to obtain refraction by means of prisms of a variety of materials such as ebonite, aluminum, and water. Perhaps the experiment of this type most favorable for detecting refraction was one by Barkla[2]. In this work X-rays of a wavelength which excited strongly the characteristic K-radiation from bromine were passed through a crystal of potassium bromide. The precision of his experiment was such that he was able to conclude that the refractive index for a wavelength of 0.5 Å probably differed from unity by less than five parts in a million.

Although these direct tests for refraction of X-rays were unsuccessful, Stenström observed[3] that for X-rays whose wavelengths are greater than about 3 Å, reflected from crystals of sugar and gypsum, Bragg's law, $n\lambda = 2\,D\sin\vartheta$, does not give accurately the angles of reflection. He interpreted the difference as due to an appreciable refraction of the X-rays as they enter the crystal. Measurements by Duane and Siegbahn and their collaborators[4] showed that discrepancies of the same type occur, though they are very small indeed, when ordinary X-rays are reflected from calcite.

The direction of the deviations in Stenström's experiments indicated that the index of refraction of the crystals employed was less than unity. If this is the case also for other substances, total reflection should occur when X-rays in air strike a polished surface at a sufficiently sharp glancing angle, just as light in a glass prism is totally reflected from a surface between the glass and air if the light strikes the surface at a sufficiently sharp angle. From a measurement of this critical angle for total reflection it should be possible to determine the index of refraction of the X-rays.

When the experiment was tried[5] the results were strictly in accord with these predictions. The apparatus was set up as shown in Fig. 1, reflecting a

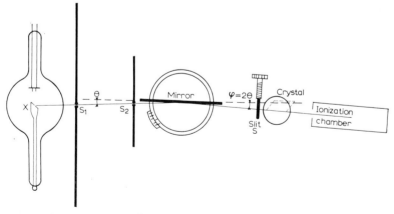

Fig. 1. Apparatus for studying the total reflection of X-rays.

narrow sheet of X-rays from a polished mirror on the crystal of a Bragg spectrometer. It was found that the beam could be reflected from the surfaces of a polished glass and silver through several minutes of arc. By studying the spectrum of the reflected beam, the critical glancing angle was found to be approximately proportional to the wavelength. For ordinary X-rays whose wavelength is one half an ångström, the critical glancing angle from crown glass was found to be about 4.5 minutes of arc, which means a reflective index differing from unity by less than one part in a million.

P C

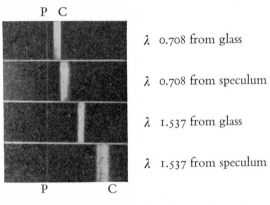

λ 0.708 from glass

λ 0.708 from speculum

λ 1.537 from glass

λ 1.537 from speculum

P   C

Fig. 2. Total reflection of X-rays from polished glass and speculum metal (Doan). P = direct beam; C = critical angle of the totally reflected beam.

Fig. 2 shows some photographs of the totally reflected beam and the critical angle for total reflection taken recently from Dr. Doan[6] working at Chicago. From the sharpness of the critical angle shown in this figure, it is evident that a precise determination of the refractive index can thus be made.

You will recall that when one measures the index of refraction of a beam of light in a glass prism it is customary to set the prism at the angle for minimum deviation. This is done primarily because it simplifies the calculation of the refractive index from measured angles. It is an interesting comment on the psychology of habit that most of the earlier investigators of the refraction X-rays by prisms also used their prisms set at the minimum deviation. Of course, since the effect to be measured was very small indeed, the adjustments should have been made to secure not the minimum deviation but the maximum possible. After almost thirty years of attempts to refract X-rays by prisms, experiments under the conditions to secure maximum refraction were first performed by Larsson, Siegbahn, and Waller[7], using the arrangement shown diagrammatically in Fig. 3. The X-rays struck the face of the prism at a fine glancing angle, just greater than the critical angle for the rays which are refracted. Thus the direct rays, the refracted rays, and the totally reflected rays of greater wavelength were all recorded on the same plate.

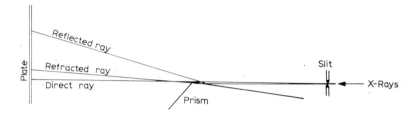

Fig. 3. Refraction of X-rays by a glass prism. (Arrangement of Larsson, Siegbahn, and Waller.)

Fig. 4 shows one of the resulting photographs. Here we see a complete dispersion spectrum of the refracted X-rays precisely similar to the spectrum obtained when the light is refracted by a prism of glass. The presence of the direct ray and the totally reflected ray on the same plate make possible all the angle measurements necessary for a precise determination of the refractive index of each spectrum line.

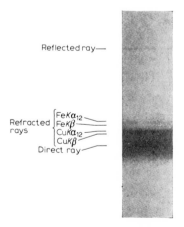

Fig. 4. Prism spectrum of X-rays obtained by Larsson, Siegbahn, and Waller.

For a generation we have been trying to obtain a quantitative test of Drude and Lorentz' dispersion theory in the ordinary optical region. But our ignorance regarding the number and the natural frequency of the electron oscillators in the refractive medium has foiled all such attempts. For the extreme frequencies of X-rays, however, the problem has become greatly simplified. In the case of substances such as glass, the X-ray frequencies are much higher than the natural frequencies of the oscillators in the medium, and the only knowledge which the theory requires is that of the number of electrons per unit volume in the dispersive medium. If we assume the number of electrons per atom to be equal to the atomic number, we are thus able to calculate at once the refractive index of the medium for X-rays. In the case of glass this calculation gives agreement with experiment within the experimental error, which is in some cases less than one per cent. So we may say that the laws of optical dispersion given by the electron theory are first established on a quantitative basis by these experiments on the refraction of X-rays.

Another way of looking at the problem is to assume the validity of the dispersion equation developed from the electron theory, and to use these measurements of refraction of X-rays to calculate the number of electrons in each atom of the refracting material. This affords us what is probably our most direct as well as our most precise means of determining this number. The precision of the experiments is now such that we can say that the number of electrons per atom effective in refracting X-rays is within less than one half of one per cent equal to the atomic number of the atom.

Thus optical refraction and reflection are extended to the region of X-rays, and this extension has brought with it more exact knowledge not only of the laws of optics but also of the structure of the atom.

The diffraction of X-rays

Early in the history of X-rays it was recognized that most of the properties of these rays might be explained if, as suggested by Wiechert[8], they consist of electromagnetic waves much shorter than those of light. Haga and Wind performed a careful series of experiments[9] to detect any possible diffraction by a wedge-shaped slit a few thousandths of an inch broad at its widest part. The magnitude of the broadening was about that which would result[10] from rays of 1.3 Å wavelength. The experiments were repeated by yet more refined methods by Walter and Pohl[11] who came to the conclusion that if any diffraction effects were present, they were considerably smaller than Haga and Wind had estimated. But on the basis of the photometric measurements of Walter and Pohl's plates by Koch[12] using his new photoelectric microphotometer, Sommerfeld found[13] that their photographs indicated an effective wavelength for hard X-rays of 4 Å, and for soft X-rays a wavelength measurably greater.

It may have been because of their difficulty that these experiments did not carry as far as their accuracy would seem to have warranted. Nevertheless it was this work perhaps more than any other that encouraged Laue to undertake his remarkable experiments on the diffraction of X-rays by crystals.

Within the last few years Walter has repeated these slit diffraction experiments, making use of the Kα-line of copper, and has obtained perfectly convincing diffraction effects[14]. Because of the difficulty in determining the width of the slit where the diffraction occurs, it was possible to make from his photographs only a rough estimate of the wavelength of X-rays. But within this rather large probable error the wavelength agreed with that determined by crystal spectrometry.

While these slit diffraction experiments were being developed, and long before they were brought to a successful conclusion, Laue and his collaborators discovered the remarkable fact that crystals act as suitable gratings for diffracting X-rays. You are all acquainted with the history of this discovery. The identity in nature of X-rays and light could no longer be doubted. It gave a tool which enabled the Braggs to determine with a definiteness previously almost unthinkable, the manner in which crystals are constructed of their elementary components. By its help, Moseley and Siegbahn have studied the spectra of X-rays, we have learned to count one by one the electrons in the different atoms, and we have found out something regarding the arrangement of these electrons. The measurement of X-ray wavelengths thus made possible gave Duane the means of making his precise determination of Planck's radiation constant. By showing the change of wavelength when X-rays are scattered, it has helped us to find the quanta of momentum of radiation which had previously been only vaguely suspected. Thus in the two great fields of modern physical inquiry, the structure of matter and the nature of radiation, the discovery of the diffraction of X-rays by crystals has opened the gateway to many new and fruitful paths of investigation. As Duc de Broglie has remarked, «if the value of a discovery is to be measured by fruitfulness of its consequences, the work of Laue and his collaborators should be considered as perhaps the most important in modern physics».

These are some of the consequences of extending the optical phenomenon of diffraction into the realm of X-rays.

There is, however, another aspect of the extension of optical diffraction into the X-ray region, which has also led to interesting results. It is the use of ruled diffraction gratings for studies of spectra. By a series of brilliant investigations, Schumann, Lyman, and Millikan, using vacuum spectrographs, have pushed the optical spectra by successive stages far into the ultraviolet. Using a concave reflection grating at nearly normal incidence, Millikan and his collaborators[15] found a line probably belonging to the L-series of aluminum, of a wavelength as short as 136.6 Å, only a twenty-fifth that of yellow light. Why his spectra stopped here, whether because of failure of his gratings to reflect shorter wavelengths, or because of lack of sensitiveness of the plates, or because his hot sparks gave no rays of shorter wavelength, was hard to say.

Röntgen had tried to get X-ray spectra by reflection from a ruled grating, but the task seemed hopeless. How could one get spectra from a reflection grating if the reflection grating would not reflect? But when it was found that X-rays could be totally reflected by fine glancing angles, hope for the success of such an experiment was revived. Carrara[16], working at Pisa, tried one of Rowland's optical gratings, but without success. Fortunately we at

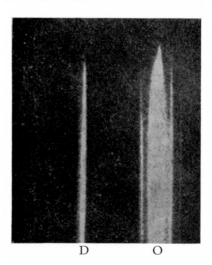

D   O

Fig. 5. Spectrum of the $K\alpha_1$-line of molybdenum, $\lambda = 0.708$ Å, from a grating ruled on speculum metal (Compton and Doan). D marks the direct beam, and O the directly reflected beam.

Chicago did not know of this failure, and with one of Michelson's gratings ruled specially for this purpose, Doan found that he could get diffraction spectra of the K-series radiations both from copper and molybdenum[17]. Fig. 5 shows one of our diffraction spectra, giving several orders of the $K\alpha_1$-line of molybdenum, obtained by reflection at a small glancing angle. This work was quickly followed by Thibaud[18], who photographed a beautiful spectrum of the K-series lines of copper from a grating of only a few hundred lines ruled on glass. That X-ray spectra could be obtained from the same type of ruled reflection gratings as those used with light was now established.

The race to complete the spectrum between the extreme ultraviolet of Millikan and the soft X-ray spectra of Siegbahn began again with renewed enthusiasm. It had seemed that the work of Millikan and his co-workers had carried the ultraviolet spectra to as short wavelengths as it was possible to go. On the X-ray side, the long wavelength limit was placed, theoretically at least, by the spacing of the reflecting layers in the crystal used as a natural grating. De Broglie, W. H. Bragg, Siegbahn, and their collaborators were finding suitable crystals of greater and greater spacing until Thoraeus and Siegbahn[19], using crystals of palmitic acid, measured the $L\alpha$-line of chromium with a wavelength 21.69 Å. But there still remained a gap of almost three octaves between these X-rays and the shortest ultraviolet in which, though radiation had been detected by photoelectric methods, no spectral measurements has been made.

Thibaud, working in de Broglie's laboratory at Paris, made a determined effort to extend the limit of the ultraviolet spectrum, using his glass grating at glancing incidence[20]. His spectra however stopped at 144 Å, a little greater than the shortest wavelength observed in Millikan's experiments.

But meanwhile, Dauvillier, also working with de Broglie, was making rapid strides working from the soft X-ray side of the gap. First[21] using a grating of palmitic acid, he found the $K\alpha$-line of carbon of wavelength 45 Å. Then[22] using for a grating a crystal of the lead salt of melissic acid, with the remarkable grating space of 87.5 Å, he measured a spectrum line of thorium as long as 121 Å, leaving only a small fraction of an octave between his longest X-ray spectrum lines and Millikan's shortest ultraviolet lines. The credit for filling in the greater part of the remaining gap must thus be given to Dauvillier.

The final bridge between the X-ray and the ultraviolet spectra has however been laid by Osgood[23], a young Scotchman working with me at Chicago. He also used soft X-rays as did Dauvillier, but instead of a crystal grating, he did his experiments with a concave glass grating in a Rowland mounting, but with the rays at glancing incidence. Fig. 6 shows a series of Osgood's spectra. The shortest wavelength here shown is the Kα-line of carbon, 45 Å, and we see a series of lines up to 211 Å. An interesting feature of the spectra is an emission band in the aluminum spectrum at about 170 Å, which is probably in some way associated with the L-series spectrum of aluminum. These spectra overlap, on the short wavelength side, Dauvillier's crystal measurements, and on the other side of the great wavelengths, Millikan's ultraviolet spectra.

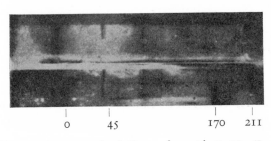

0	45	170	211

Fig. 6. Osgood's grating spectra of soft X-rays from Al, C, Mg, Fe, and Ni, showing lines from λ = 45 Å to λ = 211 Å. These are the first spectra bridging the gap between soft X-rays and the ultraviolet.

In the September number of *The Physical Review*, Hunt[24] describes similar experiments, using however a plane ruled grating at glancing incidence, in which he has measured lines from 2 Å down to the carbon line at 45 Å, thus meeting the shortest of Osgood's measurements. On the other hand, Fig. 7 shows some beautiful spectra of the extreme ultraviolet obtained recently by Dr. Hoag, working with Professor Gale at Chicago, using a concave grating at grazing incidence. These spectra extend from 200 Å to 1760 Å, overlapping Osgood's X-ray spectra on the short wavelength side and reaching the ordinary ultraviolet region on the side of the great wavelengths. Thus from the extreme infrared to the region of the ordinary X-rays we now have a continuous series of spectra from ruled gratings.

Whatever we may find regarding the nature of X-rays, it would take a bold man indeed to suggest, in light of these experiments, that they differ in nature from ordinary light.

It is too early to predict what may be the consequences of these grating measurements of X-rays. It seems clear, however, that they must lead to a new and more precise knowledge of the absolute wavelength of crystals.

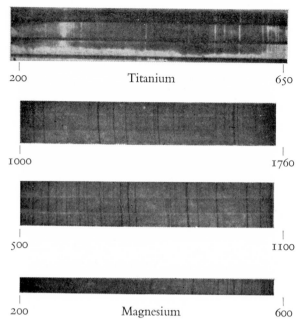

200	Titanium	650

1000		1760

500		1100

200	Magnesium	600

Fig. 7. Spectra of the extreme ultraviolet, from Mg and Ti, 200 Å to 1760 Å (Hoag).

This will in turn afford a new means of determining Avogadro's number and the electronic charge, which should be of precision comparable with that of Millikan's oil drops.

The scattering of X-rays and light

The phenomena that we have been considering are ones in which the laws which have been found to hold in the optical region apply equally well in the X-ray region. This is not the case, however, for all optical phenomena.

The theory of the diffuse scattering of light by turbid media has been examined by Drude, Lord Rayleigh, Raman, and others, and an essentially similar theory of the diffuse scattering of X-rays has been developed by Thomson, Debye, and others. Two important consequences of these theories are, (1) that the scattered radiation shall be of the same wavelength as the primary rays, and (2) that the rays scattered at 90 degrees with the primary rays shall be plane polarized. The experimental tests of these two predictions have led to interesting results.

A series of experiments performed during the last few years* has shown that secondary X-rays are of greater wavelength than the primary rays which produce them. This work is too well-known to require description. On the other hand, careful experiments to find a similar increase in wavelength in light diffusely scattered by a turbid medium have failed to show any effect[25]. An examination of the spectrum of the secondary X-rays shows that the primary beam has been split into two parts, as shown in Fig. 8, one of the same wavelength and the other of increased wavelength. When

* For an account of this work, see e.g. the writer's *X-rays and Electrons*, Chap. 9, Van Nostrand, 1926.

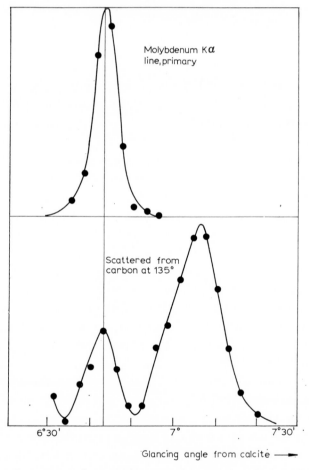

Fig. 8. A typical spectrum of scattered X-rays, showing the splitting of the primary ray into a modified and an unmodified ray.

different primary wavelengths are used, we find always the same difference in wavelength between these two components; but the relative intensity of the two components changes. For the longer wavelengths the unmodified ray has the greater energy, while for the shorter wavelengths the modified ray is predominant. In fact when hard γ-rays are employed, it is not possible to find any radiation of the original wavelength.

Thus in the wavelength of secondary radiation we have a gradually increasing departure from the classical electron theory of scattering as we go from the optical region to the region of X-rays and γ-rays.

The question arises, are these secondary X-rays of increased wavelength to be classed as scattered X-rays or as fluorescent? An important fact bearing on this point is the intensity of the secondary rays. From the theories of Thomson, Debye, and others it is possible to calculate the absolute intensity of the scattered rays. It is found that this calculated intensity agrees very nearly with the total intensity of the modified and unmodified rays, but that in many cases the observed intensity of the unmodified ray taken alone is very small compared with the calculated intensity. If the electron theory of the intensity of scattering is even approximately correct, we must thus include the modified with the unmodified rays as scattered rays.

Information regarding the origin of these secondary rays is also given by their state of polarization. We have called attention to the fact that the electron theory demands that the X-rays scattered at 90 degrees should be completely plane polarized. If the rays of increased wavelength are fluorescent, however, we should not expect them to be strongly polarized. You will remember the experiments performed by Barkla[26] some twenty years ago in which he observed strong polarization in X-rays scattered at right angles. It was this experiment which gave us our first strong evidence of the similar character of X-rays and light. But in this work the polarization was far from complete. In fact the intensity of the secondary rays at 90 degrees dropped only to one third its maximum value, where as for complete polarization it should have fallen to zero.

The fact that no such unpolarized rays exist was established by repeating Barkla's experiment[27] with scattering blocks of different sizes. When very small blocks were used, we found that the polarization was nearly complete. The lack of complete polarization in Barkla's experiments was due chiefly to the multiple scattering of the X-rays in the large blocks that he used to scatter the X-rays. It would seem that the only explanation of the complete polarization of the secondary rays is that they consist wholly of scattered rays.

According to the classical theory, an electromagnetic wave is scattered when it sets the electrons which it traverses into forced oscillations, and these oscillating electrons reradiate the energy which they receive. In order to account for the change in wavelength of the scattered rays, however, we have had to adopt a wholly different picture of the scattering process, as shown in Fig. 9. Here we do not think of the X-rays as waves but as light corpuscles, quanta, or, as we may call them, photons. Moreover, there is nothing here of the forced oscillation pictured on the classical view, but a sort of elastic collision, in which the energy and momentum are conserved.

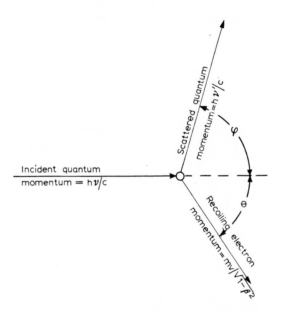

Fig. 9. An X-ray photon is deflected through an angle φ by an electron, which in turn recoils at an angle θ, taking a part of the energy of the photon.

This new picture of the scattering process leads at once to three consequences that can be tested by experiment. There is a change of wavelength

$$\delta\lambda = \frac{h}{mc}(\mathrm{1} - \cos\varphi) \qquad (\mathrm{1})$$

which accounts for the modified line in the spectra of scattered X-rays. Experiment has shown that this formula is correct within the precision of our knowledge of h, m, and c. The electron which recoils from the scattered X-rays should have the kinetic energy

$$E_{kin} = h\nu \cdot \frac{h\nu}{mc^2} \cos^2\theta \qquad (2)$$

approximately. When this theory was first proposed, no electrons of this type were known; but they were discovered by Wilson[28] and Bothe[29] within a few months after their prediction. Now we know that the number, energy, and spatial distribution of these recoil electrons are in accord with the predictions of the photon theory. Finally, whenever a photon is deflected at an angle φ, the electron should recoil at an angle θ given by the relation

$$\cot \tfrac{1}{2}\varphi = \tan \theta \qquad (3)$$

approximately.

This relation we have tested[30], using the apparatus shown diagrammatically in Fig. 10. A narrow beam of X-rays enters a Wilson expansion

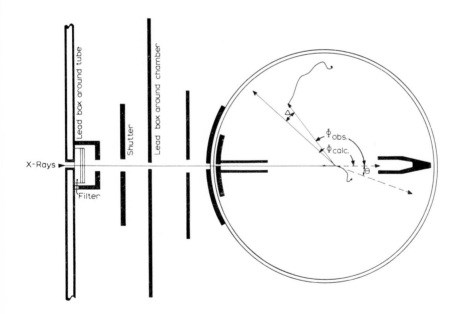

Fig. 10. An electron recoiling at an angle θ should be associated with a photon deflected through an angle φ.

chamber. Here it produces a recoil electron. If the photon theory is correct, associated with this recoil electron, a photon is scattered in the direction φ. If it should happen to eject a β-ray, the origin of this β-ray tells the direction in which the photon was scattered. Fig. 11 shows a typical photograph of the process. A measurement of the angle θ at which the recoil electron on this plate is ejected and the angle φ of the origin of the secondary β-particle, shows close agreement with the photon formula. This experiment is of especial significance, since it shows that for each recoil electron there is a scattered photon, and that the energy and momentum of the system photon plus electron are conserved in the scattering process.

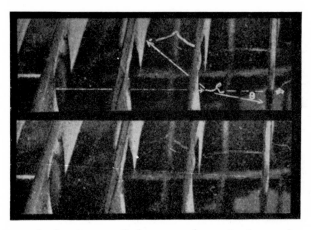

Fig. 11. Photograph showing recoil electron and associated secondary β-ray. (The upper photograph is retouched.)

The evidence for the existence of directed quanta of radiation afforded by this experiment is very direct. The experiment shows that associated with each recoil electron there is scattered X-ray energy enough to produce a secondary β-ray, and that this energy proceeds in a direction determined at the moment of ejection of the recoil electron. Unless the experiment is subject to improbably large experimental errors, therefore, the scattered X-rays proceed in the form of photons.

Thus we see that as a study of the scattering of radiation is extended into the very high frequencies of X-rays, the manner of scattering changes. For the lower frequencies the phenomena could be accounted for in terms of waves. For these higher frequencies we can find no interpretation of the scattering except in terms of the deflection of corpuscles or photons of radiation. Yet it is certain that the two types of radiation, light and X-rays, are essentially the same kind of thing. We are thus confronted with the dilemma of having before us a convincing evidence that radiation consists of waves, and at the same time that it consists of corpuscles.

It would seem that this dilemma is being solved by the new wave mechanics. De Broglie[31] has assumed that associated with every particle of matter in motion there is a wave whose wavelength is given by the relation

$$mv = h/\lambda$$

where mv is the momentum of the particle. A very similar assumption was made at about the same time by Duane[32], to account for the diffraction of X-ray photons. As applied to the motion of electrons, Schrödinger has shown the great power of this conception in studying atomic structure[33]. It now seems, through the efforts of Heisenberg, Bohr, and others, that this conception of the relation between corpuscles and waves is capable of giving us a unified view of the diffraction and interference of light, and at the same time of its diffuse scattering and the photoelectric effect. It would however take too long to describe these new developments in detail.

We have thus seen how the essentially optical properties of radiation have been recognized and studied in the realm of X-rays. A study of the refraction and specular reflection of X-rays has given an important confirmation of the electron theory of dispersion, and has enabled us to count with high precision the number of electrons in the atom. The diffraction of X-rays by crystals has given wonderfully exact information regarding the structure of crystals, and has greatly extended our knowledge of spectra. When X-rays were diffracted by ruled gratings, it made possible the study of the complete spectrum from the longest to the shortest waves. In the diffuse scattering of radiation, we have found a gradual change from the scattering of waves to the scattering of corpuscles.

Thus by a study of X-rays as a branch of optics we have found in X-rays all of the well-known wave characteristics of light, but we have found also that we must consider these rays as moving in directed quanta. It is these changes in the laws of optics when extended to the realm of X-rays that have been in large measure responsible for the recent revision of our ideas regarding the nature of the atom and of radiation.

1. W. Röntgen, *Sitzber. Würzburger Phys. Med. Ges.*, (1895). These papers are reprinted in German in *Ann. Physik*, 64 (1898) 1, and in English translation by A. Stanton in *Science*, 3 (1896) 227.

2. C. G. Barkla, *Phil. Mag.*, 31 (1916) 257.

3. W. Stenström, *Thesis Lund*, 1919.

4. W. Duane and R. A. Patterson, *Phys. Rev.*, 16 (1920) 532; M. Siegbahn, *Compt. Rend.*, 173 (1921) 1350; 174 (1922) 745.

5. A. H. Compton, *Phil. Mag.*, 45 (1923) 1121.

6. R. L. Doan, *Phil. Mag.*, [7], 4 (1927) 100.

7. A. Larsson, M. Siegbahn, and I. Waller, *Naturwiss.*, 12 (1924) 1212.

8. E. Wiechert, *Sitz. Phys.Ekon. Ges. Königsberg*, (1894).

9. H. Haga and C. H. Wind, *Wiedemann's Ann.*, 68 (1899) 884.

10. A. Sommerfeld, *Physik. Z.*, 2 (1900) 59.

11. B. Walter and R. W. Pohl, *Ann. Physik*, 29 (1909) 331.

12. P. P. Koch, *ibid.*, 38 (1912) 507.

13. A. Sommerfeld, *ibid.*, 38 (1912) 473.

14. B. Walter, *ibid.*, 74 (1924) 661; 75 (1924) 189.

15. R. A. Millikan, I. S. Bowen, R. A. Sawyer, and G. D. Shallenberger, *Proc. Natl. Acad. Sci. U.S.*, 7 (1921) 289; *Phys. Rev.*, 23 (1924) 1.

16. N. Carrara, *Nuovo Cimento*, 1 (1924) 107.

17. A. H. Compton and R. L. Doan, *Proc. Natl. Acad. Sci. U.S.*, 11 (1925) 598.

18. J. Thibaud, *Compt. Rend.*, 182 (1926) 1141.

19. M. Siegbahn and R. Thoraeus, *Arkiv Mat. Astron. Fysik*, 19 (1925) 1.

20. J. Thibaud, *J. Phys. Radium*, 8 (1927) 15.

21. A. Dauvillier, *Compt. Rend.*, 182 (1926) 1083.

22. A. Dauvillier, *J. Phys. Radium*, 8 (1927) 1.

23. T. H. Osgood, *Nature*, 119 (1927) 817; *Phys. Rev.*, 30 (1927) 567.

24. F. L. Hunt, *Phys. Rev.*, 30 (1927) 227.

25. For example, P. A. Ross, *Proc. Natl. Acad. Sci. U.S.*, 9 (1923) 246.

26. C. G. Barkla, *Proc. Roy. Soc. London*, A 77 (1906) 247.

27. A. H. Compton and C. F. Hagenow, *J. Opt. Soc. Am.*, 8 (1924) 487.

28. C. T. R. Wilson, *Proc. Roy. Soc. London*, A 104 (1923) 1.

29. W. Bothe, *Z. Physik*, 16 (1923) 319; 20 (1923) 237.

30. A. H. Compton and A. W. Simon, *Phys. Rev.*, 26 (1925) 289.

31. L. de Broglie, *Thesis Paris*, 1924.

32. W. Duane, *Proc. Natl. Acad. Sci. U.S.*, 11 (1925) 489.

33. E. Schrödinger, *Ann. Physik*, 79 (1926) 361, 489, 734; 80 (1926) 437; 81 (1926) 109; *Phys. Rev.*, 28 (1926) 1051.

Biography

Arthur Holly Compton was born at Wooster, Ohio, on September 10th, 1892, the son of Elias Compton, Professor of Philosophy and Dean of the College of Wooster. He was educated at the College, graduating Bachelor of Science in 1913, and he spent three years in postgraduate study at Princeton University receiving his M.A. degree in 1914 and his Ph.D. in 1916. After spending a year as instructor of physics at the University of Minnesota, he took a position as a research engineer with the Westinghouse Lamp Company at Pittsburgh until 1919 when he studied at Cambridge University as a National Research Council Fellow. In 1920, he was appointed Wayman Crow Professor of Physics, and Head of the Department of Physics at the Washington University, St. Louis; and in 1923 he moved to the University of Chicago as Professor of Physics. Compton returned to St. Louis as Chancellor in 1945 and from 1954 until his retirement in 1961 he was Distinguished Service Professor of Natural Philosophy at the Washington University.

In his early days at Princeton, Compton devised an elegant method for demonstrating the Earth's rotation, but he was soon to begin his studies in the field of X-rays. He developed a theory of the intensity of X-ray reflection from crystals as a means of studying the arrangement of electrons and atoms, and in 1918 he started a study of X-ray scattering. This led, in 1922, to his discovery of the increase of wavelength of X-rays due to scattering of the incident radiation by free electrons, which implies that the scattered quanta have less energy than the quanta of the original beam. This effect, nowadays known as the *Compton effect*, which clearly illustrates the particle concept of electromagnetic radiation, was afterwards substantiated by C. T. R. Wilson who, in his cloud chamber, could show the presence of the tracks of the recoil electrons. Another proof of the reality of this phenomenon was supplied by the coincidence method (developed by Compton and A. W. Simon, and independently in Germany by W. Bothe and H. Geiger), by which it could be established that individual scattered X-ray photons and recoil electrons appear at the same instant, contradicting the views then being developed by some investigators in an attempt to reconcile quantum views with the continuous waves of electromagnetic theory. For this discovery, Compton was awarded the Nobel Prize in Physics for 1927 (sharing this with C. T. R. Wilson who received the Prize for his discovery of the cloud chamber method).

In addition, Compton discovered (with C. F. Hagenow) the phenomenon of total reflection of X-rays and their complete polarization, which led to a more accurate determination of the number of electrons in an atom. He was also the first (with R. L. Doan) who obtained X-ray spectra from ruled gratings, which offers a direct method of measuring the wavelength of X-rays. By comparing these spectra with those obtained when using a crystal, the absolute value of the grating space of the crystal can be determined. The Avogadro number found by combining above value with the measured crystal density, led to a new value for the electronic charge. This outcome necessitated the revision of the Millikan oil-drop value from 4.774 to 4.803×10^{-10} e.s.u. (revealing that systematic errors had been made in the measurement of the viscosity of air, a quantity entering into the oil-drop method).

During 1930–1940, Compton led a world-wide study of the geographic variations of the intensity of cosmic rays, thereby fully confirming the observations made in 1927 by J. Clay from Amsterdam of the influence of latitude on cosmic ray intensity. He could, however, show that the intensity was correlated with geomagnetic rather than geographic latitude. This gave rise to extensive studies of the interaction of the Earth's magnetic field with the incoming isotropic stream of primary charged particles.

Compton has numerous papers on scientific record and he is the author of *Secondary Radiations Produced by X-rays* (1922), *X-Rays and Electrons* (1926, second edition 1928), *X-Rays in Theory and Experiment* (with S. K. Allison, 1935, this being the revised edition of *X-rays and Electrons*), *The Freedom of Man* (1935, third edition 1939), *On Going to College* (with others, 1940), and *Human Meaning of Science* (1940).

Dr. Compton was awarded numerous honorary degrees and other distinctions including the Rumford Gold Medal (American Academy of Arts and Sciences), 1927; Gold Medal of Radiological Society of North America, 1928; Hughes Medal (Royal Society) and Franklin Medal (Franklin Institute), 1940.

He served as President of the American Physical Society (1934), of the American Association of Scientific Workers (1939–1940), and of the American Association for the Advancement of Science (1942).

In 1941 Compton was appointed Chairman of the National Academy of Sciences Committee to Evaluate Use of Atomic Energy in War. His investigations, carried out in cooperation with E. Fermi, L. Szilard, E. P. Wigner and others, led to the establishment of the first controlled uranium fission reactors, and, ultimately, to the large plutonium-producing reactors in Hanford, Washington, which produced the plutonium for the Nagasaki bomb, in August 1945. (He also played a role in the Government's decision to use the bomb; a personal account of these matters may be found in his book, *Atomic Quest – a Personal Narrative*, 1956.)

In 1916, he married Betty Charity McCloskey. The eldest of their two sons, Arthur Allen, is in the American Foreign Service and the youngest, John Joseph, is Professor of Philosophy at the Vanderbilt University (Nashville, Tennessee). His brother Wilson is a former President of the Washington State University, and his brother Karl Taylor was formerly President of the Massachusetts Institute of Technology.

Compton's chief recreations were tennis, astronomy, photography and music.

He died on March 15th, 1962, in Berkeley, California.

CHARLES T. R. WILSON

On the cloud method of making visible ions and the tracks of ionizing particles

Nobel Lecture, December 12, 1927

In September 1894 I spent a few weeks in the Observatory which then existed on the summit of Ben Nevis, the highest of the Scottish hills. The wonderful optical phenomena shown when the sun shone on the clouds surrounding the hill-top, and especially the coloured rings surrounding the sun (coronas) or surrounding the shadow cast by the hill-top or observer on mist or cloud (glories), greatly excited my interest and made me wish to imitate them in the laboratory.

At the beginning of 1895 I made some experiments for this purpose – making clouds by expansion of moist air after the manner of Coulier and Aitken. Almost immediately I came across something which promised to be of more interest than the optical phenomena which I had intended to study. Moist air which had been freed from Aitken's dust particles, so that no cloud was formed even when a considerable degree of supersaturation was produced by expansion, did appear to give a cloud if the expansion and consequent supersaturation exceeded a certain limit. A quantitative expansion apparatus (Fig. 1) was therefore made in which given samples of moist air could repeatedly be allowed to expand suddenly without danger of contamination, and in which the increase of volume to be made could be adjusted at will.

It was found that there was a definite critical value for the expansion ratio ($v_2/v_1 = 1.25$) corresponding to an approximately fourfold supersaturation. In moist air which had been freed from Aitken's nuclei by repeatedly forming a cloud and allowing the drops to settle, no drops were formed unless the expansion exceeded this limit, while if it were exceeded, a shower of drops was seen to fall. The number of drops in the shower showed no diminution however often the process of producing the shower and allowing the drops to fall was repeated. It was evident then that the nuclei were always being regenerated in the air. A note describing these experiments was read before the Cambridge Philosophical Society in May 1895.

Further experiments with somewhat more elaborate apparatus (Fig. 2)

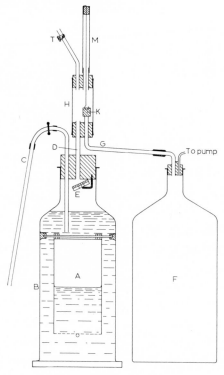

Fig. 1.

which allowed of more sudden expansion showed that there was a second critical expansion corresponding to an approximately eightfold supersaturation of the vapour. With expansions exceeding this limit, dense clouds were formed in dust-free air, the number of drops in the cloud increasing with very great rapidity as the expansion was increased beyond it and giving rise on account of their small and uniform size to very beautiful colour phenomena. The number of drops for expansions between the two limits remained small – the resulting condensation resembling a shower of rain rather than a cloud. The results were not essentially different in the various pure gases tried – although the expansion required to produce a given supersaturation was naturally different.

While the obvious explanation of the dense clouds formed when the second supersaturation limit was exceeded was that here we had condensation occurring in the absence of any nuclei other than the molecules of the vapour or gas – those responsible for the rain-like condensation which occurred when the supersaturation lay between the two limits from the first, excited

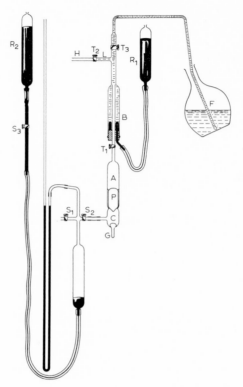

Fig. 2.

my interest. The very fact that their number was so limited and yet that they were always being regenerated, together with the fact that the supersaturation required indicated a magnitude not greatly exceeding molecular dimensions, at once suggested that we had a means of making visible and counting certain individual molecules or atoms which were at the moment in some exceptional condition. Could they be electrically charged atoms or ions?[*]

In the autumn of 1895 came the news of Röntgen's great discovery. At the beginning of 1896 J. J. Thomson was investigating the conductivity of air exposed to the new rays – and I had the opportunity of using an X-ray tube of the primitive form then used which had been made by Prof. Thomson's assistant Mr. Everett in the Cavendish Laboratory. I can well recall my delight when I found at the first trial that while no drops were formed on expansion of the cloud chamber when exposed to X-rays if the expansion were less than 1.25, a fog which took many minutes to fall was produced

[*] The striking effect of point discharges on condensation in a steam jet had been attributed to ions by H. v. Helmholtz and Richarz.

when the expansion lay between the rain-like and cloud-like limits; X-rays thus produced in large numbers nuclei of the same kind as were always being produced in very small numbers in the air within the cloud chamber.

A short note describing this experiment was communicated to the Royal Society in March 1896.* The full paper containing the detailed account of the measurement of the two cloud limits in different gases was communicated a year later.

During the following two years I investigated by means of the expansion apparatus the condensation nuclei produced in gases by X-rays, by the newly discovered uranium rays, by ultraviolet light, by point discharges and other agents.

The purely ionizing agents all produced nuclei, identical as regards the minimum supersaturation required to cause water to condense upon them.

The condensation nuclei produced by these ionizing agents were shown to be indeed themselves the ions by their behaviour in an electric field. They could be completely removed by applying an electric field before expansion – so that no cloud was formed.

Uncharged nuclei, not removable by a field, were also found to be produced in various ways and their properties were investigated.

A paper describing these investigations was communicated to the Royal Society in the autumn of 1898.

The following winter was occupied in studying separately the phenomena of condensation on positive and negative ions. It was found that the measurement of the least expansion required to condense water in ionized air or other gas had all been concerned with the negative ion; to catch the positive ion the expansion ratio v_2/v_1, had to exceed a limit of about 1.31, corresponding to an approximately sixfold supersaturation instead of the fourfold supersaturation required by the negative ion.

This paper marked the completion of a stage in my work, the behaviour of ions as condensation nuclei. It was now possible to make visible the individual ions and to distinguish between positive and negative ions.

This found its immediate application in the determination of the charge carried by an ion by Thomson and later by H. A. Wilson. The method used by the latter of partially balancing the weight of a charged drop by a known electric field and determining the change in the rate of fall did not however

* Richarz about the same time described the action of X-rays on condensation in the steam jet.

really depend essentially on the charge being due to condensation on an ion; and Millikan, whose earlier experiments were made by H. A. Wilson's method, soon abandoned the use of water drops and the expansion method.

It is, I think, of some interest that the value of the elementary charge « e », deduced directly from the degree of supersaturation required to cause negative ions to grow into visible drops, is 4.9×10^{-10} e.s.u.; it agrees within 1 per cent with Millikan's accurately determined value.

My own researches at this time were directed in another direction. Since the nuclei responsible for the rain-like condensation in air not exposed to known ionizing agents require just the same degree of supersaturation to make water condense upon them as do the ions produced by X-rays and other ionizing agents, it seemed almost certain that they also are ions. Experiments were therefore made to find if there was a measurable conduction of electricity through air in a closed vessel containing dust-free air. These led at once to positive results, and proved that the air in a closed vessel is always ionized. Quite independently and approaching the matter from a different side, Geitel was working at the subject in Germany and arrived at the same conclusion; his paper was published very shortly before mine. My own experiments were performed on a small scale, the method used being one afterwards very largely employed, in which the rate of loss of charge was measured from an insulated system consisting of a short metal rod with a gold leaf attached which was suspended in an ionization chamber in such a way that the possibility of leakage along the supports was eliminated.

These experiments were carried out in 1900, and they led me naturally to further experiments on conduction in closed vessels, to the direction of radioactive matter carried down by rain and snow, to the direct measurement of the current between the atmosphere and the earth, and to the study of atmospheric electricity generally.

With the exception of some experiments published in 1904 proving directly that the nuclei causing the ordinary rain-like condensation are removable by an electric field and are therefore ions (an experiment which required for success a somewhat larger expansion apparatus than that which had been used in the condensation experiments on the ions produced by X-rays) my experimental work on condensation phenomena was not resumed for many years.

Among the experimental work on the subject carried out by others in this period, in addition to the determination of the electronic charge, that on condensation phenomena in other vapours than water by Przibram and by

Laby should be mentioned. These investigations showed that water vapour is quite exceptional in condensing more readily on the negative than on the positive ion; a connection between the relative efficiency of the positive and negative ions and the sign of the electrical charges developed on splashing – the Lenard effect – was established.

Towards 1910 I began to make experiments with a view to increasing the usefulness of the condensation method.

I had from the time of my first experiments on condensation of water vapour on the ions had in view the possibility of determining the ionic charge by a direct method, in which the ions carrying a known charge were to be made visible by condensation, photographed and counted. The plan which I had in view on resuming the work was that of measuring an intermittent current from a negatively charged plate exposed to ultraviolet light within the cloud chamber, thus obtaining a stream of ions divided into groups, and finding the number of ions per group by the condensation method.

Again in the years which had elapsed since my earlier experiments, ideas on the corpuscular nature of α- and β-rays had become much more definite, and I had in view the possibility that the track of an ionizing particle might be made visible and photographed by condensing water on the ions which it liberated. As I succeeded in this latter aim, and Millikan had by this time rendered the other project unnecessary, the determination of «e» by the method of direct counting of drops was never carried out.

Much time was spent in making tests of the most suitable form of expansion apparatus and in finding an efficient means of instantaneous illumination of the cloud particles for the purpose of photographing them. In the spring of 1911 tests were still incomplete, but it occurred to me one day to try whether some indication of the tracks might not be made visible with the rough apparatus already constructed. The first test was made with X-rays, with little expectation of success, and in making an expansion of the proper magnitude for condensation on the ions while the air was exposed to the rays I was delighted to see the cloud chamber filled with little wisps and threads of clouds – the tracks of the electrons ejected by the action of the rays. The radium-tipped metal tongue of a spintharoscope was then placed inside the cloud chamber and the very beautiful sight of the clouds condensed along the tracks of the α-particles was seen for the first time. The long thread-like tracks of fast β-particles were also seen when a suitable source was brought near the cloud chamber.

Some rough photographs were obtained and were included in a short communication to the Royal Society made in April 1911.

The summer of 1911 was occupied in designing improved apparatus. The expansion apparatus (Fig. 3) was constructed in the workshop of the Cavendish Laboratory and is the one which I have had in use up to the present time. In the winter which followed, the photographs were obtained which formed the basis of a paper communicated to the Royal Society in the following June (1912).

The essential conditions to be fulfilled if good pictures of the tracks are to be obtained are mainly these. The expansion must be effected without stirring up the gas; this condition is secured by using a wide, shallow cloud chamber of which the floor can be made to drop suddenly and so produce the desired increase of volume. The cloud chamber must be freed not only from «dust» particles, but from ions other than those produced by the ionizing particles under observation; an electric field maintained between the roof and floor of the cloud chamber serves this purpose.

For the purpose of obtaining sharp pictures of the tracks, the order of operations has to be: firstly, the production of the necessary supersaturation by sudden expansion of the gas; secondly, the passage of the ionizing par-

Fig. 3.

ticles through the supersaturated gas; and finally, the illumination of the
cloud condensed on the ions along the track.

Perhaps the most important purpose that the photographs obtained at this
time served, was to confirm, in a way which was free from ambiguity, conclusions which had already been reached by less direct means and which in
some cases, but not in all, had come to be generally accepted.

I remember showing W. H. Bragg one of the first good pictures of α-
ray tracks very shortly after it was obtained. He at once showed me a diagram which he had just published showing examples of what he considered
likely forms for the paths of α-rays. The similarity between the actual photograph and Bragg's ideal picture was astonishing. (Lantern slides from photographs of α-particle cloud-tracks taken at this time were shown – Figs. 4
and 5.)

Fig. 4.

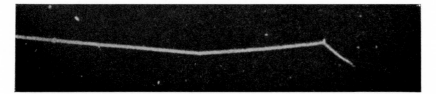

Fig. 5.

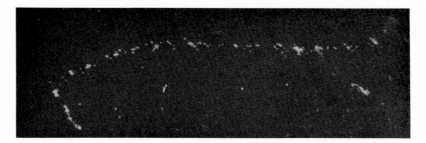

Fig. 6.

The tracks of electrons were of remarkable straightness when the velocity
was high, but slower electrons (Fig. 6) showed both sudden deflections

through large angles and gradual deviations due to an accumulation of small deflections – Rutherford's single and compound scattering. Both types of scattering were also shown in the last part of the course of the α-particles.

The pictures of the clouds condensed in air exposed to a beam of X-rays showed perfectly clearly that the primary effect of the rays is to eject electrons with considerable velocity from atoms in the path of the beam, and that the ionization is due to the action of these secondary β-particles. This was in accordance with the conclusions at which W.H.Bragg had arrived.

Information as to the nature of the ionization by β-particles was afforded by the photographs (e.g. Fig. 6). As was stated in the paper published in 1912, the ions along the track of a β-particle occur partly in pairs, partly in groups; and the groups were interpreted as indicating that in certain cases an electron ejected from an atom by a β-particle may itself have energy enough to ionize. This result appeared to be overlooked in later discussions as to the nature of ionization by β-particles.

Further photographs were taken in the winter of 1912–1913, especially illustrating the effects of X-rays. Some of these were exhibited at lectures before the Royal Institution and the French Physical Society, and published in their journals. Among these were pictures showing the effects of placing a sheet of metal, e.g. silver (Fig. 7), in the path of a beam of X-rays. These showed very clearly the absorption by the screen of the primary radiation; and the absorption by the air of the characteristic radiations from a copper or silver screen was also shown by the clouds condensed along tracks of the electrons which they ejected.

The tracks of the electrons ejected from a thin copper screen as a result of the absorption of the primary X-rays was also well shown (Fig. 8); the excess of the number ejected on the side of emergence being conspicuous. In obtaining the pictures which best showed this effect, the intensity of the radiation was reduced by introducing a plate of aluminium about 1 cm in thickness which removed especially the less penetrating rays. A very interesting feature appears in these photographs. It is described in the concluding paragraph of the *Journal de Physique* paper:

« A great number of the rays emitted by the copper and the air under the influence of the X-rays are extraordinarily long; some attain a length which in air at atmospheric pressure corresponds to nearly three centimetres. It should be added, however, that on the path of the primary X-rays one can see a large number of little patches of cloud, which perhaps represent the paths of exceedingly short cathode rays, and of which the interpretation requires further investigation. »

These very short tracks, we now know, are due to the Compton effect; they are the tracks of recoiling electrons, each of which has scattered a quantum of radiation.

At this stage of the work, some stereoscopic pictures of cloud tracks were obtained; and the advantages of such virtually three-dimensional pictures were so apparent that henceforth this method was exclusively used. A number of stereoscopic pictures of α-ray tracks and of the tracks of electrons ejected by X-rays had been obtained when war broke out.

Work on the tracks was entirely laid aside during the war. When it was resumed (at the Solar Physics Observatory, to which I was now attached) it was some time before good pictures were obtained, not till the autumn of

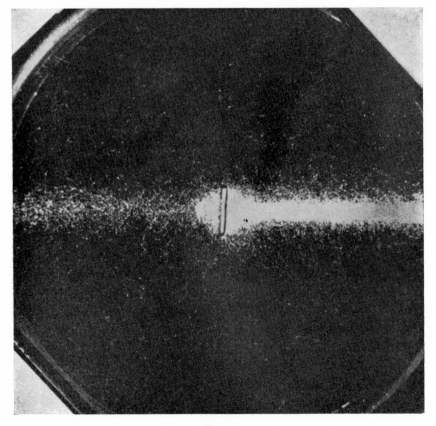

Fig. 7.

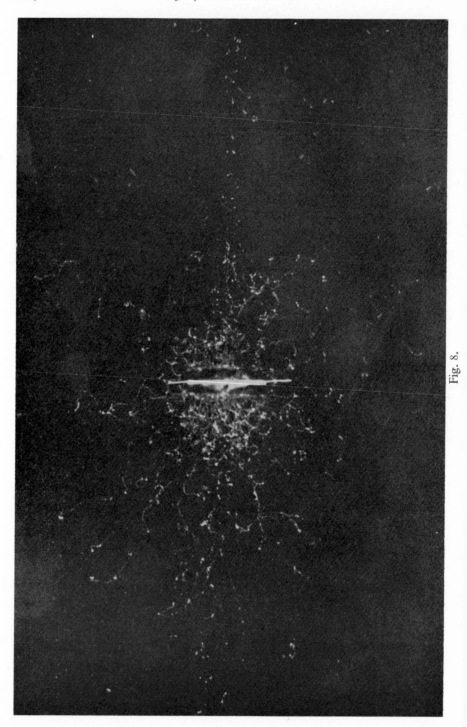

Fig. 8.

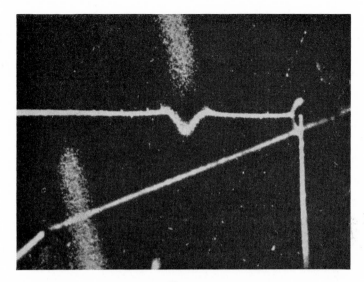

Fig. 9.

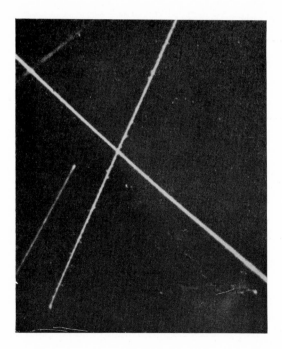

Fig. 10.

1921. A number of stereoscopic pictures of α-ray tracks were then obtained with some thorium emanation in the cloud chamber; some of these pictures were of interest and were published in November 1922. They showed well, for example (Figs. 9 and 10), the separation by an electric field of the positive and negative ions liberated along the track of an α-particle which traversed the cloud chamber before expansion; the two associated tracks of α-particles from an atom of thorium emanation and from the resulting thorium A atom; the track of the recoiling atom which has ejected an α-particle; and the tracks of δ-rays (electrons ejected by the α-particle with velocity comparable with its own) projecting from the initial portions of α-ray tracks. The tracks of δ-rays due to α-rays in hydrogen had been photographed some years before by Bumstead in America.

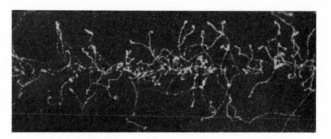

Fig. 11.

The experiments on the effects of X-rays and of the electrons ejected by them, which had been interrupted by the war, were now resumed, and a number of stereoscopic pictures were obtained between December 1921 and July 1922. These contained a large amount of material for study and the results were not ready for publication till June 1923. When the cloud chamber is momentarily traversed by a beam of X-rays of suitable intensity a picture (Fig. 11) is obtained (in three dimensions if the stereoscopic method is used) of the tracks of all the electrons ejected from a given volume of the gas by the action of the X-rays, primary and secondary. An examination of the picture shows at once: (1) the point of origin of each β-ray (electron track); (2) its initial direction (i.e. the direction in which an electron has been ejected from its parent atom by the action of the radiation); (3) its range or total length of its path; (4) the form of the track, its sudden or gradual bends, and the number and direction of emission of any secondary β-rays (branches); and (5) the variation of ionization along the track; under favourable conditions the number and distribution of the ions along the tracks may be obtained by direct counting.

The general results obtained can hardly be indicated otherwise than by showing examples of the photographs. Unfortunately I am not able to show them stereoscopically on the screen.

1. The first picture (Fig. 12) shows the absolutely straight track of a fast electron, and the devious tracks of electrons of which the energy corresponds to less than about 20,000 volts.

2. This (Fig. 13) shows the track of an electron of moderate energy: the straightness of the initial portion – a deviation through a large angle as a result of a close approach to the nucleus of an atom – the increasing curvature of the track and increasing ionization as the velocity diminishes.

3. Here (Fig. 14) the primary electron has ejected from an atom a secondary electron with energy enough to form a conspicuous branch track.

4. This (Fig. 15) is the track of a very fast electron passing through air at rather low pressure. In this picture the drops condensed on positive and negative ions are individually visible, and occur sometimes in pairs, sometimes in groups. The electron ejected from an atom by the primary β-particle has in many cases emerged with insufficient energy to produce further ionization; in other cases the energy of the ejected electron has been sufficient to produce one or more additional pairs of ions by collision.

5. In a large number of cases (e.g. Fig. 16) while the individual ions could not be counted, it was easy to determine the number of groups, i.e. the primary ionization or number of atoms from which an electron was ejected per cm of path.

6. This (Fig. 17) shows the tracks of electrons ejected by the K-radiations from silver.

7. The next picture (Fig. 18) shows the tracks of those ejected under identical conditions by the K-rays from copper.

From data such as those contained in these two pictures it was possible to measure the ranges of electrons of known initial energy. The range in air was found to be 1 cm for an electron of about 21,000 volts, and to vary according to Whiddington's law of the fourth power of the velocity. This result was utilized in determining the primary ionization for electrons of approximately known velocity.

8. The next picture (Fig. 19) was obtained by passing a very narrow beam of hard X-rays through a thin copper plate. Only two tracks appeared in the photograph, that of an electron ejected from the copper by the primary

beam, and a short one, in the air outside the primary beam, of range corresponding to ejection of an electron by copper K-radiation. We almost certainly have here the tracks of the copper K-electron whose ejection was followed by the emission of a quantum of copper K-radiation, and of the electron ejected from nitrogen or oxygen as a result of the absorption of this same quantum of copper K-radiation.

9. A quite similar picture (Fig. 20) obtained with a narrow beam of hard X-rays passing through a platinum plate.

10. Similarly related tracks may occur, both of which have their origin in the air. This picture (Fig. 21) shows the most common case (one independently discovered by Auger and explained, and very thoroughly investigated by him). Here both tracks start from the same atom; the K-radiation (or the energy which might have been spent in emitting it) being used in ejecting an outer electron from the atom from which the X-rays had ejected a K-electron.

The remaining pictures (Figs. 22, 23, and 24) show the cloud tracks obtained when horizontal beams of X-rays traversed the cloud chamber from right to left. They show, as some of the pictures obtained in 1913 had already indicated, that two classes of β-rays are produced by such rays, giving « long » tracks and « short » tracks.

A « long » track is the track of a photoelectron, i.e. of an electron ejected as the result of absorption of a quantum of X-radiation. The number of short tracks was found to be very small relatively to that of the long tracks when the wavelength of the incident radiation is as great as one ångström. It increases rapidly as the wavelength diminishes, and for short wavelengths the number greatly exceeds that for the long tracks. At the same time the short tracks which are mere « sphere tracks » when they are due to the longer waves become « fish tracks »; they begin to have a measurable range, and their appearance shows that they are due to electrons ejected nearly along the direction of propagation of the primary beam.

It was pointed out in the 1923 paper that the phenomena relating to these tracks supported A. H. Compton's theory of the scattering of X-rays, and that they are in all probability just the tracks of the recoiling electrons which according to this theory have scattered individual quanta of radiation.

It was pointed out by Compton that the relative numbers of the short and long tracks for a given wavelength of the incident radiation in these photographs are in agreement with the ratio between the scattering and absorption coefficients, and that this in itself furnishes strong support for his theory.

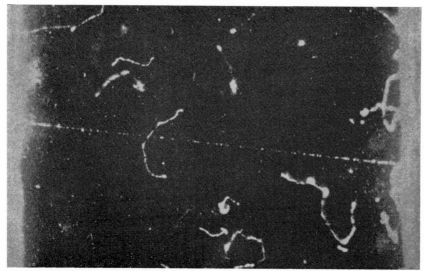

Fig. 12.

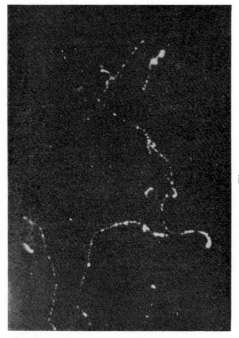

Fig. 13.

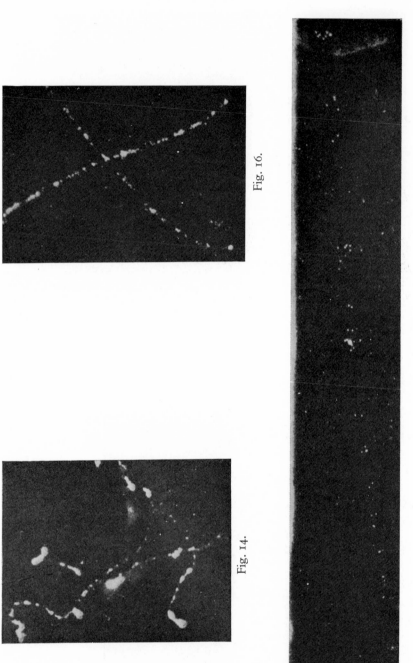

Fig. 16.

Fig. 15.

Fig. 14.

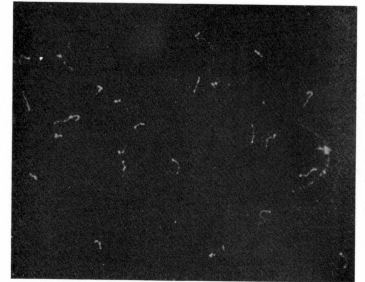

Fig. 18.

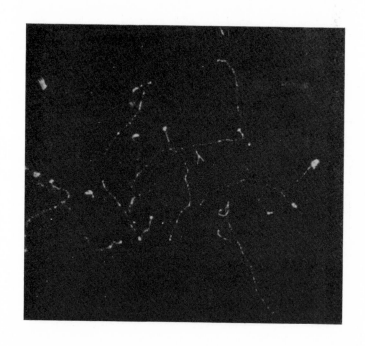

Fig. 17.

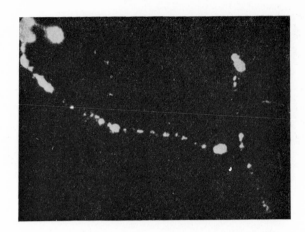

Fig. 21

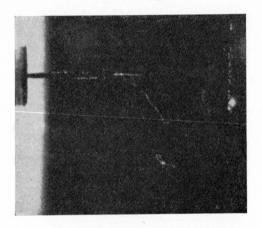

Fig. 20.

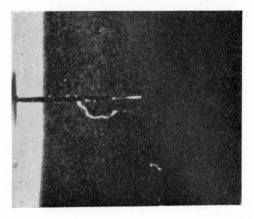

Fig. 19.

Fig. 22.

Fig. 23.

Fig. 24.

Nuttall and Williams have later investigated the relative numbers of long and short tracks in cloud photographs with homogeneous X-rays of different wavelengths in pure gases. This investigation as well as other recent cloud experiments, such as those of Compton and his collaborators, afford strong confirmation of Compton's theory and leave no room for doubt that the « fish tracks » are the tracks of the recoil electrons of that theory; each represents the scattering of a quantum of radiation.

The long tracks, i.e. the tracks of electrons ejected as a result of absorption of a quantum of radiation may be initially nearly at right angles to the beam of X-rays or may be inclined at considerable angles to this direction. In my own observations the number which had a forward component in their velocity was found considerably to exceed those with a backward component; and the ratio of the number with a forward to the number with a backward component increased with increasing frequency of the radiation. Qualitatively at least one may explain this result by saying that the momentum of the absorbed quantum is given to the ejected electron. The matter has been investigated much more fully by Auger and others.

I have tried to give some account of the history of the development of the cloud method.

During the last few years many physicists have been using the method; in some cases with refinements which made it possible to attain an accuracy much exceeding that arrived at in my experiments. It would take too long even to enumerate these investigations. But I should like to mention as examples of the applications of the method: the work of Blackett on collisions of α-particles with atomic nuclei and on atomic disintegrations thus produced, on the ranges of individual α-particles by Mlle Curie and by Miss Meitner, on δ-rays by Chadwick and Emeleus, on the mobility of radioactive ions by Dee, on X-rays and the β-rays associated with them by Bothe, by Auger, by Nuttall and Williams, and by Compton and his collaborators; and on the study of the wavelengths of γ-radiations, by measurement of the ranges of the Compton recoil electrons, by Skobelzyn.

Biography

Charles Thomson Rees Wilson was born on the 14th of February, 1869, in the parish of Glencorse, near Edinburgh. His father, John Wilson, was a farmer, and his ancestors had been farmers in the South of Scotland for generations. His mother was Annie Clerk Harper.

At the age of four he lost his father, and his mother moved with the family to Manchester, where he was at first educated at a private school, and later at Owen's College – now the University of Manchester. Here, intending to become a physician, Wilson took up mainly biology. Having been granted an entrance scholarship in 1888 he went on to Cambridge (Sidney Sussex College), where he took his degree in 1892. It was here that he became interested in the physical sciences, especially physics and chemistry. (It was also possible that Wilson's decision to abandon medicine was influenced by Balfour Stewart, who was professor of physics at Owen's College at that time – about a dozen years earlier, J. J. Thomson, who also went to Cambridge, had passed through the same College.)

When standing on the summit of Ben Nevis, the highest of the Scottish mountains, in the late summer of 1894, Wilson was struck by the beauty of coronas and « glories » (coloured rings surrounding shadows cast on mist and cloud), and he decided to imitate these natural phenomena in the laboratory (early 1895). His sharp observation and keen intellect, however, led him to suspect (after a few months' work at the Cavendish Laboratory) that the few drops reappearing again and again each time he expanded a volume of moist, dust-free air, might be the result of condensation on nuclei – possibly the ions causing the « residual » conductivity of the atmosphere – produced continuously. Wilson's hypothesis was supported after exposure (early 1896) of his primitive *cloud chamber* to the newly discovered (end of 1895) X-rays. The immense increase of the « rain-like » condensation fitted excellently with the observation made by Thomson and McClelland, immediately after Röntgen's discovery, that air was made conductive by the passage of X-rays. When, during the summer of that year, it was firmly established by Thomson and Rutherford that the conductivity was indeed due to ionization of the gas, there was no longer any doubt that ions in gases could be detected and, photographically, recorded and thus studied at leisure. Wilson's appointment as Clerk Maxwell Student, at the end of that year, enabled him to devote all his time for the next three years to research, and for a year subsequent to this he was employed by the Meteorological Council in research on atmospheric electricity. The greater part of his work on the behaviour of ions as condensation nuclei was thus carried out in the years 1895–1900, whilst after this his other occupations–mainly tutorial–prevented him from dealing sufficiently with the development of the cloud chamber. Early in 1911, however, he was the first person to see and photograph the tracks of individual α- and β-particles and electrons. (The latter were described by him as «little wisps and threads of clouds».) The event aroused great interest as the paths of the α-particles were just as W. H. Bragg had drawn them in a publication some years earlier. But it was not until 1923 that the cloud chamber was brought to perfection and led to his two, beautifully illustrated, classic papers on the tracks of electrons. Wilson's technique was promptly followed with startling success in all parts of the world–in Cambridge, by Blackett (who in 1948 received the Nobel Prize on account of his further development of the cloud chamber and his discoveries made therewith) and Kapitza; in Paris, by Irène Curie and Auger; in Berlin, by Bothe, Meitner, and Philipp; in Leningrad, by Skobelzyn; in Tokio, by Kikuchi.

Some of the most important achievements using the Wilson chamber were: the demonstration of the existence of Compton recoil electrons, thus establishing beyond any doubt the reality of the Compton effect (Compton shared the Nobel Prize with Wilson in 1927); the discovery of the positron by Anderson (who was awarded the Nobel Prize for 1936 for this feat); the visual demonstration of the processes of «pair creation» and «annihilation» of electrons and positrons by Blackett and Occhialini; and that of the transmutation of atomic nuclei carried out by Cockcroft and Walton. Thus, Rutherford's remark that the cloud chamber was «the most original and wonderful instrument in scientific history» has been fully justified.

In 1900, Wilson was made Fellow of Sidney Sussex College, and University Lecturer and Demonstrator. From then until 1918 he was in charge of the advanced teaching of practical physics at the Cavendish Laboratory, and also gave lectures on light. As well as his experimental work at the Cavendish Laboratory, he also made observations (1900–1901) on atmospheric electricity (mainly in the surroundings of Peebles in Scotland). In 1913, he was appointed Observer in Meteorological Physics at the Solar Physics Observatory, and most of his research both on the tracks of ionizing particles and on thunderstorm electricity was carried out there. In 1918, he was appointed Reader in Electrical Meteorology, and in 1925, Jacksonian Professor of Natural Philosophy. He was elected a Fellow of the Royal Society in 1900, and this Society also honoured him with the Hughes Medal (1911), a Royal Medal (1922), and the Copley Medal (1935). The Cambridge Philosophical Society awarded him the Hopkins Prize (1920), and the Royal Society of Edinburgh the Gunning Prize (1921), while the Franklin Institute presented him the Howard Potts Medal (1925).

After his retirement Wilson moved to Edinburgh, and later, at the age of 80, to the village of Carlops, close to his birthplace at the farmhouse of Crosshouse, at Glencorse. Life after this, however, was not an empty one: C.T.R. as his friends and colleagues called him, maintained social contacts, making a weekly journey by bus to the city to lunch with them. Scientifically, too, he was active to the end, finishing his long-promised manuscript on the theory of thundercloud electricity (*Proc. Roy. Soc. London*, August (1956)).

Among the few who enjoyed his personal guidance may be mentioned: Wormell (in the general field of atmospheric electricity), C. F. Powel (Nobel Prize winner 1950, for his development of the photographic method of studying nuclear processes and the discoveries made therewith on mesons), P. I. Dee and J. G. Wilson.

In 1908, Professor Wilson married Jessie Fraser, daughter of Rev. G. H. Dick of Glasgow; there were two sons and two daughters.

He died on the 15th of November, 1959, in the midst of his family.

Physics 1928

OWEN WILLANS RICHARDSON

«for his work on the thermionic phenomenon and especially for the discovery of the law named after him»

Physics 1928

Presentation Speech by Professor C.W. Oseen, Chairman of the Nobel Committee for Physics of the Royal Swedish Academy of Sciences

Your Majesty, Your Royal Highnesses, Ladies and Gentlemen.

Among the great problems that scientists conducting research in electro-technique are today trying to solve, is that of enabling two men to converse in whatever part of the world each may be. In 1928 things had reached the stage when we could begin to establish telephonic communication between Sweden and North America. On that occasion there was a telephone line of more than 22,000 kilometres in length between Stockholm and New York. From Stockholm, speech was transmitted via Berlin to England by means of a cable and overhead lines; from England by means of wireless to New York; then, via a cable and lines by land, over to Los Angeles and back to New York, and from there by means of a new line to Chicago, returning finally to New York. In spite of the great distance, the words could be heard distinctly and this is explained by the fact that there were no fewer than 166 amplifiers along the line. The principle of construction of an amplifier is very simple. A glowing filament sends out a stream of electrons. When the speech waves reach the amplifier, they oscillate in tune with the sound waves but are weakened. The speech waves are now made to put the stream of electrons in the same state of oscillation as they have themselves. So exactly does the stream of electrons adapt itself to the speech waves that the amplification could be repeated 166 times without the distinctness of speech being lost.

I should like to give another example of what has recently been attained in that department. On the 16th of February 1928, there was a conference between the American Institute of Electrical Engineers in New York and the Institution of Electrical Engineers in London. The various speeches could be heard in both places by means of loud-speakers.

Most people here present will certainly be able to call to mind those anxious days, when news of the missing Nobile expedition was awaited all over the world. Everyone will no doubt remember that the first word of the lost expedition was picked up by a wireless amateur. I think that on this occasion it was clear to many people that wireless is not only a means of diversion – and as such, one of the more prominent – but also one of the most valuable

expedients in the struggle against that sort of Nature which is still uncon-
quered.

Every owner of a valve receiving-set knows the importance of the valve
in the apparatus – the valve, the essential part of which is the glowing filament.

At the Jubilee, held in the twenty-fifth year of the reign of King Oscar II,
our medical men were enabled to take up the struggle against the tuber-
culosis, thanks to the Jubilee Fund. At the Jubilee held on Your Majesty's
70th birthday, the fight against cancer was taken up in the same manner.
We all know that Röntgen rays are one of the keenest weapons employed in
this struggle. But we know, too, that this weapon is double-edged. The rays
cannot only do good but also do harm. All depends on the accurate regulation of their strength and intensity. Quite recently, a change has taken place
in this department. Röntgen rays are obtained when rapidly moving electrons collide with a solid body. By using a glowing filament in order to
produce the electron stream, the means of regulating accurately the strength
and intensity of Röntgen rays has been obtained.

Behind the progress which has here been briefly pointed out, lies the work
of many men. But we have seen that they all have one thing in common. A
« red thread » connects them – the glowing filament.

As early as 1737, a French scientist, Du Fay by name, found out that air in
proximity to a glowing body is a conductor of electricity. Valuable researches concerning the character of this conductivity was made by Elster
and Geitel, two German scientists. Their investigations were continued by
Mr. J. J. Thomson, the Grand Old Man of English Physics of today. By
these researches they have found it probable that the conductivity of air in
proximity to a glowing metal depends on electrons in the air, which have
been made free in some way or another. So far had the researches advanced
when Mr. O. W. Richardson appeared and devoted himself to it. He began
by laying down a theory for the phenomenon. According to this theory the
phenomenon is bound up with the electrical conductivity of metals. The
latter depends on the fact that there are free electrons in a metal. At higher
temperatures these cannot, according to Mr. Richardson, be retained by the
body but they are emitted according to a fixed law. But a theory alone does
not give any knowledge of reality. That can be obtained only by means of
experimental research. So Mr. Richardson proceeded to do this. The point
was to find out if the theory was really right. The strenuous work of twelve
years was necessary to settle this question. So hard was the struggle that even

so late as in the twelfth year, there was a time when it was uncertain whether Mr. Richardson's theory was not completely wrong, and if the origin of the phenomenon was not quite different, being, for instance, chemical reactions between the metal and impurities in it. But in the end, Mr. Richardson's theory proved to be correct in all essential points. The most important fact was that Mr. Richardson's opinion about the thermion-phenomenon with fixed laws was totally confirmed. Through this fact a solid basis was obtained for the practical application of the phenomenon. Mr. Richardson's work has been the starting-point and the prop of the technical activity which has led to the progress of which I have just spoken.

Professor Richardson. You are a happy man. You possess the very thing that gives life its chief value. You can devote yourself with all your strength to the activity that you love. We constantly see the results of this activity come to light. Besides this, you are fortunate enough to see the harvest ripen to the benefit of mankind in the fields you tilled in your youth. For one who is so rich it is but a little thing to receive the greatest prize which the Royal Academy of Sciences has at its disposal as a reward for a scientific discovery. I ask you, however, to receive from our King's hand the Nobel Prize for Physics for the year 1928.

OWEN W. RICHARDSON

Thermionic phenomena and the laws which govern them

Nobel Lecture, December 12, 1929

In its broadest aspect this subject may be summarized as the branch of Physics which deals with the effect of heat on the interaction between electricity and matter. It is not altogether new. Nearly 200 years ago it was known that air in the neighbourhood of hot bodies conducted electricity. In 1873 Guthrie showed that a red-hot iron ball in air could retain a negative but not a positive charge. In a series of researches extending from 1882 to 1889, Elster and Geitel examined the charge collected on an insulated plate placed near various hot wires in diverse gases at different pressures. The observed effects were very specific and varied, but there emerged a general tendency for the plate to acquire a positive charge at low temperatures and high pressures, and a negative charge at high temperatures and low pressures. The matter became really interesting in 1899 when J. J. Thomson showed that the discharge from an incandescent carbon filament in a vacuum tube was carried by negative electrons. In 1900 McClelland showed that the currents from a negatively charged platinum wire were influenced very little, if at all, by changes in the nature and pressure of the surrounding gas, if the pressure were fairly low. These facts seemed to me to be highly significant, and I resolved to investigate the phenomenon thoroughly.

The view of these effects generally held at that time by people who had thought about them was that the electric discharges were carried by ions and electrons which were generated by the interaction of the neighbouring gas molecules with the hot body. It was left an open question as to whether this action was merely thermal, a matter of kinetic energy, or was chemical, or involved the intervention of radiation. The effects observed in the best vacua were attributed to the residual gas which could not be got rid of. This was, of course, easily possible. I felt, however, that it was very likely that interacting gases had little to do with the main phenomenon, but that the negatively charged electrons and, possibly, the positively charged ions too were coming from the heated solid. This would be reasonable from the point of view of the theories of metallic conduction which had been put forward between 1888 and 1900 by Thomson, Riecke, and Drude. I decided that the best way to make progress was to get rid of the complications due to the presence of gases and to find out what, if anything, happened when gas effects were excluded.

This was not so easy at the beginning of this century as it would be at the present time. Largely owing to the technical importance of the phenomena under consideration the art of evacuating gases has advanced enormously since then. In those days the gas had all to be got away by hand pumps. As the heating of the tube walls and other parts of the apparatus by the hot wire generates gas from them which continues almost indefinitely this is a most tedious operation. I have often heated a wire in a tube for weeks in succession in order to make sure that the currents observed were stable and not coming from residual gas. There was no ductile tungsten; the most refractory material readily available in a reasonably pure form was platinum. In 1901 I was able to show that each unit area of a platinum surface emitted a limited number of electrons. This number increased very rapidly with the temperature, so that the maximum current i at any absolute temperature T was governed by the law

$$i = AT^{\frac{1}{2}}\mathrm{c}^{-w/kT} \tag{1}$$

In this equation k is Boltzmann's constant, and A and w are specific constants of the material. This equation was completely accounted for by the simple hypothesis that the freely moving electrons in the interior of the hot conductor escaped when they reached the surface provided that the part of their energy which depended on the component of velocity normal to the surface was greater than the work function w. In 1903 I showed that the same conclusions could be drawn for sodium and more qualitatively for carbon. Further, that the differences of the work functions of different substances should be equal to their contact potential differences, and the experimental values for platinum and sodium verified this. The results also verified the conclusion that the work functions for different elements should be of the same order of magnitude as $\frac{1}{2}(e^2/d)$, where e is the electronic charge and d the radius of the atom, and also that it should vary roughly as the inverse cube root of the atomic volume. In the same year Wehnelt found that similar phenomena were exhibited by a large number of metallic oxides. The alkaline earths in particular had an exceptionally low work function and were in consequence very efficient emitters of electrons.

It is necessary to say a word or two in parenthesis about the positive ionization which is frequently observed. This is due to an emission of positive ions
which arises in various ways. When any ordinary sample of a solid is first
heated, it gives rise to a copious emission of positive ions which decays (and
sometimes recovers) with time in a manner which resembles superficially
that of radioactive substances. This effect is due to impurities. After this has
been got rid of, there may be another more stable emission characteristic of
the substance itself. There is a third type which is a direct result of interaction
between the heated solid and the surrounding gas. I devoted a good deal of
time between 1904 and 1912 to the investigation of these effects. The results
were interesting, but there is not time to consider them in any detail. I will
only mention that all three types of positive emission, when stable, were
found to obey the same temperature law $AT^{\frac{1}{2}}e^{-b/T}$ as the electronic emission
but, of course, with different constants A, b; that the carriers of the characteristic emissions were charged atoms of the metallic constituent; and that
the carriers of the temporary effect were singly charged atoms of sodium or
potassium, the latter usually predominating, which are present as contaminants.

The central idea which lies behind the theory summarized in Eq. (1) is
that of an electron gas evaporating from the hot source. If this idea is correct,
the thermionic currents should be able to flow against a small *opposing* elec-
tromotive force because the kinetic energy of the heat motion of the electron
gas molecules, in other words the electrons, will carry some of them through
it. Furthermore, we could at that time find out a great deal more about what
the electrons in an electron gas were doing than we could about the molecules of an ordinary gas. Owing to the fact that they are electrically charged,
their motion can be controlled by an external electric field. By measuring the
electronic current which flows against various directly opposing fields it is
possible to ascertain the proportion of the emitted electrons which have a
value of the component of their velocity perpendicular to the emitting surface between any assigned limits. By making observations of the spreading
of the electrons sideways under different small accelerating fields it is possible
to deduce similar information about the components of velocity parallel to
the surface. By experiments of this kind made in 1908–1909, partly with the
help of F. C. Brown, I was able to show that the distribution of velocity
among the emitted electrons was identical with the Maxwell distribution for
a gas, of equal molecular weight to that of the electron, at the temperature of
the metal. The identity was shown to hold for each velocity component.

Apart from its interest in connection with electrons, this was the first exper-imental demonstration of Maxwell's law for any gas, although the law was enunciated by Maxwell in 1859.

There were two other matters which required urgent investigation before the theory of electron emission could be regarded as securely founded. The first was this. If the electrons are really coming out of the hot body by virtue of their heat energy being able to overcome the work function w, the hot body should be cooled by this process. It is like the cooling of water by evaporation. I published a calculation of the magnitude of this effect in 1903, but the first experimental investigation was made by Wehnelt and Jentzsch in 1909. They observed a cooling effect, but the magnitude did not agree with the theory. In 1913 H. L. Cooke and I devised an improved exper-imental method of attacking this question, redetermined this cooling effect, and showed that it agreed with the value of the work function deduced from the variation of the thermionic currents with the temperature. Our conclu-sions have since been confirmed by the very accurate experiments of Davis-son and Germer made in 1922.

The other matter to which I referred is the converse of this. If a stream of electrons flows into a conductor from outside, there should be a develop-ment of heat which does not depend either on the temperature of these elec-trons or on the magnitude of the small potential differences used to drive them. H. L. Cooke and I devised and put into operation an apparatus for detecting and measuring this effect in 1910–1911. The results showed a satis-factory agreement with the value of the work function obtained by the other two methods.

Despite the steadily accumulating mass of evidence to the contrary, some of which I have briefly outlined, the view had been fairly commonly held up to about 1913 that thermionic emission was not a physical phenomenon but a secondary effect of some chemical reaction between the hot body and the surrounding gas. The advent of ductile tungsten enabled me, in 1913, to get very big currents under better vacuum conditions than had hitherto been possible and to show that the mass of the electrons emitted exceeded the mass of the chemicals which could possibly be consumed. This experiment, I think, ended that controversy so far as it could be regarded seriously.

There is a very close relationship between thermionic and photoelectric phenomena. The photoelectric threshold frequency, the least frequency v_0 which will eject an electron from a given substance, is connected with the thermionic work function w_0 by the simple relation

$$w_o = h v_o$$

where h is Planck's constant. This was established by experiments made by K. T. Compton and myself in 1912. We know that any body in thermal equilibrium at any temperature T is surrounded by a bath of radiation in which the frequency distribution is given by Planck's formula. This formula puts no finite limit on the magnitude of the frequencies occurring; so that there will always be some frequencies present for which v_o is greater than w_o/h. Such frequencies will eject electrons by photoelectric action; so that the temperature radiation alone will, by a kind of photoelectric effect integrated over the whole spectrum, give rise to an electronic emission which should increase with the temperature. In 1912 I showed that it followed from the principles of thermodynamics that this integrated photoelectric emission would follow Eq. (1) exactly with, possibly, a different value for the constant A. This conclusion was established by direct experiment later by W. Wilson, in 1917. Thermionic emission might thus well be an integrated photoelectric emission; only the absolute magnitude could decide. In 1912 there were no known data which would enable the magnitude of this integrated photoelectric effect to be ascertained, so, with the collaboration first of K. T. Compton and later of F. J. Rogers, I set about to determine the absolute values of the photoelectric yields of various substances as a function of frequency. With the help of these absolute values I was able in 1916 to calculate the electron emission from platinum at 2,000° K due to its complete blackbody spectrum. The result showed that thermionic emission is at least 5,000 times, and almost certainly 100 million times, as large; so that thermionic emission cannot be merely an integrated photoelectric effect, although it has the same thermodynamic properties. A photochemical theory of chemical reactions based on considerations analogous to these has been put forward independently by Perrin and seems to have met with very similar difficulties. If we have to make a decision now, the verdict must be, on the facts at present revealed, that the part of these effects which is of radiational origin is comparatively unimportant. I am not sure, however, that the end has been heard of this matter. I have a feeling that there is something coordinating these radiational and mechanical or chemical effects which at present is concealed from us.

I will now say a few words about the relation between thermionic phenomena and theories of metallic conduction. In so far as it can be regarded as a serious contribution to scientific knowledge, thermionics was born at the same time as the theories of metallic conduction associated with J. J. Thomson, Riecke, Drude, and Lorentz, and it grew up with them. The dominant feature of these theories is the assumption that the currents in metals are carried by electrons which are moving freely and which possess the same average amount of kinetic energy as that of the molecule of a monatomic gas at the same temperature. Since all the thermionic facts which I have outlined received a ready explanation on these theories, there came to be a presumption that they favoured them rather than others, such as that put forward by Lindemann, which supposed the electrons in metals to be normally at rest. The fact that the experiments confirmed the requirement of the former theories, that the emitted electrons should have a Maxwell distribution of kinetic energy, especially seems to have led to the spreading of this opinion. It is a requirement of classical dynamics that this distribution should hold for electrons in any part of a system in thermal equilibrium, and as it is found to be true for the external electrons, the only part of the system accessible to experimental investigation, there is a presumption that it will also be true of the internal electrons. But this presumption has no validity apart from classical dynamics. Except for the considerations dealt with in the next paragraph which were perhaps still somewhat uncertain, the ascertained facts of thermionic emission did not favour one type of theory of metallic conduction rather than another until 1922, when Davisson and Germer made a very accurate comparison of the experimental value of the work function deduced from the cooling effect with that deduced from the temperature emission formula, at different temperatures, using the same tungsten filament. An analysis of their results showed that the experimental evidence was definitely against the classical theory of metallic conductors and in favour of a type of theory which makes the kinetic energy of the internal electrons practically independent of the temperature.

In 1911 as a result of pursuing some difficulties in connection with the thermodynamic theory of electron emission I came to the conclusion that

$$i = AT^2 e^{-w/kT} \tag{2}$$

was a theoretically preferable form of the temperature emission equation to Eq. (1), with, of course, different values of the constants A and w from those used with (1). It is impossible to distinguish between these two equations by experimenting. The effect of the T^2 or $T^{\frac{1}{2}}$ term is so small compared with the exponential factor that a small change in A and w will entirely conceal it. In fact, at my instigation K. K. Smith in 1915 measured the emission from tungsten over such a wide range of temperature that the current changed by a factor of nearly 10^{12}, yet the results seemed to be equally well covered by either (1) or (2). It is, of course, very satisfactory to know that either formula will do this. There are not many physical laws which have been tested over so wide a range. The great advantage of Eq. (2) is that it makes A a universal constant; so that there is only one specific constant for each substance, namely w. The first time I mentioned explicitly that A was a universal constant was in 1915. Here I came to it as a result of a thermodynamic argument about electron emission. In 1914 I had already come to it by a different route. I had come to the conclusion that the classical statistics were not applicable to the electrons inside conductors. There was no means of ascertaining what the correct statistics were, so I endeavoured to avoid this difficulty by adopting some quantum ideas previously used by Keesom to calculate the specific heat of helium at low temperatures. In this way I determined the constant A as $0.547 \, mk^2e/h^3$ (m and e being the mass and charge of the electron, k and h Boltzmann and Planck's constants). These calculations have since been improved upon by others, but there still seems to be some doubt about the pure number factor which I made out to be 0.547. The most probable value of it seems to be 4π. Amongst those whose writings have made important contributions to this question since 1915 are von Laue (1918), Tolman (1921), Dushman (1923), Roy (1926), Sommerfeld (1927), and R. H. Fowler (1928).

By 1924 it was easy to prove that all the existing theories of metallic conduction were wrong, but just where they went wrong it was impossible to say. None of them were able to unite in a straightforward and satisfactory way such diverse facts as the law of Wiedemann and Franz, the large number of free electrons and the mean free paths required by the optical properties of metals, their known crystal structures, their small specific heats, the variation of conductivity with temperature and the existence of supraconductivity, and the relation between the thermionic cooling effect and the temperature.

This great problem was solved by Sommerfeld in 1927. Following up the work of Pauli on the paramagnetism of the alkali metals, which had just appeared, he showed that the electron gas in metals should not obey the classical statistics as in the older theories, such as that of Lorentz for example, but should obey the new statistics of Fermi and Dirac. This makes a profound change in the distribution of velocities among the electrons when their concentration is very great, as in the interior of a metal, but it makes little or no difference when the concentration is small, as in the external electron atmospheres. It thus allows us to retain the experimentally established Maxwell distribution for the external electrons. On this theory the energy of the internal electrons is the energy of their Schrödinger proper values. If the concentration of the electrons is large, as in a metal, it is fixed almost entirely by the density of the electrons and has little to do with their temperature. It is, in fact, a kind of zero-point energy. This feature immediately accounts for the very small contribution of the electrons to the specific heats of metals, which was so great a difficulty for the older theories. It appears also to be capable of accounting for the other serious difficulties.

There is one other feature of Sommerfeld's theory which I must mention as it affects the interpretation to be put on the thermionic work function w. Before the advent of this theory w was interpreted as the work required to remove a free electron at rest inside the metal to a point outside. According to Sommerfeld's theory w is equal to the difference between this work and the maximum energy of the internal electrons. The value of this is

$$\frac{h^2}{2m}\left(\frac{3n}{8\pi}\right)^{\frac{2}{3}}$$

if n is the number in unit volume. For most metallic conductors this quantity is equivalent to about 10 volts. As w is generally somewhere about 4 volts, this means that the difference between the electrostatic potential energy of a free electron inside and outside a metal is some 3 or 4 times as large as was formerly supposed. Direct experimental evidence that this is correct is furnished by the recent experiments of Davisson and Germer on the diffraction of electrons by nickel crystals.

We have seen that the classical theories of metallic conduction gave a pretty good account of those thermionic phenomena which I have so far referred to. The only clear exceptions which emerged were the magnitude of the work function in relation to temperature as deduced from the cooling effect and the calculation of the actual magnitude of the absolute constant A which enters into the $AT^2e^{-w/kT}$ formula. As this contains Planck's constant h its elucidation necessarily involved some form of quantum theory. As a historical fact, however, it was chiefly on other difficulties with the properties of metals that the older theories wrecked themselves. I come now to some thermionic phenomena with which the older theories were not so successful.

It became apparent at a very early stage that the emission of electrons from conductors at a given temperature was very susceptible to the influence of foreign substances and particularly to gaseous contaminants. This was not surprising in itself, as the phenomenon is essentially a surface phenomenon but some of the observed effects were unexpected. In 1903 H. A. Wilson made the important observation that the emission from platinum could be enormously increased by the presence of small quantities of hydrogen. In 1908 he showed that in certain circumstances this emission was a function of the pressure of the hydrogen at a fixed temperature. If the pressure was kept fixed, the currents still followed the $AT^2e^{-b/T}$ formula, but with changed values of A and b. These parameters were now functions of the pressure of such a kind that they obeyed an equation

$$b = c \log A + d \tag{3}$$

where c and d are new constants independent of both pressure and temperature. In 1913 Langmuir observed that the emission from tungsten was affected by various gases, hydrogen having a particularly depressing effect on this substance, although the effect may in reality be caused by water vapour. In 1915 I pointed out that in all these cases of contamination the currents still obeyed the $AT^2e^{-b/T}$ formula, with changed values of the parameters, but that all the values, including those for the pure metals, satisfied Eq. (3) with the same constants c and d. In 1925 A. F. A. Young and I extended the list to include potassium contaminated in a large number of ways. The number of substances which subscribe to Eq. (3) has recently been added to very considerably by several American investigators. This effect is not small, it is large. The parameter A can change by a factor of 10^{12} as a result of contamination.

Since 1915 I have felt that this result must be important both on account of its generality and of its magnitude, but I have never been able to arrive at any satisfactory reason for it. It seems now that this is one of those phenomena which are only to be accounted for with the help of the new waves of L. de Broglie. The solution of the problem we owe to R. H. Fowler and Nordheim (1928). Their explanation is similar in principle to that by which Gamow and Gurney and Condon explain the disintegration of the radioactive nucleus. They take the conventional simplified picture of a metal as a sharply bounded region of low potential energy densely packed with electrons. But as de Broglie has shown us, an electron can be regarded as a train of waves, or a wave packet, having a wavelength equal to h divided by the momentum of the electron. If such a wave is incident on the surface of the metal, it may be either reflected or transmitted. Thus the problem of the emission of electrons by a conductor may be looked upon as the problem of the reflection of the corresponding de Broglie waves at the hill of potential gradient which exists at the boundary. If the height of this hill is H, then on my old theory none of the electrons reaching the boundary would escape if their normal component N of kinetic energy were less than H, whereas all would escape for which N exceeded H. In the wave reflection problem it is still true that there is total reflection for N less than H, but the sharp discontinuity at $N = H$ has disappeared. It is found that the proportion transmitted is a continuous function of N and H, whose value tends to unity as the difference between N and H increases. This, however, makes very little difference; and when the calculations are completely carried out, it is found that Eq. (2) is still valid with the magnitude of the universal constant A unaltered in any essential way.

This result, however, depends essentially on the assumption that the potential energy increases to a permanent maximum as the electron crosses the surface. No doubt this is the correct picture for a pure metal, but for a contaminated one we may expect something different. If the contaminant is a thin layer, it may be only a few molecules thick, of a more electropositive substance, we should expect the hill to rise to a maximum height, let us say H_1, and then fall to a permanently lower level at a height H_2. On the old ideas the condition for escape would be that N should exceed the maximum height H, but in the wave problem it is possible for some of the waves to penetrate the hump H_1–H_2 provided its thickness is not large compared with the wavelength. There is a well-established optical analogue of this in the failure of total reflection when the thickness of the reflecting medium becomes comparable with the wavelength of the light. When the transmission of the de Broglie waves is calculated for this more complicated potential distribution, it is found that the emission formula (2) still holds good, but with new constants A and b, which are connected together by a relation which is equivalent to (3). I am not claiming that all the facts in this department of thermionics have been completely coordinated by these theories of Fowler and Nordheim, but it is satisfactory that we have begun to understand something about this intractable subject.

I come now to a phenomenon which is not exactly thermionic, as it is independent of temperature, but in some ways it is intimately related to thermionic effects. It has been suspected for a long time that electrons could be pulled out of metals without the co-operation of gases by sufficiently strong electric fields. The effects seemed very erratic and difficult to investigate. The reality of the phenomenon has, however, been firmly established by the work of Gossling, of Millikan and Eyring, and of Rother, during or a little prior to 1926, and by that of various experimenters since then. These currents are carried by electrons and they may be quite large. The magnitude is independent of the temperature of the emitting substance, but at the same time is a continuous function of the applied electric field. The theory of this effect was discussed at length by Schottky in 1923 and more briefly, but in relation to the new experimental data, by Millikan and Eyring in 1926. It does not seem to have been realized, however, that no rational treatment of the old particle theories would get the electrons out in a way which made the emission a continuous function of the field without at the same time being a function which was sensitive to the temperature. I noticed this important point in 1927, and accordingly I attacked the problem from a new point of view by regarding it as a Schrödinger wave problem of an electron in the field of force at the conducting surface. Perhaps the last word has not been said on this matter, but it now looks as though in this attempt I attributed too much importance to the mirror-image attraction of the electron in the surface. Whatever its ultimate importance may be, this paper first drew attention to essential physical aspects of this phenomenon and indicated in a general way the nature of its connection with thermionic effects. In 1928 the problem was attacked by Oppenheimer and, more completely, by Fowler and Nordheim, who succeeded in putting it into an exceedingly simple form. They treat it in the same way as they treated the problem of thermionic emission, namely as a problem in the reflection of de Broglie waves at a potential barrier. The only essential difference between the two problems is that the potential, instead of being constant outside the metal, now falls off as a linear function of the distance from the surface. Their solution of this problem leads to a formula which so far as I am able to judge, is in excellent agreement with the ascertained facts in this domain.

The existence of this field extraction phenomenon has a number of interesting consequences, one of which I will now mention. If we consider an evacuated enclosure containing a number of bodies having different thermionic work functions w_1, w_2, etc., they will not be in electrical equilibrium unless their surfaces are charged. The reason for this is that those with lower work functions would emit electrons at a more rapid rate than those with higher work functions. The condition for equilibrium to a first approxima- tion, and one which covers the essential features of the phenomenon, is that there should be a certain field of electric force between the different bodies. This is such that, if the potential difference between any point just outside the body with suffix 1 and any point just outside the body with suffix 2 is V_{12}, then $eV_{12} = w_1 - w_2$. V_{12} is the contact potential difference between the bodies 1 and 2. There is nothing essential to the thermionic argument which depends on the shape, size or relative position of the bodies, and the result should be the same whether they are interconnected by other conductors or insulated from each other. The quantities such as V_{12} are thus intrinsic poten- tial differences which are characteristic properties of the materials of which the conductors are made.

The field extraction phenomenon requires a modification of this conclu- sion. To simplify the argument I consider only two bodies, those with suf- fixes 1 and 2. Some portion of each of them is bounded by a plane surface, and the bodies are arranged so that these plane surfaces are parallel to one another and a distance x apart. The more distant parts of the bodies may be united by an electric circuit which includes a galvanometer. When x is con- siderable, there is equilibrium and no current passes through the galvanom- eter, because the excess electrons emitted by the more electropositive body are kept back by the potential difference V_{12}, and this equilibrium is prac- tically unaffected by the small force eV_{12}/x. But now suppose x to become very small, let us say comparable with atomic dimensions. The force eV_{12}/x now becomes large and will begin to extract electrons from the more electro- negative body. This upsets the equilibrium, which is restored by a current passing through the galvanometer. But this is a perpetuum mobile: the cur- rent can be made to do useful work. It consumes nothing and the apparatus has no moving parts. If it is argued that it may be tapping some source of heat, at least it must be a perpetuum mobile of the second kind, since it works at a constant temperature. What is the answer to this riddle? I say it is this: the contact potential difference V_{12} is not completely independent of the distance between the two bodies. When this distance becomes small, V_{12} diminishes, and this diminution takes place in such a way that the additional electron current from the more electropositive body which reaches the more electronegative body owing to the reduced value of V_{12} is just equal to the electron current which is extracted from the more electronegative body by the field. In particular when the bodies are in contact, V_{12} falls to zero or at any rate to a quantity of the order of the thermoelectric magnitudes. Well, this seems to correspond to the actual properties of the contact difference of potential, and I think it clears up an old difficulty in connection with it.

Biography

Owen Willans Richardson was born on the 26th of April, 1879, at Dewsbury, Yorkshire, England, as the only son of Joshua Henry and Charlotte Maria Richardson.

Educated at Batley Grammar School, he proceeded to Cambridge in 1897, having obtained an Entrance Major Scholarship at Trinity College; he gained First Class Honours in Natural Science at the examinations of the Universities of Cambridge and London, with particular distinctions in Physics and Chemistry. After graduating at Cambridge in 1900, he began to investigate the emission of electricity from hot bodies at the Cavendish Laboratory. In 1902 he was elected a Fellow of Trinity College, Cambridge. The law for the discovery of which the Nobel Prize was specially given, was first announced by him in a paper read before the Cambridge Philosophical Society on the 25th November, 1901, in the following words, as recorded in the published Proceedings: « If then the negative radiation is due to the corpuscles coming out of the metal, the saturation current s should obey the law $s = AT^{\frac{1}{2}}e^{-b/T}$. This law is fully confirmed by the experiments to be described. » Richardson continued working at this subject at Cambridge until 1906, when he was appointed Professor of Physics at Princeton University in America, where he remained until the end of 1913, working at thermionic emission, photoelectric action, and the gyromagnetic effect. In 1911 he was elected a member of the American Philosophical Society, and in 1913 a Fellow of the Royal Society, whereupon (1914) he returned to England as Wheatstone Professor of Physics at King's College in the University of London. Among his publications were: *The Electron Theory of Matter*, 1914 (2nd ed., 1916), *The Emission of Electricity from Hot Bodies*, 1916 (2nd ed., 1921), *Molecular Hydrogen and its Spectrum*, 1934.

He was awarded the Hughes Medal by the Royal Society (1920), especially for work on thermionics; elected President, Section A, of the British Association (1921) and President of the Physical Society, London (1926–1928); appointed Yarrow Research Professor of the Royal Society, London 1924–1944), and knighted in 1939. Since 1914 he worked at thermionics,

photoelectric effects, magnetism, the emission of electrons by chemical action, the theory of electrons, the quantum theory, the spectrum of molecular
hydrogen, soft X-rays, the fine structure of Hα and Dα. His last paper, with
E. W. Foster, appeared in 1953. He received honorary degrees from the
Universities of St. Andrews, Leeds, and London.

In 1906 he married Lilian Maud Wilson, the only sister of the well-known
physicist H. A. Wilson, who was a fellow-student with him in Cambridge.
There were two sons and one daughter of this marriage. After the death of
his wife in 1945, Richardson married the physicist Henriette Rupp in 1948;
he himself died in 1959.

Physics 1929

Prince LOUIS-VICTOR DE BROGLIE

«for his discovery of the wave nature of electrons»

Physics 1929

*Presentation Speech by Professor C. W. Oseen, Chairman of the Nobel Committee
for Physics of the Royal Swedish Academy of Sciences*

Your Majesty, Your Royal Highnesses, Ladies and Gentlemen.

The question as to the nature of light rays is one of the oldest problems in physics. In the works of the ancient philosopers are to be found an indication and a rough outline of two radically different concepts of this phenomenon. However, in a clear and definite form they appear at the time when the foundations of physics were laid, a time that bears the stamp of Newton's genius. One of these theories asserts that a light ray is composed of small particles, which we may term corpuscles, which are projected into space by light-emitting substances. The other states that light is a wave motion of one type or another. The fact that these two theories, at this elementary stage, are equally possible, is attributable to their explaining equally well the simplest law governing a light ray, viz. conditions being undisturbed it propagates in a straight line.

The 19th century sealed the victory of the wave theory. Those of us whose studies coincide with that period have certainly all learned that light is a wave motion. This conviction was based on the study of a series of phenomena which are readily accounted for by the wave theory but which, on the other hand, cannot be explained by the corpuscular theory. One of these phenomena is the diffraction undergone by a light beam when it passes through a small hole in an opaque screen. Alongside the diffracted ray there are alternate light and dark bands. This phenomenon has long been considered a decisive proof of the wave theory. Furthermore, in the course of the 19th century a very large number of other, more complex, light phenomena had been learnt of which all, without exception, were completely explainable by the wave theory, while it appeared to be impossible to account for them on the basis of the corpuscular theory. The correctness of the wave theory seemed definitely established.

The 19th century was also the period when atomic concepts have taken root into physics. One of the greatest discoveries of the final decades of that century was the discovery of the electron, the smallest negative charge of electricity occurring in the free state.

Under the influence of these two currents of ideas the concept which 19th century physics had of the universe was the following. The universe was divided into two smaller worlds. One was the world of light, of waves; the other was the world of matter, of atoms and electrons. The perceptible appearance of the universe was conditioned by the interaction of these two worlds.

Our century taught us that besides the innumerable light phenomena which testify to the truth of the wave theory, there are others which testify no less decisively to the correctness of the corpuscular theory. A light ray has the property of liberating a stream of electrons from a substance. The number of electrons liberated depends on the intensity of the ray. But the velocity with which the electrons leave the substance is the same whether the light ray originates from the most powerful light source that can be made, or whether it originates from the most distant fixed stars which are invisible to the naked eye. In this case everything occurs as if the light ray were composed of corpuscles which traversed the spaces of the universe unmodified. It thus seems that light is at once a wave motion and a stream of corpuscles. Some of its properties are explained by the former supposition, others by the second. Both must be true.

Louis de Broglie had the boldness to maintain that not all the properties of matter can be explained by the theory that it consists of corpuscles. Apart from the numberless phenomena which can be accounted for by this theory, there are others, according to him, which can be explained only by assuming that matter is, by its nature, a wave motion. At a time when no single known fact supported this theory, Louis de Broglie asserted that a stream of electrons which passed through a very small hole in an opaque screen must exhibit the same phenomena as a light ray under the same conditions. It was not quite in this way that Louis de Broglie's experimental investigation concerning his theory took place. Instead, the phenomena arising when beams of electrons are reflected by crystalline surfaces, or when they penetrate thin sheets, etc. were turned to account. The experimental results obtained by these various methods have fully substantiated Louis de Broglie's theory. It is thus a fact that matter has properties which can be interpreted only by assuming that matter is of a wave nature. An aspect of the nature of matter which is completely new and previously quite unsuspected has thus been revealed to us.

Hence there are not two worlds, one of light and waves, one of matter and corpuscles. There is only a single universe. Some of its properties can be accounted for by the wave theory, others by the corpuscular theory.

In conclusion I would like to point out that what applies to matter applies also to ourselves since, from a certain point of view, we are part of matter.

A well-known Swedish poem has as its opening words «My life is a wave». The poet could also have expressed his thought by the words: «I am a wave». Had he done so, his words would have contained a premonition of man's present deepest understanding of the nature of matter.

Monsieur Louis de Broglie. When quite young you threw yourself into the controversy raging round the most profound problem in physics. You had the boldness to assert, without the support of any known fact, that matter had not only a corpuscular nature, but also a wave nature. Experiment came later and established the correctness of your view. You have covered in fresh glory a name already crowned for centuries with honour. The Royal Academy of Sciences has sought to reward your discovery with the highest recompense of which it is capable. I would ask you to receive from the hands of our King the Nobel Physics Prize for 1929.

The wave nature of the electron

Nobel Lecture, December 12, 1929

When in 1920 I resumed my studies of theoretical physics which had long been interrupted by circumstances beyond my control, I was far from the idea that my studies would bring me several years later to receive such a high and envied prize as that awarded by the Swedish Academy of Sciences each year to a scientist: the Nobel Prize for Physics. What at that time drew me towards theoretical physics was not the hope that such a high distinction would ever crown my work; I was attracted to theoretical physics by the mystery enshrouding the structure of matter and the structure of radiations, a mystery which deepened as the strange quantum concept introduced by Planck in 1900 in his research on black-body radiation continued to encroach on the whole domain of physics.

To assist you to understand how my studies developed, I must first depict for you the crisis which physics had then been passing through for some twenty years.

For a long time physicists had been wondering whether light was composed of small, rapidly moving corpuscles. This idea was put forward by the philosophers of antiquity and upheld by Newton in the 18th century. After Thomas Young's discovery of interference phenomena and following the admirable work of Augustin Fresnel, the hypothesis of a granular structure of light was entirely abandoned and the wave theory unanimously adopted. Thus the physicists of last century spurned absolutely the idea of an atomic structure of light. Although rejected by optics, the atomic theories began making great headway not only in chemistry, where they provided a simple interpretation of the laws of definite proportions, but also in the physics of matter where they made possible an interpretation of a large number of properties of solids, liquids, and gases. In particular they were instrumental in the elaboration of that admirable kinetic theory of gases which, generalized under the name of statistical mechanics, enables a clear meaning to be given to the abstract concepts of thermodynamics. Experiment also yielded decisive proof in favour of an atomic constitution of electricity; the concept of the electricity corpuscle owes its appearance to Sir J. J. Thomson and you will all be familiar with H. A. Lorentz's use of it in his theory of electrons.

Some thirty years ago, physics was hence divided into two: firstly the physics of matter based on the concept of corpuscles and atoms which were supposed to obey Newton's classical laws of mechanics, and secondly radiation physics based on the concept of wave propagation in a hypothetical continuous medium, i.e. the light ether or electromagnetic ether. But these two physics could not remain alien one to the other; they had to be fused together by devising a theory to explain the energy exchanges between matter and radiation – and that is where the difficulties arose. While seeking to link these two physics together, imprecise and even inadmissible conclusions were in fact arrived at in respect of the energy equilibrium between matter and radiation in a thermally insulated medium: matter, it came to be said, must yield all its energy to the radiation and so tend of its own accord to absolute zero temperature! This absurd conclusion had at all costs to be avoided. By an intuition of his genius Planck realized the way of avoiding it: instead of assuming, in common with the classical wave theory, that a light source emits its radiation continuously, it had to be assumed on the contrary that it emits equal and finite quantities, *quanta*. The energy of each quantum has, moreover, a value proportional to the frequency v of the radiation. It is equal to hv, h being a universal constant since referred to as Planck's constant.

The success of Planck's ideas entailed serious consequences. If light is emitted as quanta, ought it not, once emitted, to have a granular structure? The existence of radiation quanta thus implies the corpuscular concept of light. On the other hand, as shown by Jeans and H. Poincaré, it is demonstrable that if the motion of the material particles in light sources obeyed the laws of classical mechanics it would be impossible to derive the exact law of blackbody radiation, Planck's law. It must therefore be assumed that traditional dynamics, even as modified by Einstein's theory of relativity, is incapable of accounting for motion on a very small scale.

The existence of a granular structure of light and of other radiations was confirmed by the discovery of the photoelectric effect. If a beam of light or of X-rays falls on a piece of matter, the latter will emit rapidly moving electrons. The kinetic energy of these electrons increases linearly with the frequency of the incident radiation and is independent of its intensity. This phenomenon can be explained simply by assuming that the radiation is composed of quanta hv capable of yielding all their energy to an electron of the irradiated body: one is thus led to the theory of light quanta proposed by Einstein in 1905 and which is, after all, a reversion to Newton's corpuscular theory, completed by the relation for the proportionality between the energy of the corpuscles and the frequency. A number of arguments were put forward by Einstein in support of his viewpoint and in 1922 the discovery by A. H. Compton of the X-ray scattering phenomenon which bears his name confirmed it. Nevertheless, it was still necessary to adopt the wave theory to account for interference and diffraction phenomena and no way whatsoever of reconciling the wave theory with the existence of light corpuscles could be visualized.

As stated, Planck's investigations cast doubts on the validity of very small scale mechanics. Let us consider a material point which describes a small trajectory which is closed or else turning back on itself. According to classical dynamics there are numberless motions of this type which are possible complying with the initial conditions, and the possible values for the energy of the moving body form a continuous sequence. On the other hand Planck was led to assume that only certain preferred motions, *quantized* motions, are possible or at least stable, since energy can only assume values forming a discontinuous sequence. This concept seemed rather strange at first but its value had to be recognized because it was this concept which brought Planck to the correct law of black-body radiation and because it then proved its fruitfulness in many other fields. Lastly, it was on the concept of atomic motion quantization that Bohr based his famous theory of the atom; it is so familiar to scientists that I shall not summarize it here.

The necessity of assuming for light two contradictory theories – that of waves and that of corpuscles – and the inability to understand why, among the infinity of motions which an electron ought to be able to have in the atom according to classical concepts, only certain ones were possible: such were the enigmas confronting physicists at the time I resumed my studies of theoretical physics.

When I started to ponder these difficulties two things struck me in the main. Firstly the light-quantum theory cannot be regarded as satisfactory since it defines the energy of a light corpuscle by the relation $W = h\nu$ which contains a frequency ν. Now a purely corpuscular theory does not contain any element permitting the definition of a frequency. This reason alone renders it necessary in the case of light to introduce simultaneously the corpuscle concept and the concept of periodicity.

On the other hand the determination of the stable motions of the electrons in the atom involves whole numbers, and so far the only phenomena in which whole numbers were involved in physics were those of interference and of eigenvibrations. That suggested the idea to me that electrons themselves could not be represented as simple corpuscles either, but that a periodicity had also to be assigned to them too.

I thus arrived at the following overall concept which guided my studies: for both matter and radiations, light in particular, it is necessary to introduce the corpuscle concept and the wave concept at the same time. In other words the existence of corpuscles accompanied by waves has to be assumed in all cases. However, since corpuscles and waves cannot be independent because, according to Bohr's expression, they constitute two complementary forces of reality, it must be possible to establish a certain parallelism between the motion of a corpuscle and the propagation of the associated wave. The first objective to achieve had, therefore, to be to establish this correspondence.

With that in view I started by considering the simplest case: that of an isolated corpuscle, i.e. a corpuscle free from all outside influence. We wish to associate a wave with it. Let us consider first of all a reference system $0x_0y_0z_0$ in which the corpuscle is immobile: this is the «intrinsic» system of the corpuscle in the sense of the relativity theory. In this system the wave will be stationary since the corpuscle is immobile: its phase will be the same at every point; it will be represented by an expression of the form $\sin 2\pi \nu_0 (t_0 - \tau_0)$; t_0 being the intrinsic time of the corpuscle and τ_0 a constant.

In accordance with the principle of inertia in every Galilean system, the corpuscle will have a rectilinear and uniform motion. Let us consider such a Galilean system and let $v = \beta c$ be the velocity of the corpuscle in this system; we shall not restrict generality by taking the direction of the motion as the x-axis. In compliance with Lorentz' transformation, the time t used by an observer of this new system will be associated with the intrinsic time t_0 by the relation:

$$t_0 = \frac{t - \dfrac{\beta x}{c}}{\sqrt{1 - \beta^2}}$$

and hence for this observer the phase of the wave will be given by

$$\sin 2\pi \frac{\nu_0}{\sqrt{1 - \beta^2}} \left(t - \frac{\beta x}{c} - \tau_0 \right).$$

For him the wave will thus have a frequency:

$$\nu = \frac{\nu_0}{\sqrt{1 - \beta^2}}$$

and will propagate in the direction of the x-axis at the phase velocity:

$$V = \frac{c}{\beta} = \frac{c^2}{\nu}$$

By the elimination of β between the two preceding formulae the following relation can readily be derived which defines the refractive index of the vacuum n for the waves considered:

$$n = \sqrt{1 - \frac{\nu_0{}^2}{\nu^2}}$$

A « group velocity » corresponds to this « law of dispersion ». You will be aware that the group velocity is the velocity of the resultant amplitude of a group of waves of very close frequencies. Lord Rayleigh showed that this velocity U satisfies equation:

$$\frac{1}{U} = \frac{\partial (n\nu)}{\partial \nu}$$

Here $U = v$, that is to say that the group velocity of the waves in the system $xyzt$ is equal to the velocity of the corpuscle in this system. This relation is of very great importance for the development of the theory.

The corpuscle is thus defined in the system $xyzt$ by the frequency ν and the phase velocity V of its associated wave. To establish the parallelism of which we have spoken, we must seek to link these parameters to the mechanical parameters, energy and quantity of motion. Since the proportionality between energy and frequency is one of the most characteristic relations of the quantum theory, and since, moreover, the frequency and the energy transform in the same way when the Galilean reference system is changed, we may simply write

$$\text{energy} = h \times \text{frequency,} \quad \text{or } W = h\nu$$

where h is Planck's constant. This relation must apply in all Galilean systems and in the intrinsic system of the corpuscle where the energy of the corpuscle, according to Einstein, reduces to its internal energy $m_0 c^2$ (m_0 being the rest mass) we have

$$h\nu_0 = m_0 c^2$$

This relation defines the frequency ν_0 as a function of the rest mass m_0 or inversely.

The quantity of movement is a vector $\vec{p}$ equal to

$$\frac{m_0 v}{\sqrt{1 - \beta^2}}$$

and we have:

$$(p) = \frac{m_0 v}{\sqrt{1 - \beta^2}} = \frac{W v}{c^2} = \frac{h \nu}{V} = \frac{h}{\lambda}$$

The quantity λ is the distance between two consecutive peaks of the wave, i.e. the « wavelength ». Hence:

$$\lambda = \frac{h}{p}$$

This is a fundamental relation of the theory.

The whole of the foregoing relates to the very simple case where there is no field of force at all acting on the corpuscles. I shall show you very briefly how to generalize the theory in the case of a corpuscle moving in a constant field of force deriving from a potential function $F(xyz)$. By reasoning which I shall pass over, we are then led to assume that the propagation of the wave corresponds to a refractive index which varies from point to point in space in accordance with the formula:

$$n(xyz) = \sqrt{\left[1 - \frac{F(xyz)}{h\nu}\right]^2 - \frac{\nu_0^2}{\nu^2}}$$

or to a first approximation if the corrections introduced by the theory of relativity are negligible

$$n(xyz) = \sqrt{\frac{2\,(E - F)}{m_0 c^2}}$$

with $E = W - m_0 c^2$. The constant energy W of the corpuscle is still associated with the constant frequency ν of the wave by the relation

$$W = h\nu$$

while the wavelength λ which varies from one point to another of the force field is associated with the equally variable quantity of motion p by the following relation

$$\lambda(xyz) = \frac{h}{p\,(xyz)}$$

Here again it is demonstrated that the group velocity of the waves is equal to the velocity of the corpuscle. The parallelism thus established between the corpuscle and its wave enables us to identify Fermat's principle for the waves and the principle of least action for the corpuscles (constant fields). Fermat's principle states that the ray in the optical sense which passes through two points A and B in a medium having an index $n(xyz)$ varying from one point to another but constant in time is such that the integral $\int_A^B n\,dl$ taken along this ray is extreme. On the other hand Maupertuis' principle of least action teaches us the following: the trajectory of a corpuscle passing through two points A and B in space is such that the integral $\int_A^B p\,dl$ taken along the trajectory is extreme, provided, of course, that only the motions corresponding to a given energy value are considered. From the relations derived above between the mechanical and the wave parameters, we have:

$$n = \frac{c}{V} = \frac{c}{\nu} \cdot \frac{1}{\lambda} = \frac{c}{h\nu} \cdot \frac{h}{\lambda} = \frac{c}{W} p = \text{const. } p$$

since W is constant in a constant field. It follows that Fermat's and Maupertuis' principles are each a translation of the other and the possible trajectories of the corpuscle are identical to the possible rays of its wave.

These concepts lead to an interpretation of the conditions of stability introduced by the quantum theory. Actually, if we consider a closed trajectory C in a constant field, it is very natural to assume that the phase of the associated wave must be a uniform function along this trajectory. Hence we may write:

$$\int_c \frac{dl}{\lambda} = \int_c \frac{1}{h} p\, dl = \text{integer}$$

This is precisely Planck's condition of stability for periodic atomic motions. The conditions of quantum stability thus emerge as analogous to resonance phenomena and the appearance of integers becomes as natural here as in the theory of vibrating cords and plates.

The general formulae which establish the parallelism between waves and corpuscles may be applied to corpuscles of light on the assumption that here the rest mass m_0 is infinitely small. Actually, if for a given value of the energy W, m_0 is made to tend towards zero, v and V are both found to tend towards c and at the limit the two fundamental formulae are obtained on which Einstein had based his light-quantum theory

$$W = h\nu \qquad p = \frac{h\nu}{c}$$

Such are the main ideas which I developed in my initial studies. They showed clearly that it was possible to establish a correspondence between waves and corpuscles such that the laws of mechanics correspond to the laws of geometrical optics. In the wave theory, however, as you will know, geometrical optics is only an approximation: this approximation has its limits of validity and particularly when interference and diffraction phenomena are involved, it is quite inadequate. This prompted the thought that classical mechanics is also only an approximation relative to a vaster wave mechanics. I stated as much almost at the outset of my studies, i.e. « A new mechanics must be developed which is to classical mechanics what wave optics is to geometrical optics ». This new mechanics has since been developed, thanks mainly to the fine work done by Schrödinger. It is based on wave propagation equations and strictly defines the evolution in time of the wave associated with a corpuscle. It has in particular succeeded in giving a new and more satisfactory form to the quantization conditions of intra-atomic motion since the classical quantization conditions are justified, as we have seen, by the application of geometrical optics to the waves associated with the intra-atomic corpuscles, and this application is not strictly justified.

I cannot attempt even briefly to sum up here the development of the new mechanics. I merely wish to say that on examination it proved to be identical with a mechanics independently developed, first by Heisenberg, then by Born, Jordan, Pauli, Dirac, etc.: quantum mechanics. The two mechanics, wave and quantum, are equivalent from the mathematical point of view.

We shall content ourselves here by considering the general significance of the results obtained. To sum up the meaning of wave mechanics it can be stated that: « A wave must be associated with each corpuscle and only the study of the wave's propagation will yield information to us on the successive positions of the corpuscle in space ». In conventional large-scale mechanical phenomena the anticipated positions lie along a curve which is the trajectory in the conventional meaning of the word. But what happens if the wave does not propagate according to the laws of optical geometry, if, say, there are interferences and diffraction? Then it is no longer possible to assign to the corpuscle a motion complying with classical dynamics, that much is certain. Is it even still possible to assume that at each moment the corpuscle occupies a well-defined position in the wave and that the wave in its propagation carries the corpuscle along in the same way as a wave would carry along a cork? These are difficult questions and to discuss them would take us too far and even to the confines of philosophy. All that I shall say about them here is that nowadays the tendency in general is to assume that it is not constantly possible to assign to the corpuscle a well-defined position in the wave. I must restrict myself to the assertion that when an observation is carried out enabling the localization of the corpuscle, the observer is invariably induced to assign to the corpuscle a position in the interior of the wave and the probability of it being at a particular point M of the wave is proportional to the square of the amplitude, that is to say the intensity at M.

This may be expressed in the following manner. If we consider a cloud of corpuscles associated with the same wave, the intensity of the wave at each point is proportional to the cloud density at that point (i.e. to the number of corpuscles per unit volume around that point). This hypothesis is necessary to explain how, in the case of light interferences, the light energy is concentrated at the points where the wave intensity is maximum: if in fact it is assumed that the light energy is carried by light corpuscles, photons, then the photon density in the wave must be proportional to the intensity.

This rule in itself will enable us to understand how it was possible to verify the wave theory of the electron by experiment.

Let us in fact imagine an indefinite cloud of electrons all moving at the same velocity in the same direction. In conformity with the fundamental ideas of wave mechanics we must associate with this cloud an indefinite plane wave of the form

$$a \sin 2\pi \left[\frac{W}{h} t - \frac{\alpha x + \beta y + \gamma z}{\lambda} \right]$$

where $\alpha\beta\gamma$ are the cosines governing the propagation direction and where the wavelength λ is equal to h/p. With electrons which are not extremely fast, we may write

$$p = m_0 v$$

and hence

$$\lambda = \frac{h}{m_0 v}$$

where m_0 is the rest mass of the electron.

You will be aware that in practice, to obtain electrons moving at the same velocity, they are made to undergo a drop in potential P and we have

$$\tfrac{1}{2} m_0 v^2 = eP$$

Hence,

$$\lambda = \frac{h}{\sqrt{2 m_0 eP}}$$

Numerically this gives

$$\lambda = \frac{12.24}{\sqrt{P}} \, 10^{-8} \text{ cm} \quad (P \text{ in volts})$$

Since it is scarcely possible to use electrons other than such that have undergone a voltage drop of at least some tens of volts, you will see that the wavelength λ predicted by theory is at most of the order of 10^{-8} cm, i.e. of the
order of the Ångström unit. It is also the order of magnitude of X-ray wavelengths.

Since the wavelength of the electron waves is of the order of that of X-
rays, it must be expected that crystals can cause diffraction of these waves
completely analogous to the Laue phenomenon. Allow me to refresh your
memories what is the Laue phenomenon. A natural crystal such as rock salt,
for example, contains nodes composed of the atoms of the substances making
up the crystal and which are regularly spaced at distances of the order of an
Ångström. These nodes act as diffusion centres for the waves and if the
crystal is impinged upon by a wave, the wavelength of which is also of the
order of an Ångström, the waves diffracted by the various nodes are in phase
agreement in certain well-defined directions and in these directions the total
diffracted intensity is a pronounced maximum. The arrangement of these
diffraction maxima is given by the nowadays well-known mathematical
theory developed by von Laue and Bragg which defines the position of the
maxima as a function of the spacing of the nodes in the crystal and of the
wavelength of the incident wave. For X-rays this theory has been admirably
confirmed by von Laue, Friedrich, and Knipping and thereafter the diffraction of X-rays in crystals has become a commonplace experience. The accurate measurement of X-ray wavelengths is based on this diffraction: is
there any need to remind this in the country where Siegbahn and co-workers
are continuing their fine work?

For X-rays the phenomenon of diffraction by crystals was a natural consequence of the idea that X-rays are waves analogous to light and differ from
it only by having a smaller wavelength. For electrons nothing similar could
be foreseen as long as the electron was regarded as a simple small corpuscle.
However, if the electron is assumed to be associated with a wave and the
density of an electron cloud is measured by the intensity of the associated
wave, then a phenomenon analogous to the Laue phenomenon ought to be
expected for electrons. The electron wave will actually be diffracted in-
tensely in the directions which can be calculated by means of the Laue-Bragg
theory from the wavelength $\lambda = h/mv$, which corresponds to the known
velocity v of the electrons impinging on the crystal. Since, according to our
general principle, the intensity of the diffracted wave is a measure of the
density of the cloud of diffracted electrons, we must expect to find a great

many diffracted electrons in the directions of the maxima. If the phenomenon actually exists it should thus provide decisive experimental proof in
favour of the existence of a wave associated with the electron with wavelength h/mv, and so the fundamental idea of wave mechanics will rest on
firm experimental foundations.

Now, experiment which is the final judge of theories, has shown that the
phenomenon of electron diffraction by crystals actually exists and that it
obeys exactly and quantitatively the laws of wave mechanics. To Davisson
and Germer, working at the Bell Laboratories in New York, falls the honour
of being the first to observe the phenomenon by a method analogous to that
of von Laue for X-rays. By duplicating the same experiments but replacing
the single crystal by a crystalline powder in conformity with the method
introduced for X-rays by Debye and Scherrer, Professor G. P. Thomson of
Aberdeen, son of the famous Cambridge physicist Sir J. J. Thomson, found
the same phenomena. Then Rupp in Germany, Kikuchi in Japan, Ponte in
France and others reproduced them, varying the experimental conditions.
Today, the existence of the phenomenon is beyond doubt and the slight
difficulties of interpretation posed by the first experiments of Davisson and
Germer appear to have been satisfactorily solved.

Rupp has even managed to bring about electron diffraction in a particularly striking form. You will be familiar with what are termed diffraction
gratings in optics: these are glass or metal surfaces, plane or slightly curved,
on which have been mechanically traced equidistant lines, the spacing between which is comparable in order of magnitude with the wavelengths of
light waves. The waves diffracted by these lines interfere, and the interferences give rise to maxima of diffracted light in certain directions depending on the interline spacing, on the direction of the light impinging on the
grating, and on the wavelength of this light. For a long time it proved impossible to achieve similar phenomena with this type of man-made diffraction grating using X-rays instead of light. The reason was that the wavelength of X-rays is much smaller than that of light and no instrument can
draw lines on a surface, the spacing between which is of the order of magnitude of X-ray wavelengths. A number of ingenious physicists (Compton,
J. Thibaud) found how to overcome the difficulty. Let us take an ordinary
optical diffraction grating and observe it almost tangentially to its surface.
The lines of the grating will appear to us much closer together than they
actually are. For X-rays impinging at this almost skimming incidence on the
grating the effect will be as if the lines were very closely set and diffraction

phenomena analogous to those of light will occur. This is what the above-mentioned physicists confirmed. But then, since the electron wavelengths are of the order of X-ray wavelengths, it must also be possible to obtain diffraction phenomena by directing a beam of electrons on to an optical diffraction grating at a very low angle. Rupp succeeded in doing so and was thus able to measure the wavelength of electron waves by comparing them directly with the spacing of the mechanically traced lines on the grating.

Thus to describe the properties of matter as well as those of light, waves and corpuscles have to be referred to at one and the same time. The electron can no longer be conceived as a single, small granule of electricity; it must be associated with a wave and this wave is no myth; its wavelength can be measured and its interferences predicted. It has thus been possible to predict a whole group of phenomena without their actually having been discovered. And it is on this concept of the duality of waves and corpuscles in Nature, expressed in a more or less abstract form, that the whole recent development of theoretical physics has been founded and that all future development of this science will apparently have to be founded.

Biography

Prince Louis-Victor de Broglie of the French Academy, Permanent Secretary of the Academy of Sciences, and Professor at the Faculty of Sciences at Paris University, was born at Dieppe (Seine Inférieure) on 15th August, 1892, the son of Victor, Duc de Broglie and Pauline d'Armaillé. After studying at the Lycée Janson of Sailly, he passed his school-leaving certificate in 1909. He applied himself first to literary studies and took his degree in history in 1910. Then, as his liking for science prevailed, he studied for a science degree, which he gained in 1913. He was then conscripted for military service and posted to the wireless section of the army, where he remained for the whole of the war of 1914–1918. During this period he was stationed at the Eiffel Tower, where he devoted his spare time to the study of technical problems. At the end of the war Louis de Broglie resumed his studies of general physics. While taking an interest in the experimental work carried out by his elder brother, Maurice, and co-workers, he specialized in theoretical physics and, in particular, in the study of problems involving quanta. In 1924 at the Faculty of Sciences at Paris University he delivered a thesis *Recherches sur la Théorie des Quanta* (Researches on the quantum theory), which gained him his doctor's degree. This thesis contained a series of important findings which he had obtained in the course of about two years. The ideas set out in that work, which first gave rise to astonishment owing to their novelty, were subsequently fully confirmed by the discovery of electron diffraction by crystals in 1927 by Davisson and Germer; they served as the basis for developing the general theory nowadays known by the name of *wave mechanics*, a theory which has utterly transformed our knowledge of physical phenomena on the atomic scale.

After the maintaining of his thesis and while continuing to publish original work on the new mechanics, Louis de Broglie took up teaching duties. On completion of two year's free lectures at the Sorbonne he was appointed to teach theoretical physics at the Institut Henri Poincaré which had just been built in Paris. The purpose of that Institute is to teach and develop mathematical and theoretical physics. The incumbent of the chair of theoretical physics at the Faculty of Sciences at the University of Paris since 1932, Louis de Broglie runs a course on a different subject each year at the Institut Henri Poincaré, and several of these courses have been published. Many French and foreign students have come to work with him and a great deal of doctorate theses have been prepared under his guidance.

Between 1930 and 1950, Louis de Broglie's work has been chiefly devoted to the study of the various extensions of wave mechanics: Dirac's electron theory, the new theory of light, the general theory of spin particles, applications of wave mechanics to nuclear physics, etc. He has published numerous notes and several papers on this subject, and is the author of more than twenty-five books on the fields of his particular interests.

Since 1951, together with young colleagues, Louis de Broglie has resumed the study of an attempt which he made in 1927 under the name of the *theory of the double solution* to give a causal interpretation to wave mechanics in the classical terms of space and time, an attempt which he had then abandoned in the face of the almost universal adherance of physicists to the purely probabilistic interpretation of Born, Bohr, and Heisenberg. Back again in this his former field of research, he has obtained a certain number of new and encouraging results which he has published in notes to *Comptes Rendus de l'Académie des Sciences* and in various expositions.

After crowning Louis de Broglie's work on two occasions, the Académie des Sciences awarded him in 1929 the Henri Poincaré medal (awarded for the first time), then in 1932, the Albert I of Monaco prize. In 1929 the Swedish Academy of Sciences conferred on him the Nobel Prize for Physics « for his discovery of the wave nature of electrons ». In 1952 the first Kalinga Prize was awarded to him by UNESCO for his efforts to explain aspects of modern physics to the layman. In 1956 he received the gold medal of the French National Scientific Research Centre. He has made major contributions to the fostering of international scientific co-operation.

Elected a member of the Academy of Sciences of the French Institute in 1933, Louis de Broglie has been its Permanent Secretary for the mathematical sciences since 1942. He has been a member of the Bureau des Longitudes since 1944. He holds the Grand Cross of the Légion d'Honneur and is an Officer of the Order of Leopold of Belgium. He is an honorary doctor of the Universities of Warsaw, Bucharest, Athens, Lausanne, Quebec, and Brussels, and a member of eighteen foreign academies in Europe, India, and the U.S.A.

Professor de Broglie's most important publications are:

Recherches sur la théorie des quanta (Researches on the quantum theory), Thesis Paris, 1924.

Ondes et mouvements (Waves and motions), Gauthier-Villars, Paris, 1926.

Rapport au 5e Conseil de Physique Solvay, Brussels, 1927.

La mécanique ondulatoire (Wave mechanics), Gauthier-Villars, Paris, 1928.

Une tentative d'interprétation causale et non linéaire de la mécanique ondulatoire: la théorie de la double solution, Gauthier-Villars, Paris, 1956.

English translation: *Non-linear Wave Mechanics: A Causal Interpretation*, Elsevier, Amsterdam, 1960.

Introduction à la nouvelle théorie des particules de M. Jean-Pierre Vigier et de ses collaborateurs, Gauthier-Villars, Paris, 1961.

English translation: *Introduction to the Vigier Theory of Elementary Particles*, Elsevier, Amsterdam, 1963.

Étude critique des bases de l'interprétation actuelle de la mécanique ondulatoire, Gauthier-Villars, Paris, 1963.

English translation: *The Current Interpretation of Wave Mechanics: A Critical Study*, Elsevier, Amsterdam, 1964.

Physics 1930

Sir CHANDRASEKHARA

VENKATA RAMAN

«for his work on the scattering of light and for the discovery of the effect named after him»

Physics 1930

Presentation Speech by Professor H. Pleijel, Chairman of the Nobel Committee for Physics of the Royal Swedish Academy of Sciences

Your Majesty, Your Royal Highnesses, Ladies and Gentlemen.

The Academy of Sciences, has resolved to award the Nobel Prize in Physics for 1930 to Sir Venkata Raman for his work on the scattering of light and for the discovery of the effect named after him.

The diffusion of light is an optical phenomenon, which has been known for a long time. A ray of light is not perceptible unless it strikes the eye directly. If, however, a bundle of rays of light traverses a medium in which extremely fine dust is present, the ray of light will scatter to the sides and the path of the ray through the medium will be discernible from the side. We can represent the course of events in this way; the small particles of dust begin to oscillate owing to electric influence from the ray of light, and they form centres from which light is disseminated in all directions. The wavelength, or the number of oscillations per second, in the light thus diffused is here the same as in the original ray of light. But this effect has different degrees of strength for light with different wavelengths. It is stronger for the short wavelengths than for the long ones, and consequently it is stronger for the blue part of the spectrum than for the red part. Hence if a ray of light containing all the colours of the spectrum passes through a medium, the yellow and the red rays will pass through the medium without appreciable scattering, whereas the blue rays will be scattered to the sides. This effect has received the name of the « Tyndall effect ».

Lord Rayleigh, who has made a study of this effect, has put forward the hypothesis that the blue colours of the sky and the reddish colouring that is observed at sunrise and sunset is caused by the diffusion of light owing to the fine dust or the particles of water in the atmosphere. The blue light from the sky would thus be light-scattered to the sides, while the reddish light would be light that passes through the lower layers of the atmosphere and which has become impoverished in blue rays owing to scattering. Later, in 1899, Rayleigh threw out the suggestion that the phenomenon in question might be due to the fact that the molecules of air themselves exercised a scattering effect on the rays of light.

In 1914 Cabannes succeeded in showing experimentally that pure and dust-less gases also have the capacity of scattering rays of light.

But a closer examination of scattering in different substances in solid, liquid, or gaseous form showed that the scattered light did not in certain respects exactly follow the laws which, according to calculation, should hold good for the Tyndall effect. The hypothesis which formed the basis of this effect would seem to involve, amongst other things, that the rays scattered to the sides were polarized. This, however, did not prove to be exactly the case.

This divergence from what was to be expected was made the starting-point of a searching study of the nature of scattered light, in which study Raman was one of those who took an active part. Raman sought to find the explanation of the anomalies in asymmetry observed in the molecules. During these studies of his in the phenomenon of scattering, Raman made, in 1928, the unexpected and highly surprising discovery that the scattered light showed not only the radiation that derived from the primary light but also a radiation that contained other wavelengths, which were foreign to the primary light.

In order to study more closely the properties of the new rays, the primary light that was emitted from a powerful mercury lamp was filtered in such a way as to yield a primary light of one single wavelength. The light scattered from that ray in a medium was watched in a spectrograph, in which every wavelength or frequency produces a line. Here he found that, in addition to the mercury line chosen, there was obtained a spectrum of new sharp lines, which appeared in the spectrograph on either side of the original line. When another mercury line was employed, the same extra spectrum showed itself round it. Thus, when the primary light was moved, the new spectrum followed, in such a way that the frequency distance between the primary line and the new lines always remained the same.

Raman investigated the universal character of the phenomenon by using a large number of substances as a scattering medium, and everywhere found the same effect.

The explanation of this phenomenon, which has received the name of the « Raman effect » after its discoverer, has been found by Raman himself, with the help of the modern conception of the nature of light. According to that conception, light cannot be emitted from or absorbed by material otherwise than in the form of definite amounts of energy or what are known as « light quanta ». Thus the energy of light would possess a kind of atomic character. A quantum of light is proportionate to the frequency of rays of light, so that in the case of a frequency twice as great, the quanta of the rays of light will also be twice as great.

In order to illustrate the conditions when an atom emits or absorbs light energy, we can, according to Bohr, picture to ourselves the atom as consisting of a nucleus, charged with positive electricity round which negative electrons rotate in circular paths at various distances from the centre. The path of every such electron possesses a certain energy, which is different for different distances from the central body.

Only certain paths are stable. When the electron moves in such a path, no energy is emitted. When, on the other hand, an electron falls from a path with higher energy to one with lower energy – that is to say, from an outer path to an inner path – light is emitted with a frequency that is characteristic of these two paths, and the energy of radiation consists of a quantum of light. Thus the atom can give rise to as many frequencies as the number of different transitions between the stable paths. There is a line in the spectrum corresponding to each frequency.

An incoming radiation cannot be absorbed by the atom unless its light quantum is identical with one of the light quanta that the atom can emit.

Now the Raman effect seems to conflict with this law. The positions of the Raman-lines in the spectrum do not correspond, in point of fact, with the frequencies of the atom itself, and they move with the activating ray. Raman has explained this apparent contradiction and the coming into existence of the lines by the effect of combination between the quantum of light coming from without and the quanta of light that are released or bound in the atom. If the atom, at the same time as it receives from without a quantum of light, emits a quantum of light of a different magnitude, and if the difference between these two quanta is identical with the quantum of light which is bound or released when an electron passes from one path to another, the quantum of light coming from without is absorbed. In that case the atom will emit an extra frequency, which either will be the sum of or the difference between the activating ray and a frequency in the atom itself. In this case these new lines group themselves round the incoming primary frequency on either side of it, and the distance between the activating frequency and the nearest Raman-lines will be identical with the lowest oscillation frequencies of the atom or with its ultrared spectrum. What has been said as to the atom and its oscillations also holds good of the molecule.

In this way we get the ultrared spectrum moved up to the spectral line of the activating light. The discovery of the Raman-line has proved to be of extraordinarily great importance for our knowledge of the structure of molecules.

So far, indeed, there have been all but insuperable difficulties in the way of studying these ultrared oscillations, because that part of the spectrum lies so far away from the region where the photographic plate is sensitive. Raman's discovery has now overcome these difficulties, and the way has been opened for the investigation of the oscillations of the nucleus of the molecules. We choose the primary ray within that range of frequency where the photographic plate is sensitive. The ultrared spectrum, in the form of the Raman-lines, is moved up to that region and, in consequence of that, exact measurements of its lines can be effected.

In the same way the ultraviolet spectrum can be investigated with the help of the Raman effect. Thus we have obtained a simple and exact method for the investigation of the entire sphere of oscillation of the molecules.

Raman himself and his fellow-workers have, during the years that have elapsed since the discovery was made, investigated the frequencies in a large number of substances in a solid, liquid, and gaseous state. Investigations have been made as to whether different conditions of aggregation affect atoms and molecules, and the molecular conditions in electrolytic dissociation and the ultrared absorption spectrum of crystals have been studied.

Thus the Raman effect has already yielded important results concerning the chemical constitution of substances; and it is to foresee that the extremely valuable tool that the Raman effect has placed in our hands will in the immediate future bring with it a deepening of our knowledge of the structure of matter.

Sir Venkata Raman. The Royal Academy of Sciences has awarded you the Nobel Prize in Physics for your eminent researches on the diffusion of gases and for your discovery of the effect that bears your name. The Raman effect has opened new routes to our knowledge of the structure of matter and has already given most important results.

I now ask you to receive the prize from the hands of His Majesty.

Sir Chandrasekhara V. Raman

The molecular scattering of light

Nobel Lecture, December 11, 1930

The colour of the sea

In the history of science, we often find that the study of some natural phenomenon has been the starting-point in the development of a new branch of knowledge. We have an instance of this in the colour of skylight, which has inspired numerous optical investigations, and the explanation of which, proposed by the late Lord Rayleigh, and subsequently verified by observation, forms the beginning of our knowledge of the subject of this lecture. Even more striking, though not so familiar to all, is the colour exhibited by oceanic waters. A voyage to Europe in the summer of 1921 gave me the first opportunity of observing the wonderful blue opalescence of the Mediterranean Sea. It seemed not unlikely that the phenomenon owed its origin to the scattering of sunlight by the molecules of the water. To test this explanation, it appeared desirable to ascertain the laws governing the diffusion of light in liquids, and experiments with this object were started immediately on my return to Calcutta in September, 1921. It soon became evident, however, that the subject possessed a significance extending far beyond the special purpose for which the work was undertaken, and that it offered unlimited scope for research. It seemed indeed that the study of light-scattering might carry one into the deepest problems of physics and chemistry, and it was this belief which led to the subject becoming the main theme of our activities at Calcutta from that time onwards.

The theory of fluctuations

From the work of the first few months, it became clear that the molecular scattering of light was a very general phenomenon which could be studied not only in gases and vapours but also in liquids and in crystalline and amorphous solids, and that it was primarily an effect arising from molecular disarray in the medium and consequent local fluctuations in its optical density. Except in amorphous solids, such molecular disarray could presumably be ascribed to thermal agitation, and the experimental results appeared to support this view. The fact that molecules are optically anisotropic and can orientate freely in liquids was found to give rise to an additional type of scattering. This could be distinguished from the scattering due to fluctuations in density by reason of its being practically unpolarized, whereas the latter was completely polarized in the transverse direction. The whole subject was critically reviewed and the results till then obtained were set out in an essay published by the Calcutta University Press in February 1922.

The various problems requiring solution indicated in this essay were investigated with the aid of a succession of able collaborators. It is possible to mention briefly only a few of the numerous investigations which were carried out at Calcutta during the six years 1922 to 1927. The scattering of light in fluids was studied by Ramanathan over a wide range of pressures and temperatures with results which appeared to support the « fluctuation » theory of its origin. His work also disclosed the remarkable changes in the state of polarization which accompany the variations of intensity with temperature in vapours and in liquids. Liquid mixtures were investigated by Kameswara Rao, and furnished optical proof of the existence in such systems, of simultaneous fluctuations of density, composition, and molecular orientation. Srivastava studied the scattering of light in crystals in relation to the thermal fluctuations of density and their increase with temperature. Ramdas investigated the scattering of light by liquid surfaces due to thermal agitation, and established a relation between surface-tension and surface-opalescence. He also traced the transition from surface-opalescence to volume-opalescence which occurs at the critical temperature. Sogani investigated X-ray diffraction in liquids, in order to connect it with their optical behaviour, and test the application of fluctuation theory to X-ray scattering.

The anisotropy of molecules

As stated above, the state of polarization of the light scattered in fluids is connected with the optical anisotropy of the molecules. Much of the work done at Calcutta during the years 1922 to 1927 was intended to obtain data concerning this property and to establish its relations with various optical phenomena. Krishnan examined a great many liquids, and by his work showed very clearly the dependence of the optical anisotropy of the molecule on its chemical constitution. Ramakrishna Rao studied the depolarization of scattered light in a very large number of gases and vapours, and obtained information of high importance for the progress of the subject. Venkateswaran studied the scattering of light in aqueous solutions to find the influence on it of electrolytic dissociation. Ramachandra Rao investigated liquids having highly elongated molecules and also highly polar substances over a wide range of temperatures, and discovered the influence of molecular shape and molecular association on the depolarization of scattered light in liquids.

The interpretation of the observations with liquids involved the development of a molecular theory of light-scattering in dense media which was undertaken by Ramanathan, myself, and Krishnan. A revised opalescence formula was derived which differed from that of Einstein and yielded results in better agreement with observation. Krishnan and myself also published a series of investigations showing how the optical anisotropy of the molecules deduced from light-scattering could be utilized to interpret the optical and dielectric behaviour of fluids, and also the electric, magnetic, and mechanical birefringence exhibited by them. The conclusions derived from these studies enabled a connection to be established between the molecular anisotropy observed in fluids and the optical, electric, and magnetic aeolotropy exhibited by solids in the crystalline state.

A new phenomenon

The investigations referred to above were in the main guided by the classical electromagnetic theory of light, the application of which to the problems of light-scattering is chiefly associated with the names of Rayleigh and of Einstein. Nevertheless, the possibility that the corpuscular nature of light might come into evidence in scattering was not overlooked and was in fact elaborately discussed in the essay of February 1922 which was published at least a year before the well-known discoveries of Compton on X-ray scattering. While our experiments in the main appeared to support the electromagnetic theory of light, evidence came to hand at a very early stage of the investigations of the existence of a phenomenon which seemed to stand outside the classical scheme of thought. The scattering of light in transparent fluids is extremely feeble, much weaker in fact than the Tyndall effect usually observed in turbid media. It was experimentally discovered that associated with the Rayleigh-Einstein type of molecular scattering, was another and still feebler type of secondary radiation, the intensity of which was of the order of magnitude of a few hundredths of the classical scattering, and differed from it in not having the same wavelength as the primary or incident radiation. The first observation of this phenomenon was made at Calcutta in April 1923 by Ramanathan who was led to it in attempting to explain why in certain liquids (water, ether, methyl and ethyl alcohols), the depolarization of scattered light varied with the wavelength of the incident radiation. Ramanathan found that after exhaustive chemical purification and repeated slow distillation of the liquid in vacuum, the new radiation persisted undiminished in intensity, showing that it was a characteristic property of the substance studied and not due to any fluorescent impurity. Krishnan observed a similar effect in many other liquids in 1924, and a somewhat more conspicuous phenomenon was observed by me in ice and in optical glasses.

The optical analogue of the Compton effect

The origin of this puzzling phenomenon naturally interested us, and in the summer of 1925, Venkateswaran attempted to investigate it by photographing the spectrum of the scattered light from liquids, using sunlight filtered through colour screens, but was unable to report any decisive results. Ramakrishna Rao in his studies on the depolarization of scattering during 1926 and 1927 looked carefully for a similar phenomenon in gases and vapours, but without success. This problem was taken up again by Krishnan towards the end of 1927. While his work was in progress, the first indication of the true nature of the phenomenon came to hand from a different quarter. One of the problems interesting us at this time was the behaviour in light-scattering of highly viscous organic liquids which were capable of passing over into the glassy state. Venkateswaran undertook to study this question, and reported the highly interesting result that the colour of sunlight scattered in a highly purified sample of glycerine was a brilliant green instead of the usual blue. The phenomenon appeared to be similar to that discovered by Ramanathan in water and the alcohols, but of much greater intensity, and, therefore, more easily studied. No time was lost in following up the matter. Tests were made with a series of filters transmitting narrow regions of the solar spectrum and placed in the path of the incident beam, which showed that in every case the colour of the scattered light was different from that of the incident light, and was displaced from it towards the red. The radiations were also strongly polarized. These facts indicated a clear analogy between the empirical characters of the phenomenon and the Compton effect. The work of Compton had made familiar the idea that the wavelength of radiation could be degraded in the process of scattering, and the observations with glycerine suggested to me that the phenomenon which had puzzled us ever since 1923 was in fact the optical analogue of the Compton effect. This idea naturally stimulated further investigation with other substances.

The chief difficulty which had hitherto oppressed us in the study of the new phenomenon was its extreme feebleness in general. This was overcome by using a 7-inch refracting telescope in combination with a short-focus lens to condense sunlight into a pencil of very great intensity. With these arrangements and using complementary light-filters in the path of the incident and scattered beams, as was done by Ramanathan in 1923, to isolate the modified radiations, it was found that they could be readily observed in a great many liquids, and that in many cases they were strongly polarized. Krishnan, who very materially assisted me in these investigations, found at the same time that the phenomenon could be observed in several organic vapours, and even succeeded in visually determining the state of polarization of the modified radiations from them. Compressed gases such as CO_2 and N_2O, crystalline ice, and optical glasses also were found to exhibit the modified radiations. These observations left little doubt that the phenomenon was really a species of light-scattering analogous to the Compton effect.

The spectroscopic characters of the new effect

Thanks to the vastly more powerful illumination made available by the 7-inch refractor, the spectroscopic examination of the effect, which had been abandoned in 1925 as indecisive, now came within the reach of direct visual study. With a Zeiss cobalt-glass filter placed in the path of the incident beam and one or other of a series of organic liquids as the scattering substance, a band in the blue-green region was observed by me in the spectrum of the scattered light, separated by a dark interval from the indigo-violet region transmitted by the filter. *Both* of these regions in the spectrum became sharper when the region of transmission was narrowed by the insertion of an additional filter in the incident beam. This suggested the employment, instead of sunlight, of the highly monochromatic radiations given by a mercury arc in combination with a condenser of large aperture and a cobalt-glass filter.

With these arrangements the spectrum of the scattered light from a variety of liquids and solids was visually examined, and the startling observation was made that the spectrum generally included a number of sharp lines or bands on a diffuse background which were not present in the light of the mercury arc.

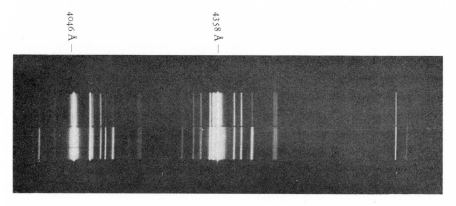

Fig. 1. Spectrum of carbon tetrachloride.

The quartz mercury lamp was so powerful and convenient a source of monochromatic illumination that, at least in the case of liquids and solids, photographing the spectrum of scattered light was found to present no extra-ordinary difficulties. The earliest pictures of the phenomenon were in fact taken with a portable quartz spectrograph of the smallest size made by the firm of Hilger. With a somewhat larger instrument of the same type, Krishnan obtained very satisfactory spectrograms with liquids and with crystals on which measurements of the desired precision could be made, and on which the presence of lines displaced towards the violet was first definitely established. The experimental difficulties were naturally greater in the case of gases or vapours, though they could be lessened by working with the substance under pressure. With an improvised instrument of large aperture (F/1.8), Ramdas obtained the first spectrograms with a gaseous substance (ether vapour) at atmospheric pressure.

In interpreting the observed phenomena, the analogy with the Compton effect was adopted as the guiding principle. The work of Compton had gained general acceptance for the idea that the scattering of radiation is a unitary process in which the conservation principles hold good. Accepting this idea it follows at once that, if the scattering particle gains any energy during the encounter with the quantum, the latter is deprived of energy to the same extent, and accordingly appears after scattering as a radiation of diminished frequency. From thermodynamic principles, it follows that the reverse process should also be possible. Adopting these ideas, the actual observations could be interpreted, and the agreement of the observed displacements with the infrared frequencies of the molecules made it clear that the new method opened up an illimitable field of experimental research in the study of the structure of matter.

Interpretation of the effect

It appears desirable to emphasize that though the conservation principle of Compton is useful in interpreting the effects disclosed by experiment, it is by itself insufficient to explain the observed phenomena. As is well known from studies on molecular spectra, a gaseous molecule has four different species of energy of increasing orders of magnitude, namely those corresponding to translatory motion, rotation, vibration, and electronic excitation. Each of these, except the first, is quantized and may be represented by an integer in an extended sequence of quantum numbers. The aggregate energy of a molecule may, therefore, assume any one out of a very large number of possible values. If we assume that an exchange of energy occurs in the collision between the molecule and the quantum, and limit ourself to the cases in which the final energy of the molecule is less than that of the incident quantum, we arrive at the result that the spectrum of the scattered light should contain an immense number of new lines and should in fact rival in its complexity the band spectrum of the molecule observed in the emission or absorption of light. Nothing more different from what is actually observed can be imagined than the foregoing picture. The most conspicuous feature revealed by experiment is the beautiful simplicity of the spectra of even complicated polyatomic molecules obtained in light-scattering, a simplicity that is in striking contrast to the extreme complexity of their emission or absorption spectra. It is this simplicity that gives to the study of light-scattering its special significance and value. It is clear that the effect actually observed was not and could not have been foreseen from an application of the conservation principles.

The general principle of correspondence between the quantum and classical theories enunciated by Niels Bohr enables us, on the other hand, to obtain a real insight into the actual phenomena. The classical theory of light-scattering tells us that if a molecule scatters light while it is moving, rotating or vibrating, the scattered radiations may include certain frequencies, different from those of the incident waves. This classical picture, in many respects, is surprisingly like what we actually observe in the experiments. It explains why the frequency shifts observed fall into three classes, translational, rotational and vibrational, of different orders of magnitude. It explains the observed selection rules, as for instance, why the frequencies of vibration deduced from scattered light include only the fundamentals and not the overtones and combinations which are so conspicuous in emission and absorption spectra. The classical theory can even go further and give us a rough indication of the intensity and polarization of the radiations of altered frequency. Nevertheless, the classical picture has to be modified in essential respects to give even a qualitative description of the phenomena, and we have, therefore, to invoke the aid of quantum principles. The work of Kramers and Heisenberg, and the newer developments in quantum mechanics which have their root in Bohr's correspondence principle seem to offer a promising way of approach towards an understanding of the experimental results. But until we know much more than we do at present regarding the structure of molecules, and have sufficient quantitative experimental knowledge of the effect, it would be rash to suggest that they afford a complete explanation of it.

The significance of the effect

The universality of the phenomenon, the convenience of the experimental technique and the simplicity of the spectra obtained enable the effect to be used as an experimental aid to the solution of a wide range of problems in physics and chemistry. Indeed, it may be said that it is this fact which constitutes the principal significance of the effect. The frequency differences determined from the spectra, the width and character of the lines appearing in them, and the intensity and state of polarization of the scattered radiations enable us to obtain an insight into the ultimate structure of the scattering substance. As experimental research has shown, these features in the spectra are very definitely influenced by physical conditions, such as temperature and state of aggregation, by physico-chemical conditions, such as mixture, solution, molecular association and polymerization, and most essentially by chemical constitution. It follows that the new field of spectroscopy has practically unrestricted scope in the study of problems relating to the structure of matter. We may also hope that it will lead us to a fuller understanding of the nature of light, and of the interactions between matter and light.

Some concluding remarks

From a physical point of view, the quantitative study of the effect with the simplest molecules holds out the largest hope of fundamental advances. The beautiful work of McLennan with liquefied gases, and of R. W. Wood and Rasetti are pioneer investigations in this field which command the highest admiration. The quantitative study of the effect with crystals of the simplest possible chemical constitution is naturally of great importance. The case of the diamond, which has been investigated by Ramaswamy, Robertson, and Fox, and with especial completeness by Bhagavantam, is of special interest. Very surprising results have been obtained with this substance, which may be the pathway to a fuller understanding of the nature of the crystalline state. I should also like to draw attention to the work of Krishnamurti, who has traced a remarkable dependence of the intensity of the spectral lines observed in scattering on the nature of the chemical bond, and followed the transition from the homopolar to the heteropolar type of chemical combination. Krishnamurti's observation that the paramagnetism of crystals apparently influences the observed intensity of the displaced lines is one of the most remarkable ever made in this new field of research.

Biography

Chandrasekhara Venkata Raman was born at Trichinopoly in Southern India on November 7th, 1888. His father was a lecturer in mathematics and physics so that from the first he was immersed in an academic atmosphere. He entered Presidency College, Madras, in 1902, and in 1904 passed his B.A. examination, winning the first place and the gold medal in physics; in 1907 he gained his M.A. degree, obtaining the highest distinctions.

His earliest researches in optics and acoustics–the two fields of investigation to which he has dedicated his entire career–were carried out while he was a student.

Since at that time a scientific career did not appear to present the best possibilities, Raman joined the Indian Finance Department in 1907; though the duties of his office took most of his time, Raman found opportunities for carrying on experimental research in the laboratory of the Indian Association for the Cultivation of Science at Calcutta (of which he became Honorary Secretary in 1919).

In 1917 he was offered the newly endowed Palit Chair of Physics at Calcutta University, and decided to accept it. After 15 years at Calcutta he became Professor at the Indian Institute of Science at Bangalore (1933–1948), and since 1948 he is Director of the Raman Institute of Research at Bangalore, established and endowed by himself. He also founded the *Indian Journal of Physics* in 1926, of which he is the Editor. Raman sponsored the establishment of the Indian Academy of Sciences and has served as President since its inception. He also initiated the *Proceedings* of that academy, in which much of his work has been published, and is President of the Current Science Association, Bangalore, which publishes *Current Science (India)*.

Some of Raman's early memoirs appeared as *Bulletins of the Indian Association for the Cultivation of Science* (Bull. 6 and 11, dealing with the «Maintenance of Vibrations»; Bull. 15, 1918, dealing with the theory of the musical instruments of the violin family). He contributed an article on the theory of musical instruments to the 8th Volume of the *Handbuch der Physik*, 1928. In 1922 he published his work on the «Molecular Diffraction of Light», the first of a series of investigations with his collaborators which ultimately led to his discovery, on the 28th of February, 1928, of the radiation effect which bears his name (« A new radiation», *Indian J. Phys.*, 2 (1928) 387), and which gained him the 1930 Nobel Prize in Physics.

Other investigations carried out by Raman were: his experimental and theoretical studies on the diffraction of light by acoustic waves of ultrasonic and hypersonic frequencies (published 1934–1942), and those on the effects produced by X-rays on infrared vibrations in crystals exposed to ordinary light. In 1948 Raman, through studying the spectroscopic behaviour of crystals, approached in a new manner fundamental problems of crystal dynamics. His laboratory has been dealing with the structure and properties of diamond, the structure and optical behaviour of numerous iridescent substances (labradorite, pearly felspar, agate, opal, and pearls).

Among his other interests have been the optics of colloids, electrical and magnetic anisotropy, and the physiology of human vision.

Raman has been honoured with a large number of honorary doctorates and memberships of scientific societies. He was elected a Fellow of the Royal Society early in his career (1924), and was knighted in 1929.

Physics 1931

Prize not awarded

Physics 1932 and 1933

WERNER HEISENBERG

[1932]

«for the creation of quantum mechanics, the application of which has, among other things, led to the discovery of the allotropic forms of hydrogen»

ERWIN SCHRÖDINGER

PAUL ADRIEN MAURICE DIRAC

[1933]

«for the discovery of new productive forms of atomic theory»

Physics 1932 and 1933

Presentation Speech by Professor H. Pleijel, Chairman of the Nobel Committee for Physics of the Royal Swedish Academy of Sciences

Your Majesty, Your Royal Highnesses, Ladies and Gentlemen.

This year's Nobel Prizes for Physics are dedicated to the new atomic physics. The prizes, which the Academy of Sciences has at its disposal, have namely been awarded to those men, Heisenberg, Schrödinger, and Dirac, who have created and developed the basic ideas of modern atomic physics.

It was Planck who, in 1900, first expressed the thought that light had atomic properties, and the theory put forward by Planck was later more exhaustively developed by Einstein. The conviction, arrived at by different paths, was that matter could not create or absorb light, other than in quantities of energy which represented the multiple of a specific unit of energy. This unit of energy received the name of light quantum or photon. The magnitude of the photon is different for different colours of light, but if the quantity of energy of a photon is divided by the frequency of oscillation of the ray of light, the same number is always obtained, the so-called Planck's constant h. This constant is thus of a universal nature and forms one of the foundation stones for modern atomic physics.

Since light too was thus divided into atoms it appeared that all phenomena could be explained as interactions between atoms of various kinds. Mass was also attributed to the atom of light, and the effects which were observed when light rays were incident upon matter could be explained with the help of the law for the impact of bodies.

Not many years passed before the found connection between the photon and the light ray led to an analogous connection between the motion of matter and the propagation of waves being sought for.

For a long time it had been known that the customary description of the propagation of light in the form of rays of light, which are diffracted and reflected on transmission from one medium to another, was only an approximation to the true circumstances, which only held good so long as the wavelength of the light was infinitesimally small compared with the dimensions of the body through which the light passed, and of the instruments with which it was observed. In reality light is propagated in the form of waves which spread out in all directions according to the laws for the propagation of waves.

Prince Louis de Broglie conceived the brilliant idea of seeking an analogy between the path of the light ray and the track of a material point. He wondered whether the track of a particle of matter, like the path of a ray of light, might only be an approximate expression for reality, prescribed by the coarseness of our senses, and whether one here was not also dealing with wave motion. Using Einstein's theory of relativity, he was equally successful in representing the motion of matter as a combination of waves which were propagating themselves with velocities greater than that of light. Matter is formed or represented by a great number of this kind of waves which have somewhat different velocities of propagation and such phase that they combine at the point in question. Such a system of waves forms a crest which propagates itself with quite a different velocity from that of its component waves, this velocity being the so-called group velocity. Such a wave crest represents a material point which is thus either formed by it or connected with it, and is called a wave packet. De Broglie now found that the velocity of the material point was in fact the group velocity of the matter-wave.

De Broglie's theory of matter-waves subsequently received experimental confirmation. If a relatively slowly travelling electron meets a crystal surface, diffraction and reflection phenomena appear in the same way as if an incident beam of waves were concerned.

As a result of this theory one is forced to the conclusion to conceive of matter as not being durable, or that it can have definite extension in space. The waves, which form the matter, travel, in fact, with different velocity and must, therefore, sooner or later separate. Matter changes form and extent in space. The picture which has been created, of matter being composed of unchangeable particles, must be modified.

One of the physical phenomena whose correct explanation has proved most difficult, is the appearance of the spectra of countless lines 'and' bands which are obtained if light is split up by optical instruments when produced by atoms and molecules as a result of their vibrations. It has been known for a long time that each such line corresponds to light of a certain frequency, which varies according to where the line appears in the various parts of the colour spectrum.

A correct explanation of the intensities of all these lines and their positions in the spectrum is of fundamental significance since it gives us an insight into the structure of the atoms and molecules and the relationships within them.

It was Bohr who, in 1913, expressed the idea that Planck's constant should be taken as the determining factor for movements within the atom, as well as for the emission and absorption of light waves.

Bohr assumed, after Rutherford, that an atom consists of an inner, heavy, positively charged particle, around which negative, light electrons circulate in closed paths, held to the nucleus by the attraction. According to whether the path of the electron is further away, or closer from the nucleus, the electron possesses different velocity and different energy. Bohr now put forward the hypothesis that only such paths exist where the energy of the electron, as a result of its motion in the path, is a whole multiple of a quantum of light corresponding to the rotation frequency of the electron. Light, Bohr now assumed, appears if an electron suddenly transfers from one path to another, and the frequency of the light ray emitted, is obtained if the change of energy experienced during transfer is divided by Planck's constant. The frequencies which Bohr thus obtained held good for a hydrogen atom which has only one electron, but when his method was applied to more complicated atoms and to certain optical phenomena, theory and practice did not agree. The fact that Bohr's hypothesis met the case for the hydrogen atom, however, suggested that Planck's constant was, in one way or another, a determining factor for the light-vibrations of the atoms. On the other hand, one had the feeling that it could not be right to apply the laws of classical mechanics to the rapid movements in the atoms. Efforts made from various sides to develop and improve Bohr's theory proved also in vain. New ideas were required to solve the problem of oscillations of atoms and molecules.

This solution followed in 1925 upon the works of Heisenberg, Schrödinger, and Dirac in which different starting-points and methods were applied.

I will first of all dwell upon Schrödinger's contribution since it is more closely than the others connected to the state of the development which atomic physics had attained at that period of time, particularly as a result of de Broglie's above-mentioned theory of matter-waves.

Since the electrons were the seat of outgoing waves, Schrödinger thought that it should be possible to find a wave equation for the motions executed by the electrons which would define these waves in the same way as the wave equation which determined the propagation of light. From the solution of this wave equation one should be able to select those oscillations which were feasible for the motions within the atoms. He was successful, too, in determining the wave equation for a series of different motions of the electron, and it turned out that these equations gave finite solutions only when the energy of the system had specific discrete values, determined by Planck's constant. In Bohr's theory these discrete energy values of the electron paths were only hypothetical, but in Schrödinger's, on the contrary, they appeared as completely determined by the form of the wave equation. Schrödinger himself, and others after him, have applied his wave theory to various optical problems including the interpretation of the phenomena accompanying the impact between light rays and electrons, investigations into the behaviour of atoms in electric and magnetic fields, the diffraction of light rays, etc. In every direction, values and formulae have been obtained using Schrödinger's theory, which have been in closer agreement with experience than the older theories were. Schrödinger's wave equation has provided a convenient and simple method for handling problems to do with light spectra, and has become an indispensible tool for the present-day physicist.

Somewhat before the appearance of Schrödinger's theory Heisenberg brought out his famous quantum mechanics. Heisenberg started off from quite different standpoints and viewed his problem, from the very beginning, from so broad an angle that it took care of systems of electrons, atoms, and molecules. According to Heisenberg one must start from such physical quantities as permit of direct observation, and the task consists of finding the laws which link these quantities together. The quantities first of all to be considered are the frequencies and intensities of the lines in the spectra of atoms and molecules. Heisenberg now considered the combination of all the oscillations of such a spectrum as *one* system, for the mathematical handling of which, he set out certain symbolical rules of calculation. It had formerly been determined already that certain kinds of motions within the atom must be viewed as independent from one another to a certain degree, in the same way that a specific difference is made in classical mechanics between parallel motion and rotational motion. It should be mentioned in this connection that in order to explain the properties of a spectrum it had been necessary to assume self-rotation of the positive nuclei and the electrons. These different kinds of motion for atoms and molecules produce different systems in Heisenberg's quantum mechanics. As the fundamental factor of Heisenberg's theory can be put forward the rule set out by him with reference to the relationship between the position coordinate and the velocity of an electron, by which rule Planck's constant is introduced into the quantum-mechanics calculations as a determining factor.

Although Heisenberg's and Schrödinger's theories had different starting-points and were developed by the use of different processes of thought, they produced the same results for problems treated by both theories.

Heisenberg's quantum mechanics has been applied by himself and others to the study of the properties of the spectra of atoms and molecules, and has yielded results which agree with experimental research. It can be said that Heisenberg's quantum mechanics has made possible a systemization of spectra of atoms. It should also be mentioned that Heisenberg, when he applied his theory to molecules consisting of two similar atoms, found among other things that the hydrogen molecule must exist in two different forms which should appear in some given ratio to each other. This prediction of Heisenberg's was later also experimentally confirmed.

Dirac has set up a wave mechanics which starts from the most general conditions. From the start he put forward the requirement that the postulate of the relativity theory be fulfilled. Viewed from this general formulation of the problems it appeared that the self-rotation of the electron which had previously come into the theory as an hypothesis stipulated by experimental facts, now appeared as a result of the general theory of Dirac.

Dirac divided the initial wave equation into two simpler ones, each providing solutions independently. It now appeared that one of the solution systems required the existence of positive electrons having the same mass and charge as the known negative electrons. This initially posed considerable difficulty for Dirac's theory, since positively charged particles were known only in the form of the heavy atom nucleus. This difficulty which at first opposed the theory has now become a brilliant confirmation of its validity. For later on, positive electrons, the positrons, whose existence was stipulated in Dirac's theoretical investigation, have been found by experiment.

The new quantum mechanics has changed to a great extent all our concepts of the relationships existing within the microscopic world, made up of atoms and molecules. We have already mentioned that as a result of the new wave mechanics we have had to modify our conception on the unchangeability of material particles. But more than this. Heisenberg has shown that according to quantum mechanics it is inconceivable to determine, at a given instant of time, both the position taken up by a particle and its velocity. Closer study of quantum mechanics shows in fact that the more one attempts to fix exactly the position of a particle, the more uncertain the determination of its velocity becomes, and vice versa. It must be further considered, that it is impossible to carry out the measurement of the situation in an atom or molecule without the employed instruments, il-

lumination, etc. themselves altering the situation which is under examination. The light emitted from the electrons becomes modified in the optical
instruments. The relationships go still deeper however. As a result of the
introduction of light quanta, quantum mechanics must abandon the requirement of causality within the microcosmic world. A ray of light on being
incident upon an optical instrument is resolved. However, the photon is in-
divisible. It must be realized then, that some photons will behave in one way,
others in another way at the resolution. The only assertion that can be made
regarding causality is that the physical laws signify a certain probability that
one or another incident will take place. Since we can only perceive average
values because of the imperfection of our senses and instruments, it is probabilities which are covered in our physical laws, and the question has been
raised, whether in the physical world there is in fact any other accordance
with laws than a statistical one.

Professor Heisenberg.   It has fallen to you whilst young in years, to have
given to physics, by means of the theory of quantum mechanics established
by you, a general method for the solution of the manifold problems which
have come to the fore as a result of restless experimental researches into the
theory of radiation. From a study of the properties of the molecules, you
have succeeded, among other things, in predicting that the hydrogen molecules would appear in two forms, which later has been confirmed. Your
quantum mechanics has created new concepts, and has led physics into fresh
trains of thought, which have now already proved of fundamental importance for our knowledge of the phenomena of physics.

    The Royal Academy of Sciences has awarded you the Nobel Prize for
Physics for 1932 in recognition of these studies, and I beg you to accept this
distinction from the hands of His Majesty the King.

Professor Schrödinger.   Through a study of the wave properties of matter
you have succeeded in establishing a new system of mechanics which also
holds good for motion within the atoms and molecules. With the aid of this
so-called wave mechanics you have found the solution to a number of
problems in atomic physics. Your theory provides a simple and convenient
method for the study of the properties of atoms and molecules under various
external conditions and it has become a great aid to the development of
physics.

    For your discovery of new fruitful forms of atomic physics and the application of these, the Royal Academy of Sciences has decided to award you the Nobel Prize. I request you to receive this from the hands of His Majesty the King.

Professor Dirac.   The theory of wave mechanics which you have developed is characterized by its universality, since from the beginning you have imposed the condition that the postulate of the theory of relativity has to be fulfilled. In this way you have shown that the existence of the spin of electrons and its qualities are a consequence of this theory and not merely a hypothesis.

Further you have succeeded in dividing the wave equation into two, which results in two systems of solutions one of which requires the existence of a positive electron of the same size and charge as the negative electron. The experimental discovery of the existence of the positron has in a brilliant way confirmed your theory.

For the discovery of new fertile forms of the theory of atoms presented by you and for its applications the Royal Academy of Sciences has awarded you the Nobel Prize, and I now ask you to receive this prize from the hands of His Majesty the King.

WERNER HEISENBERG

The development of quantum mechanics

Nobel Lecture, December 11, 1933

Quantum mechanics, on which I am to speak here, arose, in its formal content, from the endeavour to expand Bohr's principle of correspondence to a complete mathematical scheme by refining his assertions. The physically new viewpoints that distinguish quantum mechanics from classical physics were prepared by the researches of various investigators engaged in analysing the difficulties posed in Bohr's theory of atomic structure and in the radiation theory of light.

In 1900, through studying the law of black-body radiation which he had discovered, Planck had detected in optical phenomena a discontinuous phenomenon totally unknown to classical physics which, a few years later, was most precisely expressed in Einstein's hypothesis of light quanta. The impossibility of harmonizing the Maxwellian theory with the pronouncedly visual concepts expressed in the hypothesis of light quanta subsequently compelled research workers to the conclusion that radiation phenomena can only be understood by largely renouncing their immediate visualization. The fact, already found by Planck and used by Einstein, Debye, and others, that the element of discontinuity detected in radiation phenomena also plays an important part in material processes, was expressed systematically in Bohr's basic postulates of the quantum theory which, together with the Bohr-Sommerfeld quantum conditions of atomic structure, led to a qualitative interpretation of the chemical and optical properties of atoms. The acceptance of these basic postulates of the quantum theory contrasted uncompromisingly with the application of classical mechanics to atomic systems, which, however, at least in its qualitative affirmations, appeared indispensable for understanding the properties of atoms. This circumstance was a fresh argument in support of the assumption that the natural phenomena in which Planck's constant plays an important part can be understood only by largely foregoing a visual description of them. Classical physics seemed the limiting case of visualization of a fundamentally unvisualizable microphysics, the more accurately realizable the more Planck's constant vanishes relative to the parameters of the system. This view of classical mechanics as a limiting case of quantum mechanics also gave rise to Bohr's principle of correspondence which, at least in qualitative terms, transferred a number of conclusions formulated in classical mechanics to quantum mechanics. In connection with the principle of correspondence there was also discussion whether the quantum-mechanical laws could in principle be of a statistical nature; the possibility became particularly apparent in Einstein's derivation of Planck's law of radiation. Finally, the analysis of the relation between radiation theory and atomic theory by Bohr, Kramers, and Slater resulted in the following scientific situation:

According to the basic postulates of the quantum theory, an atomic system is capable of assuming discrete, stationary states, and therefore discrete energy values; in terms of the energy of the atom the emission and absorption of light by such a system occurs abruptly, in the form of impulses. On the other hand, the visualizable properties of the emitted radiation are described by a wave field, the frequency of which is associated with the difference in energy between the initial and final states of the atom by the relation

$$E_{\mathrm{I}} - E_2 = h\nu$$

To each stationary state of an atom corresponds a whole complex of parameters which specify the probability of transition from this state to another. There is no direct relation between the radiation classically emitted by an orbiting electron and those parameters defining the probability of emission; nevertheless Bohr's principle of correspondence enables a specific term of the Fourier expansion of the classical path to be assigned to each transition of the atom, and the probability for the particular transition follows qualitatively similar laws as the intensity of those Fourier components. Although therefore in the researches carried out by Rutherford, Bohr, [Sommerfeld and others, the comparison of the atom with a planetary system of electrons leads to a qualitative interpretation of the optical and chemical properties of atoms, nevertheless the fundamental dissimilarity between the atomic spectrum and the classical spectrum of an electron system imposes the need to relinquish the concept of an electron path and to forego a visual description of the atom.

The experiments necessary to define the electron-path concept also furnish an important aid in revising it. The most obvious answer to the question how the orbit of an electron in its path within the atom could be observed namely, will perhaps be to use a microscope of extreme resolving power. But since the specimen in this microscope would have to be illuminated with light having an extremely short wavelength, the first light quantum from the light source to reach the electron and pass into the observer's eye would eject the electron completely from its path in accordance with the laws of the Compton effect. Consequently only one point of the path would be observable experimentally at any one time.

In this situation, therefore, the obvious policy was to relinquish at first the concept of electron paths altogether, despite its substantiation by Wilson's experiments, and, as it were, to attempt subsequently how much of the electron-path concept can be carried over into quantum mechanics.

In the classical theory the specification of frequency, amplitude, and phase of all the light waves emitted by the atom would be fully equivalent to specifying its electron path. Since from the amplitude and phase of an emitted wave the coefficients of the appropriate term in the Fourier expansion of the electron path can be derived without ambiguity, the complete electron path therefore can be derived from a knowledge of all amplitudes and phases. Similarly, in quantum mechanics, too, the whole complex of amplitudes and phases of the radiation emitted by the atom can be regarded as a complete description of the atomic system, although its interpretation in the sense of an electron path inducing the radiation is impossible. In quantum mechanics, therefore, the place of the electron coordinates is taken by a complex of parameters corresponding to the Fourier coefficients of classical motion along a path. These, however, are no longer classified by the energy of state and the number of the corresponding harmonic vibration, but are in each case associated with two stationary states of the atom, and are a measure for the transition probability of the atom from one stationary state to another. A complex of coefficients of this type is comparable with a matrix such as occurs in linear algebra. In exactly the same way each parameter of classical mechanics, e.g. the momentum or the energy of the electrons, can then be assigned a corresponding matrix in quantum mechanics. To proceed from here beyond a mere description of the empirical state of affairs it was necessary to associate systematically the matrices assigned to the various parameters in the same way as the corresponding parameters in classical mechanics are associated by equations of motions. When, in the interest of achieving the closest possible correspondence between classical and quantum mechanics, the addition and multiplication of Fourier series were tentatively taken as the example for the addition and multiplication of the quantum-theory complexes, the product of two parameters represented by matrices appeared to be most naturally represented by the product matrix in the sense of linear algebra – an assumption already suggested by the formalism of the Kramers-Ladenburg dispersion theory.

It thus seemed consistent simply to adopt in quantum mechanics the equations of motion of classical physics, regarding them as a relation between the matrices representing the classical variables. The Bohr- Sommerfeld quantum conditions could also be re-interpreted in a relation between the matrices, and together with the equations of motion they were sufficient to define all matrices and hence the experimentally observable properties of the atom.

Born, Jordan, and Dirac deserve the credit for expanding the mathematical scheme outlined above into a consistent and practically usable theory. These investigators observed in the first place that the quantum conditions can be written as commutation relations between the matrices representing the momenta and the coordinates of the electrons, to yield the equations (p_r, momentum matrices; q_r, coordinate matrices):

$$p_r q_s - q_s p_r = \frac{h}{2\pi i} . \delta_{rs} \qquad q_r q_s - q_s q_r = 0 \qquad p_r p_s - p_s p_r = 0$$

$$\delta_{rs} = \begin{cases} 1 \text{ for } r = s \\ 0 \text{ for } r \neq s \end{cases}$$

By means of these commutation relations they were able to detect in quantum mechanics as well the laws which were fundamental to classical mechanics: the invariability in time of energy, momentum, and angular momentum.

The mathematical scheme so derived thus ultimately bears an extensive formal similarity to that of the classical theory, from which it differs outwardly by the commutation relations which, moreover, enabled the equations of motion to be derived from the Hamiltonian function.

In the physical consequences, however, there are very profound differences between quantum mechanics and classical mechanics which impose the need for a thorough discussion of the physical interpretation of quantum mechanics. As hitherto defined, quantum mechanics enables the radiation emitted by the atom, the energy values of the stationary states, and other parameters characteristic for the stationary states to be treated. The theory hence complies with the experimental data contained in atomic spectra. In all those cases, however, where a visual description is required of a transient event, e.g. when interpreting Wilson photographs, the formalism of the theory does not seem to allow an adequate representation of the experimental state of affairs. At this point Schrödinger's wave mechanics, meanwhile developed on the basis of de Broglie's theses, came to the assistance of quantum mechanics.

In the course of the studies which Mr. Schrödinger will report here himself he converted the determination of the energy values of an atom into an eigenvalue problem defined by a boundary-value problem in the coordinate space of the particular atomic system. After Schrödinger had shown the mathematical equivalence of wave mechanics, which he had discovered, with quantum mechanics, the fruitful combination of these two different areas of physical ideas resulted in an extraordinary broadening and enrichment of the formalism of the quantum theory. Firstly it was only wave mechanics which made possible the mathematical treatment of complex atomic systems, secondly analysis of the connection between the two theories led to what is known as the transformation theory developed by Dirac and Jordan. As it is impossible within the limits of the present lecture to give a detailed discussion of the mathematical structure of this theory, I should just like to point out its fundamental physical significance. Through the adoption of the physical principles of quantum mechanics into its expanded formalism, the transformation theory made it possible in completely general terms to calculate for atomic systems the probability for the occurrence of a particular, experimentally ascertainable, phenomenon under given experimental conditions. The hypothesis conjectured in the studies on the radiation theory and enunciated in precise terms in Born's collision theory, namely that the wave function governs the probability for the presence of a corpuscle, appeared to be a special case of a more general pattern of laws and to be a natural consequence of the fundamental assumptions of quantum mechanics. Schrödinger, and in later studies Jordan, Klein, and Wigner as well, had succeeded in developing as far as permitted by the principles of the quantum theory de Broglie's original concept of visualizable matter waves occurring in space and time, a concept formulated even before the development of quantum mechanics. But for that the connection between Schrödinger's concepts and de Broglie's original thesis would certainly have seemed a looser one by this statistical interpretation of wave mechanics and by the greater emphasis on the fact that Schrödinger's theory is concerned with waves in multidimensional space. Before proceeding to discuss the explicit significance of quantum mechanics it is perhaps right for me to deal briefly with this question as to the existence of matter waves in three-dimensional space, since the solution to this problem was only achieved by combining wave and quantum mechanics.

A long time before quantum mechanics was developed Pauli had inferred from the laws in the Periodic System of the elements the well-known principle that a particular quantum state can at all times be occupied by only a single electron. It proved possible to transfer this principle to quantum mechanics on the basis of what at first sight seemed a surprising result: the entire complex of stationary states which an atomic system is capable of adopting breaks down into definite classes such that an atom in a state belonging to one class can never change into a state belonging to another class under the action of whatever perturbations. As finally clarified beyond question by the studies of Wigner and Hund, such a class of states is characterized by a definite symmetry characteristic of the Schrödinger eigenfunction with respect to the transposition of the coordinates of two electrons. Owing to the fundamental identity of electrons, any external perturbation of the atom remains unchanged when two electrons are exchanged and hence causes no transitions between states of various classes. The Pauli principle and the Fermi-Dirac statistics derived from it are equivalent with the assumption that only that class of stationary states is achieved in nature in which the eigenfunction changes its sign when two electrons are exchanged. According to Dirac, selecting the symmetrical system of terms would lead not to the Pauli principle, but to Bose-Einstein electron statistics.

Between the classes of stationary states belonging to the Pauli principle or to Bose-Einstein statistics, and de Broglie's concept of matter waves there is a peculiar relation. A spatial wave phenomenon can be treated according to the principles of the quantum theory by analysing it using the Fourier theorem and then applying to the individual Fourier component of the wave motion, as a system having one degree of freedom, the normal laws of quantum mechanics. Applying this procedure for treating wave phenomena by the quantum theory, a procedure that has also proved fruitful in Dirac's studies of the theory of radiation, to de Broglie's matter waves, exactly the same results are obtained as in treating a whole complex of material particles according to quantum mechanics and selecting the symmetrical system of terms. Jordan and Klein hold that the two methods are mathematically equivalent even if allowance is also made for the interaction of the electrons, i.e. if the field energy originating from the continuous space charge is included in the calculation in de Broglie's wave theory. Schrödinger's considerations of the energy-momentum tensor assigned to the matter waves can then also be adopted in this theory as consistent components of the formalism. The studies of Jordan and Wigner show that modifying the commutation relations underlying this quantum theory of waves results in a formalism equivalent to that of quantum mechanics based on the assumption of Pauli's exclusion principle.

These studies have established that the comparison of an atom with a planetary system composed of nucleus and electrons is not the only visual picture of how we can imagine the atom. On the contrary, it is apparently no less correct to compare the atom with a charge cloud and use the correspondence to the formalism of the quantum theory borne by this concept to derive qualitative conclusions about the behaviour of the atom. However, it is the concern of wave mechanics to follow these consequences.

Reverting therefore to the formalism of quantum mechanics; its application to physical problems is justified partly by the original basic assumptions of the theory, partly by its expansion in the transformation theory on the basis of wave mechanics, and the question is now to expose the explicit significance of the theory by comparing it with classical physics.

In classical physics the aim of research was to investigate objective processes occurring in space and time, and to discover the laws governing their progress from the initial conditions. In classical physics a problem was considered solved when a particular phenomenon had been proved to occur objectively in space and time, and it had been shown to obey the general rules of classical physics as formulated by differential equations. The manner in which the knowledge of each process had been acquired, what observations may possibly have led to its experimental determination, was completely immaterial, and it was also immaterial for the consequences of the classical theory, which possible observations were to verify the predictions of the theory. In the quantum theory, however, the situation is completely different. The very fact that the formalism of quantum mechanics cannot be interpreted as visual description of a phenomenon occurring in space and time shows that quantum mechanics is in no way concerned with the objective determination of space-time phenomena. On the contrary, the formalism of quantum mechanics should be used in such a way that the probability for the outcome of a further experiment may be concluded from the determination of an experimental situation in an atomic system, providing that the system is subject to no perturbations other than those necessitated by performing the two experiments. The fact that the only definite known result to be ascertained after the fullest possible experimental investigation of the system is the probability for a certain outcome of a second experiment shows, however, that each observation must entail a discontinuous change in the formalism describing the atomic proces sand therefore also a discontinuous change in the physical phenomenon itself. Whereas in the classical theory the kind of observation has no bearing on the event, in the quantum theory the disturbance associated with each observation of the atomic phenomenon has a decisive role. Since, furthermore, the result of an observation as a rule leads only to assertions about the probability of certain results of subsequent observations, the fundamentally unverifiable part of each perturbation must, as shown by Bohr, be decisive for the non-contradictory operation of quantum mechanics. This difference between classical and atomic physics is understandable, of course, since for heavy bodies such as the planets moving around the sun the pressure of the sunlight which is reflected at their surface and which is necessary for them to be observed is negligible; for the smallest building units of matter, however, owing to their low mass, every observation has a decisive effect on their physical behaviour.

The perturbation of the system to be observed caused by the observation is also an important factor in determining the limits within which a visual description of atomic phenomena is possible. If there were experiments which permitted accurate measurement of all the characteristics of an atomic system necessary to calculate classical motion, and which, for example, supplied accurate values for the location and velocity of each electron in the system at a particular time, the result of these experiments could not be utilized at all in the formalism, but rather it would directly contradict the formalism. Again, therefore, it is clearly that fundamentally unverifiable part of the perturbation of the system caused by the measurement itself which hampers accurate ascertainment of the classical characteristics and thus permits quantum mechanics to be applied. Closer examination of the formalism shows that between the accuracy with which the location of a particle can be ascertained and the accuracy with which its momentum can simultaneously be known, there is a relation according to which the product of the probable errors in the measurement of the location and momentum is invariably at least as large as Planck's constant divided by 4π. In a very general form, therefore, we should have

$$\Delta p \, \Delta q \geqslant \frac{h}{4\pi}$$

where p and q are canonically conjugated variables. These uncertainty relations for the results of the measurement of classical variables form the necessary conditions for enabling the result of a measurement to be expressed in the formalism of the quantum theory. Bohr has shown in a series of examples how the perturbation necessarily associated with each observation indeed ensures that one cannot go below the limit set by the uncertainty relations. He contends that in the final analysis an uncertainty introduced by the concept of measurement itself is responsible for part of that perturbation remaining fundamentally unknown. The experimental determination of whatever space-time events invariably necessitates a fixed frame – say the system of coordinates in which the observer is at rest – to which all measurements are referred. The assumption that this frame is «fixed» implies neglecting its momentum from the outset, since «fixed» implies nothing other, of course, than that any transfer of momentum to it will evoke no perceptible effect. The fundamentally necessary uncertainty at this point is then transmitted via the measuring apparatus into the atomic event.

Since in connection with this situation it is tempting to consider the possibility of eliminating all uncertainties by amalgamating the object, the measuring apparatuses, and the observer into one quantum-mechanical system, it is important to emphasize that the act of measurement is necessarily visualizable, since, of course, physics is ultimately only concerned with the systematic description of space-time processes. The behaviour of the observer as well as his measuring apparatus must therefore be discussed according to the laws of classical physics, as otherwise there is no further physical problem whatsoever. Within the measuring apparatus, as emphasized by Bohr, all events in the sense of the classical theory will therefore be regarded as determined, this also being a necessary condition before one can, from a result of measurements, unequivocally conclude what has happened. In quantum theory, too, the scheme of classical physics which objectifies the results of observation by assuming in space and time processes obeying laws is thus carried through up to the point where the fundamental limits are imposed by the unvisualizable character of the atomic events symbolized by Planck's constant. A visual description for the atomic events is possible only within certain limits of accuracy – but within these limits the laws of classical physics also still apply. Owing to these limits of accuracy as defined by the uncertainty relations, moreover, a visual picture of the atom free from ambiguity has not been determined. On the contrary the corpuscular and the wave concepts are equally serviceable as a basis for visual interpretation.

The laws of quantum mechanics are basically statistical. Although the parameters of an atomic system are determined in their entirety by an experiment, the result of a future observation of the system is not generally accurately predictable. But at any later point of time there are observations which yield accurately predictable results. For the other observations only the probability for a particular outcome of the experiment can be given. The degree of certainty which still attaches to the laws of quantum mechanics is, for example, responsible for the fact that the principles of conservation for energy and momentum still hold as strictly as ever. They can be checked with any desired accuracy and will then be valid according to the accuracy with which they are checked. The statistical character of the laws of quantum mechanics, however, becomes apparent in that an accurate study of the energetic conditions renders it impossible to pursue at the same time a particular event in space and time.

For the clearest analysis of the conceptual principles of quantum mechanics we are indebted to Bohr who, in particular, applied the concept of complementarity to interpret the validity of the quantum-mechanical laws. The uncertainty relations alone afford an instance of how in quantum mechanics the exact knowledge of one variable can exclude the exact knowledge of another. This complementary relationship between different aspects of one and the same physical process is indeed characteristic for the whole structure of quantum mechanics. I had just mentioned that, for example, the determination of energetic relations excludes the detailed description of space-time processes. Similarly, the study of the chemical properties of a molecule is complementary to the study of the motions of the individual electrons in the molecule, or the observation of interference phenomena complementary to the observation of individual light quanta. Finally, the areas of validity of classical and quantum mechanics can be marked off one from the other as follows: Classical physics represents that striving to learn about Nature in which essentially we seek to draw conclusions about objective processes from observations and so ignore the consideration of the influences which every observation has on the object to be observed; classical physics, therefore, has its limits at the point from which the influence of the observation on the event can no longer be ignored. Conversely, quantum mechanics makes possible the treatment of atomic processes by partially foregoing their space-time description and objectification.

So as not to dwell on assertions in excessively abstract terms about the interpretation of quantum mechanics, I would like briefly to explain with a well-known example how far it is possible through the atomic theory to achieve an understanding of the visual processes with which we are concerned in daily life. The interest of research workers has frequently been focused on the phenomenon of regularly shaped crystals suddenly forming from a liquid, e.g. a supersaturated salt solution. According to the atomic theory the forming force in this process is to a certain extent the symmetry characteristic of the solution to Schrödinger's wave equation, and to that extent crystallization is explained by the atomic theory. Nevertheless this process retains a statistical and – one might almost say – historical element which cannot be further reduced: even when the state of the liquid is completely known before crystallization, the shape of the crystal is not determined by the laws of quantum mechanics. The formation of regular shapes is just far more probable than that of a shapeless lump. But the ultimate shape owes its genesis partly to an element of chance which in principle cannot be analysed further.

Before closing this report on quantum mechanics, I may perhaps be allowed to discuss very briefly the hopes that may be attached to the further development of this branch of research. It would be superfluous to mention that the development must be continued, based equally on the studies of de Broglie, Schrödinger, Born, Jordan, and Dirac. Here the attention of the research workers is primarily directed to the problem of reconciling the claims of the special relativity theory with those of the quantum theory. The extraordinary advances made in this field by Dirac about which Mr. Dirac will speak here, meanwhile leave open the question whether it will be possible to satisfy the claims of the two theories without at the same time determining the Sommerfeld fine-structure constant. The attempts made hitherto to achieve a relativistic formulation of the quantum theory are all based on visual concepts so close to those of classical physics that it seems impossible to determine the fine-structure constant within this system of concepts. The expansion of the conceptual system under discussion here should, furthermore, be closely associated with the further development of the quantum theory of wave fields, and it appears to me as if this formalism, notwithstanding its thorough study by a number of workers (Dirac, Pauli, Jordan, Klein, Wigner, Fermi) has still not been completely exhausted. Important pointers for the further development of quantum mechanics also emerge from the experiments involving the structure of the atomic nuclei. From their analysis by means of the Gamow theory, it would appear that between the elementary particles of the atomic nucleus forces are at work which differ somewhat in type from the forces determining the structure of the atomic shell; Stern's experiments seem, furthermore, to indicate that the behaviour of the heavy elementary particles cannot be represented by the formalism of Dirac's theory of the electron. Future research will thus have to be prepared for surprises which may otherwise come both from the field of experience of nuclear physics as well as from that of cosmic radiation. But however the development proceeds in detail, the path so far traced by the quantum theory indicates that an understanding of those still unclarified features of atomic physics can only be acquired by foregoing visualization and objectification to an extent greater than that customary hitherto. We have probably no reason to regret this, because the thought of the great epistemological difficulties with which the visual atom concept of earlier physics had to contend gives us the hope that the abstracter atomic physics developing at present will one day fit more harmoniously into the great edifice of Science.

Biography

Werner Heisenberg was born on 5th December, 1901, at Würzburg. He was the son of Dr. August Heisenberg and his wife 'Annie Wecklein. His father later became Professor of the Middle and Modern Greek languages in the University of Munich. It was probably due to his influence that Heisenberg remarked, when the Japanese physicist Yukawa discovered the particle now known as the meson and the term « mesotron » was proposed for it, that the Greek word « mesos » has no « tr » in it, with the result that the name « mesotron » was changed to « meson ».

Heisenberg went to the Maximilian school at Munich until 1920, when he went to the University of Munich to study physics under Sommerfeld, Wien, Pringsheim, and Rosenthal. During the winter of 1922–1923 he went to Göttingen to study physics under Max Born, Franck, and Hilbert. In 1923 he took his Ph.D. at the University of Munich and then became Assistant to Max Born at the University of Göttingen, and in 1924 he gained the *venia legendi* at that University.

From 1924 until 1925 he worked, with a Rockefeller Grant, with Niels Bohr, at the University of Copenhagen, returning for the summer of 1925 to Göttingen.

In 1926 he was appointed Lecturer in Theoretical Physics at the University of Copenhagen under Niels Bohr and in 1927, when he was only 26, he was appointed Professor of Theoretical Physics at the University of Leipzig.

In 1929 he went on a lecture tour to the United States, Japan, and India.

In 1941 he was appointed Professor of Physics at the University of Berlin and Director of the Kaiser Wilhelm Institute for Physics there.

At the end of the Second World War he, and other German physicists, were taken prisoner by American troops and sent to England, but in 1946 he returned to Germany and reorganized, with his colleagues, the Institute for Physics at Göttingen. This Institute was, in 1948, renamed the Max Planck Institute for Physics.

In 1948 Heisenberg stayed for some months in Cambridge, England, to give lectures, and in 1950 and 1954 he was invited to lecture in the United

States. In the winter of 1955–1956 he gave the Gifford Lectures at the University of St. Andrews, Scotland, these lectures being subsequently published as a book.

During 1955 Heisenberg was occupied with preparations for the removal of the Max Planck Institute for Physics to Munich. Still Director of this Institute, he went with it to Munich and in 1958 he was appointed Professor of Physics in the University of Munich. His Institute was then being renamed the Max Planck Institute for Physics and Astrophysics.

Heisenberg's name will always be associated with his theory of quantum mechanics, published in 1925, when he was only 23 years old. For this theory and the applications of it which resulted especially in the discovery of allotropic forms of hydrogen, Heisenberg was awarded the Nobel Prize for Physics for 1932.

His new theory was based only on what can be observed, that is to say, on the radiation emitted by the atom. We cannot, he said, always assign to an electron a position in space at a given time, nor follow it in its orbit, so that we cannot assume that the planetary orbits postulated by Niels Bohr actually exist. Mechanical quantities, such as position, velocity, etc. should be represented, not by ordinary numbers, but by abstract mathematical structures called « matrices » and he formulated his new theory in terms of matrix equations.

Later Heisenberg stated his famous *principle of uncertainty*, which lays it down that the determination of the position and momentum of a mobile particle necessarily contains errors the product of which cannot be less than the quantum constant h and that, although these errors are negligible on the human scale, they cannot be ignored in studies of the atom.

From 1957 onwards Heisenberg was interested in work on problems of plasma physics and thermonuclear processes, and also much work in close collaboration with the International Institute of Atomic Physics at Geneva. He was for several years Chairman of the Scientific Policy Committee of this Institute and subsequently remained a member of this Committee.

When he became, in 1953, President of the Alexander von Humboldt Foundation, he did much to further the policy of this Foundation, which was to invite scientists from other countries to Germany and to help them to work there.

Since 1953 his own theoretical work was concentrated on the unified field theory of elementary particles which seems to him to be the key to an understanding of the physics of elementary particles.

Apart from many medals and prizes, Heisenberg received an honorary doctorate of the University of Bruxelles, of the Technological University Karlsruhe, and recently (1964) of the University of Budapest; he is also recipient of the Order of Merit of Bavaria, and the Grand Cross for Federal Services with Star (Germany). He is a Fellow of the Royal Society of London and a Knight of the Order of Merit (Peace Class). He is a member of the Academies of Sciences of Göttingen, Bavaria, Saxony, Prussia, Sweden, Rumania, Norway, Spain, The Netherlands, Rome (Pontifical), the German Akademie der Naturforscher Leopoldina (Halle), the Accademia dei Lincei (Rome), and the American Academy of Sciences. During 1949–1951 he was President of the Deutsche Forschungsrat (German Research Council) and in 1953 he became President of the Alexander von Humboldt Foundation.

One of his hobbies is classical music: he is a distinguished pianist. In 1937 Heisenberg married Elisabeth Schumacher. They have seven children, and live in Munich.

ERWIN SCHRÖDINGER

The fundamental idea of wave mechanics

Nobel Lecture, December 12, 1933

On passing through an optical instrument, such as a telescope or a camera lens, a ray of light is subjected to a change in direction at each refracting or reflecting surface. The path of the rays can be constructed if we know the two simple laws which govern the changes in direction: the law of refraction which was discovered by Snellius a few hundred years ago, and the law of reflection with which Archimedes was familiar more than 2,000 years ago. As a simple example, Fig. 1 shows a ray A–B which is subjected to refraction at each of the four boundary surfaces of two lenses in accordance with the law of Snellius.

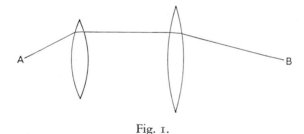

Fig. 1.

Fermat defined the total path of a ray of light from a much more general point of view. In different media, light propagates with different velocities, and the radiation path gives the appearance as if the light must arrive at its destination *as quickly as possible*. (Incidentally, it is permissible here to consider *any two* points along the ray as the starting- and end-points.) The least deviation from the path actually taken would mean a delay. This is the famous Fermat *principle of the shortest light time*, which in a marvellous manner determines the entire fate of a ray of light by a single statement and also includes the more general case, when the nature of the medium varies not suddenly at individual surfaces, but gradually from place to place. The atmosphere of the earth provides an example. The more deeply a ray of light penetrates into it from outside, the more slowly it progresses in an increasingly denser air. Although the differences in the speed of propagation are infinitesimal, Fermat's principle in these circumstances demands that the light ray should curve earthward (see Fig. 2), so that it remains a little longer in the higher «faster» layers and reaches its destination more quickly than by the shorter straight path (broken line in the figure; disregard the square,

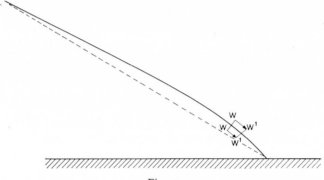

Fig. 2.

WWW¹W¹ for the time being). I think, hardly any of you will have failed to observe that the sun when it is deep on the horizon appears to be not circular but flattened: its vertical diameter looks to be shortened. This is a result of the curvature of the rays.

According to the wave theory of light, the light rays, strictly speaking, have only fictitious significance. They are not the physical paths of some particles of light, but are a mathematical device, the so-called orthogonal trajectories of wave surfaces, imaginary guide lines as it were, which point in the direction normal to the wave surface in which the latter advances (cf. Fig. 3 which shows the simplest case of concentric spherical wave surfaces and accordingly rectilinear rays, whereas Fig. 4 illustrates the case of curved

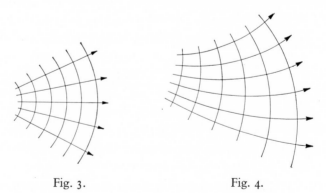

Fig. 3.   Fig. 4.

rays). It is surprising that a general principle as important as Fermat's relates directly to these mathematical guide lines, and not to the wave surfaces, and one might be inclined for this reason to consider it a mere mathematical curiosity. Far from it. It becomes properly understandable only from the point of view of wave theory and ceases to be a divine miracle. From the wave point of view, the so-called *curvature* of the light ray is far more readily understandable as a *swerving* of the wave surface, which must obviously occur when neighbouring parts of a wave surface advance at different speeds; in exactly the same manner as a company of soldiers marching forward will carry out the order « right incline » by the men taking steps of varying lengths, the right-wing man the smallest, and the left-wing man the longest. In atmospheric refraction of radiation for example (Fig. 2) the section of wave surface WW must necessarily swerve to the right towards W^1W^1 because its left half is located in slightly higher, thinner air and thus advances more rapidly than the right part at lower point. (In passing, I wish to refer to one point at which the *Snellius'* view fails. A horizontally emitted light ray should remain horizontal because the refraction index does not vary in the horizontal direction. In truth, a horizontal ray curves more strongly than any other, which is an obvious consequence of the theory of a swerving wave front.) On detailed examination the Fermat principle is found to be completely *tantamount* to the trivial and obvious statement that–given local distribution of light velocities–the wave front must swerve in the manner indicated. I cannot prove this here, but shall attempt to make it plausible. I would again ask you to visualize a rank of soldiers marching forward. To ensure that the line remains dressed, let the men be connected by a long rod which each holds firmly in his hand. No orders as to direction are given; the only order is: let each man march or run as fast as he can. If the nature of the ground varies slowly from place to place, it will be now the right wing, now the left that advances more quickly, and changes in direction will occur spontaneously. After some time has elapsed, it will be seen that the entire path travelled is not rectilinear, but somehow curved. That this curved path is exactly that by which the destination attained at any moment could be attained *most rapidly* according to the nature of the terrain, is at least quite plausible, since each of the men did his best. It will also be seen that the swerving also occurs invariably in the direction in which the terrain is worse, so that it will come to look in the end as if the men had intentionally « bypassed » a place where they would advance slowly.

The Fermat principle thus appears to be the *trivial quintessence* of the wave theory. It was therefore a memorable occasion when Hamilton made the discovery that the true movement of mass points in a field of forces (e.g. of a planet on its orbit around the sun or of a stone thrown in the gravitational field of the earth) is also governed by a very similar general principle, which carries and has made famous the name of its discoverer since then. Admittedly, the Hamilton principle does not say exactly that the mass point chooses the quickest way, but it does say something *so* similar – the analogy with the principle of the shortest travelling time of light is *so* close, that one was faced with a puzzle. It seemed as if Nature had realized one and the same law twice by entirely different means: first in the case of light, by means of a fairly obvious play of rays; and again in the case of the mass points, which was anything but obvious, unless somehow wave nature were to be attributed to them also. And this, it seemed impossible to do. Because the « mass points » on which the laws of mechanics had really been confirmed experimentally at that time were only the large, visible, sometimes *very* large bodies, the planets, for which a thing like « wave nature » appeared to be out of the question.

The smallest, elementary components of matter which we today, much more specifically, call « mass points », were purely hypothetical at the time. It was only after the discovery of radioactivity that constant refinements of methods of measurement permitted the properties of these particles to be studied in detail, and now permit the paths of such particles to be photographed and to be measured very exactly (stereophotogrammetrically) by the brilliant method of C.T.R. Wilson. As far as the measurements extend they confirm that the same mechanical laws are valid for particles as for large bodies, planets, etc. However, it was found that neither the molecule nor the individual atom can be considered as the « ultimate component »: but even the atom is a system of highly complex structure. Images are formed in our minds of the structure of atoms *consisting of* particles, images which seem to have a certain similarity with the planetary system. It was only natural that the attempt should at first be made to consider as valid the same laws of motion that had proved themselves so amazingly satisfactory on a large scale. In other words, Hamilton's mechanics, which, as I said above, culminates in the Hamilton principle, were applied also to the « inner life » of the atom. That there is a very close analogy between Hamilton's principle and Fermat's optical principle had meanwhile become all but forgotten. If it was remembered, it was considered to be nothing more than a curious trait of the mathematical theory.

Now, it is very difficult, without further going into details, to convey a proper conception of the success or failure of these classical-mechanical images of the atom. On the one hand, Hamilton's principle in particular proved to be the most faithful and reliable guide, which was simply indispensable; on the other hand one had to suffer, to do justice to the facts, the rough interference of entirely new incomprehensible postulates, of the so-called quantum conditions and quantum postulates. Strident disharmony in the symphony of classical mechanics–yet strangely familiar–played as it were on the same instrument. In mathematical terms we can formulate this as follows: whereas the Hamilton principle merely postulates that a given integral must be a minimum, without the numerical value of the minimum being established by this postulate, it is now demanded that the numerical value of the minimum should be restricted to integral multiples of a universal natural constant, Planck's quantum of action. This incidentally. The situation was fairly desperate. Had the old mechanics failed completely, it would not have been so bad. The way would then have been free to the development of a new system of mechanics. As it was, one was faced with the difficult task of saving the *soul* of the old system, whose inspiration clearly held sway in this microcosm, while at the same time flattering it as it were into accepting the quantum conditions not as gross interference but as issuing from its own innermost essence.

The way out lay just in the possibility, already indicated above, of attributing to the Hamilton principle, also, the operation of a wave mechanism on which the point-mechanical processes are essentially based, just as one had long become accustomed to doing in the case of phenomena relating to light and of the Fermat principle which governs them. Admittedly, the individual path of a mass point loses its proper physical significance and becomes as fictitious as the individual isolated ray of light. The essence of the theory, the minimum principle, however, remains not only intact, but reveals its true and simple meaning only under the wave-like aspect, as already explained. Strictly speaking, the new theory is in fact not *new*, it is a completely organic development, one might almost be tempted to say a more elaborate exposition, of the old theory.

How was it then that this new more « elaborate » exposition led to notably different results; what enabled it, when applied to the atom, to obviate difficulties which the old theory could not solve? What enabled it to render gross interference acceptable or even to make it its own?

Again, these matters can best be illustrated by analogy with optics. Quite properly, indeed, I previously called the Fermat principle the quintessence of the wave theory of light: nevertheless, it cannot render dispensible a more exact study of the wave process itself. The so-called refraction and interference phenomena of light can only be understood if we trace the wave process in detail because what matters is not only the eventual destination of the wave, but also whether at a given moment it arrives there with a wave peak or a wave trough. In the older, coarser experimental arrangements, these phenomena occurred as small details only and escaped observation. Once they were noticed and were interpreted correctly, by means of waves, it was easy to devise experiments in which the wave nature of light finds expression not only in small details, but on a very large scale in the entire character of the phenomenon.

Allow me to illustrate this by two examples, first, the example of an optical instrument, such as telescope, microscope, etc. The object is to obtain a sharp image, i.e. it is desired that all rays issuing from a point should be reunited in a point, the so-called focus (cf. Fig. 5a). It was at first believed that it was only geometrical-optical difficulties which prevented this: they are indeed considerable. Later it was found that even in the best designed instru-

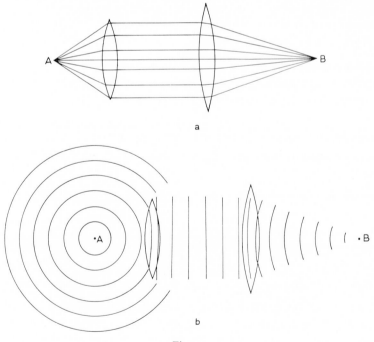

a

b

Fig. 5.

ments focussing of the rays was considerably inferior than would be expected if each ray exactly obeyed the Fermat principle independently of the neighbouring rays. The light which issues from a point and is received by the instrument is reunited behind the instrument not in a single point any more, but is distributed over a small circular area, a so-called diffraction disc, which, otherwise, is in most cases a circle only because the apertures and lens contours are generally circular. For, the cause of the phenomenon which we call *diffraction* is that not all the spherical waves issuing from the object point can be accommodated by the instrument. The lens edges and any apertures merely cut out a part of the wave surfaces (cf. Fig. 5b) and–if you will permit me to use a more suggestive expression–the injured margins resist rigid unification in a point and produce the somewhat blurred or vague image. The degree of blurring is closely associated with the *wavelength* of the light and is completely inevitable because of this deep-seated theoretical relationship. Hardly noticed at first, it governs and restricts the performance of the modern microscope which has mastered all other errors of reproduction. The images obtained of structures not much coarser or even still finer than the wavelengths of light are only remotely or not at all similar to the original.

A second, even simpler example is the shadow of an opaque object cast on a screen by a small point light source. In order to construct the shape of the shadow, each light ray must be traced and it must be established whether or not the opaque object prevents it from reaching the screen. The *margin* of the shadow is formed by those light rays which only just brush past the edge of the body. Experience has shown that the shadow margin is not absolutely sharp even with a point-shaped light source and a sharply defined shadow-casting object. The reason for this is the same as in the first example. The wave front is as it were bisected by the body (cf. Fig. 6) and the traces of this injury result in blurring of the margin of the shadow which would be incomprehensible if the individual light rays were independent entities advancing independently of one another without reference to their neighbours.

This phenomenon – which is also called diffraction – is not as a rule very noticeable with large bodies. But if the shadow-casting body is very small at least in one dimension, diffraction finds expression firstly in that no proper shadow is formed at all, and secondly – much more strikingly – in that the small body itself becomes as it were its own source of light and radiates light in all directions (preferentially to be sure, at small angles relative to the inci-

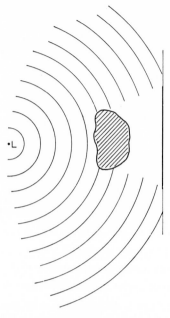

Fig. 6.

dent light). All of you are undoubtedly familiar with the so-called « motes of dust» in a light beam falling into a dark room. Fine blades of grass and spiders' webs on the crest of a hill with the sun behind it, or the errant locks of hair of a man standing with the sun behind often light up mysteriously by diffracted light, and the visibility of smoke and mist is based on it. It comes not really from the body itself, but from its immediate surroundings, an area in which it causes considerable interference with the incident wave fronts. It is interesting, and important for what follows, to observe that the area of interference always and in every direction has at least the extent of one or a few wavelengths, no matter how small the disturbing particle may be. Once again, therefore, we observe a close relationship between the phenomenon of diffraction and wavelength. This is perhaps best illustrated by reference to another wave process, i.e. sound. Because of the much greater wavelength, which is of the order of centimetres and metres, shadow formation recedes in the case of sound, and diffraction plays a major, and practically important, part: we can easily *hear* a man calling from behind a high wall or around the corner of a solid house, even if we cannot *see* him.

Let us return from optics to mechanics and explore the analogy to its fullest extent. In optics the *old* system of mechanics corresponds to intellectually operating with isolated mutually independent light rays. The new undulatory mechanics corresponds to the wave theory of light. What is gained by changing from the old view to the new is that the diffraction phenomena can be accommodated or, better expressed, what is gained is something that is strictly analogous to the diffraction phenomena of light and which on the whole must be very unimportant, otherwise the old view of mechanics would not have given full satisfaction so long. It is, however, easy to surmise that the neglected phenomenon may in some circumstances make itself very much felt, will entirely dominate the mechanical process, and will face the old system with insoluble riddles, if *the entire mechanical system is comparable in extent with the wavelengths of the « waves of matter»* which play the same part in mechanical processes as that played by the light waves in optical processes.

This is the reason why in these minute systems, the atoms, the old view was bound to fail, which though remaining intact as a close approximation for gross mechanical processes, but is no longer adequate for the delicate interplay in areas of the order of magnitude of one or a few wavelengths. It was astounding to observe the manner in which all those strange additional requirements developed spontaneously from the new undulatory view, whereas they had to be forced upon the old view to adapt them to the inner life of the atom and to provide some explanation of the observed facts.

Thus, the salient point of the whole matter is that the diameters of the atoms and the wavelength of the hypothetical material waves are of approximately the same order of magnitude. And now you are bound to ask whether it must be considered mere chance that in our continued analysis of the structure of matter we should come upon the order of magnitude of the wavelength at this of all points, or whether this is to some extent comprehensible. Further, you may ask, how we know that this is so, since the material waves are an entirely new requirement of this theory, unknown anywhere else. Or is it simply that this is an *assumption* which had to be made?

The agreement between the orders of magnitude is no mere chance, nor is any special assumption about it necessary; it follows automatically from the theory in the following remarkable manner. That the heavy *nucleus* of the atom is very much smaller than the atom and may therefore be considered as a point centre of attraction in the argument which follows may be considered as experimentally established by the experiments on the scattering of alpha rays done by Rutherford and Chadwick. Instead of the *electrons* we introduce hypothetical waves, whose wavelengths are left entirely open, because we know nothing about them yet. This leaves a letter, say *a*, indicating a still unknown figure, in our calculation. We are, however, used to this in such calculations and it does not prevent us from calculating that the nucleus of the atom must produce a kind of diffraction phenomenon in these waves, similarly as a minute dust particle does in light waves. Analogously, it follows that there is a close relationship between the extent of the area of interference with which the nucleus surrounds itself and the wavelength, and that the two are of the same order of magnitude. What this is, we have had to leave open; but the most important step now follows: *we identify the area of interference, the diffraction halo, with the atom; we assert that the atom in reality is merely the diffraction phenomenon of an electron wave captured as it were by the nucleus of the atom.* It is no longer a matter of chance that the size of the atom and the wavelength are of the same order of magnitude: it is a matter of course. We know the numerical value of neither, because we still have in our calculation the *one* unknown constant, which we called *a*. There are two possible ways of determining it, which provide a mutual check on one another. First, we can so select it that the manifestations of life of the atom, above all the spectrum lines emitted, come out correctly quantitatively; these can after all be measured very accurately. Secondly, we can select *a* in a manner such that the diffraction halo acquires the size required for the atom. These two determinations of *a* (of which the second is admittedly far more imprecise because « size of the atom » is no clearly defined term) *are in complete agreement with one another.* Thirdly, and lastly, we can remark that the constant remaining unknown, physically speaking, does not in fact have the dimension of a length, but of an action, i.e. energy × time. It is then an obvious step to substitute for it the numerical value of Planck's universal quantum of action, which is accurately known from the laws of heat radiation. It will be seen that *we return*, with the full, now considerable accuracy, *to the first* (most accurate) *determination.*

Quantitatively speaking, the theory therefore manages with a minimum of new assumptions. It contains a single available constant, to which a numerical value familiar from the older quantum theory must be given, first to attribute to the diffraction halos the right size so that they can be reasonably identified with the atoms, and secondly, to evaluate quantitatively and correctly all the manifestations of life of the atom, the light radiated by it, the ionization energy, etc.

I have tried to place before you the fundamental idea of the wave theory of matter in the simplest possible form. I must admit now that in my desire not to tangle the ideas from the very beginning, I have painted the lily. Not as regards the high degree to which all sufficiently, carefully drawn conclusions are confirmed by experience, but with regard to the conceptual ease and simplicity with which the conclusions are reached. I am not speaking here of the mathematical difficulties, which always turn out to be trivial in the end, but of the conceptual difficulties. It is, of course, easy to say that we turn from the concept of a *curved path* to a system of wave surfaces normal to it. The wave surfaces, however, even if we consider only small parts of them (see Fig. 7) include at least a narrow *bundle* of possible curved paths,

Fig. 7.

to all of which they stand in the same relationship. According to the old view, but not according to the new, one of them in each concrete individual case is distinguished from all the others which are «only possible», as that «really travelled». We are faced here with the full force of the logical opposition between an

either – or   (point mechanics)

and a

both – and   (wave mechanics)

This would not matter much, if the old system were to be dropped entirely and to be *replaced* by the new. Unfortunately, this is not the case. From the point of view of wave mechanics, the infinite array of possible point paths would be merely fictitious, none of them would have the prerogative over the others of being that really travelled in an individual case. I have, however, already mentioned that we have yet really observed such individual particle paths in some cases. The wave theory can represent this, either not at all or only very imperfectly. We find it confoundedly difficult to interpret the traces we *see* as nothing more than narrow bundles of equally possible paths between which the wave surfaces establish cross-connections. Yet, these cross-connections are necessary for an understanding of the diffraction and interference phenomena which can be demonstrated for the same particle with the same plausibility – and that on a large scale, not just as a consequence of the theoretical ideas about the interior of the atom, which we mentioned earlier. Conditions are admittedly such that we can always manage to make do in each concrete individual case without the two different aspects leading to different expectations as to the result of certain experiments. We cannot, however, manage to make do with such old, familiar, and seemingly indispensible terms as « real» or « only possible»; we are never in a position to say what really *is* or what really *happens*, but we can only say what will be *observed* in any concrete individual case. Will we have to be permanently satisfied with this...? On principle, yes. On principle, there is nothing new in the postulate that in the end exact science should aim at nothing more than the description of what can really be observed. The question is only whether from now on we shall have to refrain from tying description to a clear hypothesis about the real nature of the world. There are many who wish to pronounce such abdication even today. But I believe that this means making things a little too easy for oneself.

I would define the present state of our knowledge as follows. The ray or the particle path corresponds to a *longitudinal* relationship of the propagation process (i.e. *in the direction* of propagation), the wave surface on the other hand to a *transversal* relationship (i.e. *normal* to it). *Both* relationships are without doubt real; one is proved by photographed particle paths, the other by interference experiments. To combine both in a uniform system has proved impossible so far. Only in extreme cases does either the transversal, shell-shaped or the radial, longitudinal relationship predominate to such an extent that we *think* we can make do with the wave theory alone or with the particle theory alone.

Biography

Erwin Schrödinger was born on August 12, 1887, in Vienna, the only child of Rudolf Schrödinger, who was married to a daughter of Alexander Bauer, his Professor of Chemistry at the Technical College of Vienna. Erwin's father came from a Bavarian family which generations before had settled in Vienna. He was a highly gifted man with a broad education. After having finished his chemistry studies, he devoted himself for years to Italian painting. After this he took up botany, which resulted in a series of papers on plant phylogeny.

Schrödinger's wide interests dated from his school years at the Gymnasium, where he not only had a liking for the scientific disciplines, but also appreciated the severe logic of ancient grammar and the beauty of German poetry. (What he abhorred was memorizing of data and learning from books.)

From 1906 to 1910 he was a student at the University of Vienna, during which time he came under the strong influence of Fritz Hasenöhrl, who was Boltzmann's successor. It was in these years that Schrödinger acquired a mastery of eigenvalue problems in the physics of continuous media, thus laying the foundation for his future great work. Hereafter, as assistant to Franz Exner, he, together with his friend K. W. F. Kohlrausch, conducted practical work for students (without himself, as he said, learning what experimenting was). During the First World War he served as an artillery officer.

In 1920 he took up an academic position as assistant to Max Wien, followed by positions at Stuttgart (extraordinary professor), Breslau (ordinary professor), and at the University of Zurich (replacing von Laue) where he settled for six years. In later years Schrödinger looked back to his Zurich period with great pleasure–it was here that he enjoyed so much the contact and friendship of many of his colleagues, among whom were Hermann Weyl and Peter Debye. It was also his most fruitful period, being actively engaged in a variety of subjects of theoretical physics. His papers at that time dealt with specific heats of solids, with problems of thermodynamics (he was greatly interested in Boltzmann's probability theory) and of atomic spectra; in addition, he indulged in physiological studies of colour (as a result of his contacts with Kohlrausch and Exner, and of Helmholtz's lectures). His great discovery, Schrödinger's wave equation, was made at the end of this epoch–during the first half of 1926.

It came as a result of his dissatisfaction with the quantum condition in Bohr's orbit theory and his belief that atomic spectra should really be determined by some kind of eigenvalue problem. For this work he shared with Dirac the Nobel Prize for 1933.

In 1927 Schrödinger moved to Berlin as Planck's successor. Germany's capital was then a centre of great scientific activity and he enthusiastically took part in the weekly colloquies among colleagues, many of whom «exceeding him in age and reputation». With Hitler's coming to power (1933), however, Schrödinger decided he could not continue in Germany. He came to England and for a while held a fellowship at Oxford. In 1936 he was offered a position at Graz, which he accepted only after much deliberation and because his longing for his native country outweighed his caution. With the annexation of Austria in 1938, he was immediately in difficulty because his leaving Germany in 1933 was taken to be an unfriendly act. Soon afterwards he managed to escape to Italy, from where he proceeded to Princeton University. After a short stay he moved to the newly created Institute for Advanced Studies in Dublin, where he became Director of the School for Theoretical Physics. He remained in Dublin until his retirement in 1955.

All this time Schrödinger continued his research and published many papers on a variety of topics, including the problem of unifying gravitation and electromagnetism, which also absorbed Einstein and which is still unsolved; (he was also the author of the well-known little book «What is Life?», 1944). He remained greatly interested in the foundations of atomic physics. Schrödinger disliked the generally accepted dual description in terms of waves and particles, with a statistical interpretation for the waves, and tried to set up a theory in terms of waves only. This led him into controversy with other leading physicists.

Throughout his scientific career and also in his personal life, Schrödinger never tried to achieve a specific goal, nor did he follow any extensive project. He always found it difficult to work with others, even with his own pupils.

His unconventional way of life may probably be best illustrated by the fact that he would always carry his belongings in a rucksack on his back, and walk to the hotel from the station, even on such occasions as the Solvay Conferences in Brussels.

After his retirement he returned to an honoured position in Vienna. He died on the 4th of January, 1961, after a long illness, survived by his faithful companion, Annemarie Bertel, whom he married in 1920.

P A U L   A. M.   D I R A C

Theory of electrons and positrons

Nobel Lecture, December 12, 1933

Matter has been found by experimental physicists to be made up of small particles of various kinds, the particles of each kind being all exactly alike. Some of these kinds have definitely been shown to be composite, that is, to be composed of other particles of a simpler nature. But there are other kinds which have not been shown to be composite and which one expects will never be shown to be composite, so that one considers them as elementary and fundamental.

From general philosophical grounds one would at first sight like to have as few kinds of elementary particles as possible, say only one kind, or at most two, and to have all matter built up of these elementary kinds. It appears from the experimental results, though, that there must be more than this. In fact the number of kinds of elementary particle has shown a rather alarming tendency to increase during recent years.

The situation is perhaps not so bad, though, because on closer investigation it appears that the distinction between elementary and composite particles cannot be made rigorous. To get an interpretation of some modern experimental results one must suppose that particles can be created and annihilated. Thus if a particle is observed to come out from another particle, one can no longer be sure that the latter is composite. The former may have been created. The distinction between elementary particles and composite particles now becomes a matter of convenience. This reason alone is sufficient to compel one to give up the attractive philosophical idea that all matter is made up of one kind, or perhaps two kinds of bricks.

I should like here to discuss the simpler kinds of particles and to consider *what can be inferred about them from purely theoretical arguments*. The simpler kinds of particle are:

(i) the photons or light-quanta, of which light is composed;

(ii) the electrons, and the recently discovered positrons (which appear to be a sort of mirror image of the electrons, differing from them only in the sign of their electric charge);

(iii) the heavier particles – protons and neutrons.

Of these, I shall deal almost entirely with the electrons and the positrons – not because they are the most interesting ones, but because in their case the theory has been developed further. There is, in fact, hardly anything that can be inferred theoretically about the properties of the others. The photons, on the one hand, are so simple that they can easily be fitted into any theoretical scheme, and the theory therefore does not put any restrictions on their properties. The protons and neutrons, on the other hand, seem to be too complicated and no reliable basis for a theory of them has yet been discovered.

The question that we must first consider is how theory can give any information at all about the properties of elementary particles. There exists at the present time a general quantum mechanics which can be used to describe the motion of any kind of particle, no matter what its properties are. The general quantum mechanics, however, is valid only when the particles have small velocities and fails for velocities comparable with the velocity of light, when effects of relativity come in. There exists no relativistic quantum mechanics (that is, one valid for large velocities) which can be applied to particles with arbitrary properties. Thus when one subjects quantum mechanics to relativistic requirements, one imposes restrictions on the properties of the particle. In this way one can deduce information about the particles from purely theoretical considerations, based on general physical principles.

This procedure is successful in the case of electrons and positrons. It is to be hoped that in the future some such procedure will be found for the case of the other particles. I should like here to outline the method for electrons and positrons, showing how one can deduce the spin properties of the electron, and then how one can infer the existence of positrons with similar spin properties and with the possibility of being annihilated in collisions with electrons.

We begin with the equation connecting the kinetic energy W and momentum p_r, $(r = 1, 2, 3)$, of a particle in relativistic classical mechanics

$$\frac{W^2}{c^2} - p_r^2 - m^2 c^2 = 0 \tag{1}$$

From this we can get a wave equation of quantum mechanics, by letting the left-hand side operate on the wave function ψ and understanding W and p_r to be the operators $ih\partial/\partial t$ and $-ih\partial/\partial x_r$. With this understanding, the wave equation reads

$$\left[\frac{W^2}{c^2} - p_r^2 - m^2 c^2\right] \psi = 0 \tag{2}$$

Now it is a general requirement of quantum mechanics that its wave equations shall be linear in the operator W or $\partial/\partial t$, so this equation will not do. We must replace it by some equation linear in W, and in order that this equation may have relativistic invariance it must also be linear in the p's.

We are thus led to consider an equation of the type

$$\left[\frac{W}{c} - \alpha_r p_r - \alpha_0 mc\right] \psi = 0 \tag{3}$$

This involves four new variables α_r and α_0, which are operators that can operate on ψ. We assume they satisfy the following conditions,

$$\alpha_\mu^2 = 1 \qquad \alpha_\mu \alpha_\nu + \alpha_\nu \alpha_\mu = 0$$

for

$$\mu \neq \nu \text{ and } \mu, \nu = 0, 1, 2, 3$$

and also the α's commute with the p's and W. These special properties for the α's make Eq. (3) to a certain extent equivalent to Eq. (2), since if we then multiply (3) on the left-hand side by $W/c + \alpha_r p_r + \alpha_0 mc$ we get exactly (2).

The new variables α, which we have to introduce to get a relativistic wave equation linear in W, give rise to the spin of the electron. From the general principles of quantum mechanics one can easily deduce that these variables α give the electron a spin angular momentum of half a quantum and a magnetic moment of one Bohr magneton in the reverse direction to the angular momentum. These results are in agreement with experiment. They were, in fact, first obtained from the experimental evidence provided by spectroscopy and afterwards confirmed by the theory.

The variables α also give rise to some rather unexpected phenomena concerning the motion of the electron. These have been fully worked out by Schrödinger. It is found that an electron which seems to us to be moving slowly, must actually have a very high frequency oscillatory motion of small amplitude superposed on the regular motion which appears to us. As a result of this oscillatory motion, the velocity of the electron at any time equals the velocity of light. This is a prediction which cannot be directly verified by experiment, since the frequency of the oscillatory motion is so high and its amplitude is so small. But one must believe in this consequence of the theory, since other consequences of the theory which are inseparably bound up with this one, such as the law of scattering of light by an electron, are confirmed by experiment.

There is one other feature of these equations which I should now like to discuss, a feature which led to the prediction of the positron. If one looks at Eq. (1), one sees that it allows the kinetic energy W to be either a positive quantity greater than mc^2 or a negative quantity less than $-mc^2$. This result is preserved when one passes over to the quantum equation (2) or (3). These quantum equations are such that, when interpreted according to the general scheme of quantum dynamics, they allow as the possible results of a measurement of W either something greater than mc^2 or something less than $-mc^2$.

Now in practice the kinetic energy of a particle is always positive. We thus see that our equations allow of two kinds of motion for an electron, only one of which corresponds to what we are familiar with. The other corresponds to electrons with a very peculiar motion such that the faster they move, the less energy they have, and one must put energy into them to bring them to rest.

One would thus be inclined to introduce, as a new assumption of the theory, that only one of the two kinds of motion occurs in practice. But this gives rise to a difficulty, since we find from the theory that if we disturb the electron, we may cause a transition from a positive-energy state of motion to a negative-energy one, so that, even if we suppose all the electrons in the world to be started off in positive-energy states, after a time some of them would be in negative-energy states.

Thus in allowing negative-energy states, the theory gives something which appears not to correspond to anything known experimentally, but which we cannot simply reject by a new assumption. We must find some meaning for these states.

An examination of the behaviour of these states in an electromagnetic field shows that they correspond to the motion of an electron with a positive charge instead of the usual negative one – what the experimenters now call a positron. One might, therefore, be inclined to assume that electrons in negative-energy states are just positrons, but this will not do, because the observed positrons certainly do not have negative energies. We can, however, establish a connection between electrons in negative-energy states and positrons, in a rather more indirect way.

We make use of the exclusion principle of Pauli, according to which there can be only one electron in any state of motion. We now make the assumptions that in the world as we know it, nearly all the states of negative energy for the electrons are occupied, with just one electron in each state, and that a uniform filling of all the negative-energy states is completely un-observable to us. Further, *any unoccupied negative-energy state, being a departure from uniformity, is observable and is just a positron.*

An unoccupied negative-energy state, or *hole*, as we may call it for brevity, will have a positive energy, since it is a place where there is a shortage of negative energy. A hole is, in fact, just like an ordinary particle, and its identification with the positron seems the most reasonable way of getting over the difficulty of the appearance of negative energies in our equations. On this view the positron is just a mirror-image of the electron, having exactly the same mass and opposite charge. This has already been roughly confirmed by experiment. The positron should also have similar spin prop-erties to the electron, but this has not yet been confirmed by experiment.

From our theoretical picture, we should expect an ordinary electron, with positive energy, to be able to drop into a hole and fill up this hole, the energy being liberated in the form of electromagnetic radiation. This would mean a process in which an electron and a positron annihilate one another. The converse process, namely the creation of an electron and a positron from electromagnetic radiation, should also be able to take place. Such processes appear to have been found experimentally, and are at present being more closely investigated by experimenters.

The theory of electrons and positrons which I have just outlined is a self-consistent theory which fits the experimental facts so far as is yet known. One would like to have an equally satisfactory theory for protons. One might perhaps think that the same theory could be applied to protons. This would require the possibility of existence of negatively charged protons forming a mirror-image of the usual positively charged ones. There is, how-ever, some recent experimental evidence obtained by Stern about the spin magnetic moment of the proton, which conflicts with this theory for the proton. As the proton is so much heavier than the electron, it is quite likely that it requires some more complicated theory, though one cannot at the present time say what this theory is.

In any case I think it is probable that negative protons can exist, since as far as the theory is yet definite, there is a complete and perfect symmetry between positive and negative electric charge, and if this symmetry is really fundamental in nature, it must be possible to reverse the charge on any kind of particle. The negative protons would of course be much harder to produce experimentally, since a much larger energy would be required, corresponding to the larger mass.

If we accept the view of complete symmetry between positive and negative electric charge so far as concerns the fundamental laws of Nature, we must regard it rather as an accident that the Earth (and presumably the whole solar system), contains a preponderance of negative electrons and positive protons. It is quite possible that for some of the stars it is the other way about, these stars being built up mainly of positrons and negative protons. In fact, there may be half the stars of each kind. The two kinds of stars would both show exactly the same spectra, and there would be no way of distinguishing them by present astronomical methods.

Biography

Paul Adrien Maurice Dirac was born on 8th August, 1902, at Bristol, England, his father being Swiss and his mother English. He was educated at the Merchant Venturer's Secondary School, Bristol, then went on to Bristol University. Here, he studied electrical engineering, obtaining the B.Sc. (Engineering) degree in 1921. He then studied mathematics for two years at Bristol University, later going on to St. John's College, Cambridge, as a research student in mathematics. He received his Ph.D. degree in 1926. The following year he became a Fellow of St. John's College and, in 1932, Lucasian Professor of Mathematics at Cambridge.

Dirac's work has been concerned with the mathematical and theoretical aspects of quantum mechanics. He began work on the new quantum mechanics as soon as it was introduced by Heisenberg in 1925 – independently producing a mathematical equivalent which consisted essentially of a non-commutative algebra for calculating atomic properties – and wrote a series of papers on the subject, published mainly in the Proceedings of the Royal Society, leading up to his relativistic *theory of the electron* (1928) and the *theory of holes* (1930). This latter theory required the existence of a positive particle having the same mass and charge as the known (negative) electron. This, the *positron* was discovered experimentally at a later date (1932) by C. D. Anderson, while its existence was likewise proved by Blackett and Occhialini (1933) in the phenomena of « pair production » and « annihilation ».

The importance of Dirac's work lies essentially in his famous wave equation, which introduced special relativity into Schrödinger's equation. Taking into account the fact that, mathematically speaking, relativity theory and quantum theory are not only distinct from each other, but also oppose each other, Dirac's work could be considered a fruitful reconciliation between the two theories.

Dirac's publications include the books *Quantum Theory of the Electron* (1928) and *The Principles of Quantum Mechanics* (1930; 3rd ed. 1947).

He was elected a Fellow of the Royal Society in 1930, being awarded the

Society's Royal Medal and the Copley Medal. He was elected a member of the Pontifical Academy of Sciences in 1961.

Dirac has travelled extensively and studied at various foreign universities, including Copenhagen, Göttingen, Leyden, Wisconsin, Michigan, and Princeton (in 1934, as Visiting Professor). In 1929, after having spent five months in America, he went round the world, visiting Japan together with Heisenberg, and then returned across Siberia.

In 1937 he married Margit Wigner, of Budapest.

Physics 1934

Prize not awarded.

Physics 1935

JAMES CHADWICK

«for his discovery of the neutron»

Physics 1935

Presentation Speech by Professor H. Pleijel, Chairman of the Nobel Committee for Physics of the Royal Swedish Academy of Sciences

Your Majesty, Your Royal Highnesses, Ladies and Gentlemen.

This year like two years ago the Academy of Sciences awards the Nobel Prize for Physics as a reward for discoveries in the world of atoms and molecules. However, a fundamental difference is to be observed between the prizewinners of this year and the prizes that were awarded last time. The latter formed the reward for investigations of more theoretical nature, viz. the discovery of laws regulating the great many phenomena having been brought into light by experimental research. This year the Nobel Prize for Physics is awarded as a reward for a discovery, confirmed in an experimental way, of a new fundamental building-stone of atoms and molecules, viz. the discovery of the so-called *neutron*. By a combination of intuition, logical thought, and experimental research Professor J. Chadwick, the laureate of this year, has succeeded in proving the existence of the neutron and establishing its properties.

One of the Nobel Prize winners for the year 1933, Professor Heisenberg, had concluded by his researches that, owing to reasons of principle as well as to the roughness of our senses and our instruments, it would be impossible for us to arrive at an exact knowledge of what takes place within the atoms. However, experimental research has made undaunted progress, and by the aid of refined methods and new instruments today's Nobel Prize winners in Physics and Chemistry have succeeded in presenting science with a new and deeper knowledge of the structure and qualities of matter.

The Nobel Prize for Physics for this year is awarded as a reward for the discovery of the *neutron*.

The neutron is a heavy particle without any electric charge and of the same weight as the nucleus of an atom of hydrogen.

At the decomposition of the radioactive substances and at the disintegration of atoms and molecules two kinds of particles were always found. One of them that has been called *electron*, has an extremely small weight, amounting to about $\frac{1}{2000}$ of the weight of an atom of hydrogen. The electron is charged with negative electricity, the quantity of the charge being always the same, in whatever way the electron may have appeared. The other kind of particles proved to have a weight of the same size as that of the atom of hydrogen, or a multiple of the same. This heavy particle is always combined with a charge of positive electricity, whose quantity turned out to be equal to or a multiple of the charge of the electron. The smallest particle with positive charge, found in this way, consists of the nucleus of the atom of hydrogen, and its positive charge equals the negative charge of the electron. This smallest, heavy particle with positive charge has received the name of *proton*. Owing to the disintegration of atoms always resulting in protons and electrons, the theory was established that the atoms were composed of protons and electrons. The atom was thought of as having the form of a planetary system where the central body consists of protons, combined to a nucleus; outside this nucleus the negative light electrons circle like the planets round the sun. The number of electrons is different with different substances. The lightest element, hydrogen, has only one electron, helium has two, etc.

That the atom may be in a neutral state of electricity, the positive charge of the nucleus must be the same as the total charge of the exterior electrons. The simplest relation would here have been that the number of protons in the nucleus had been the same as that of the electrons circling about the nucleus. This proved, however, not to be the case. In the atoms belonging to different elements it was found that, apart from hydrogen, the nucleus had about twice as many protons as the number of exterior electrons. Thus e.g. helium has the weight four in relation to the nucleus of hydrogen but only two exterior electrons. That the atom may be neutral in electric respect, the supposition is necessary that the surplus of positive electricity that the nucleus thus receives owing to the greater number of protons, was compensated by negative electrons also entering the nucleus. The nucleus of helium was thus supposed to consist of four protons and two electrons, and about this nucleus there circle two electrons.

At first this idea of the atom could be made to agree fairly well with experience. The nucleus-charge resulting determines the character of the atom and its place among the elements. The number of exterior electrons and the distribution of their paths at different distances from the nucleus are determinative of the physical and chemical qualities of the element; if one electron suddenly passes from one path to another, light is emitted, and if electrons from the paths closer to the nucleus are flung from the atom, X-rays are emitted, and so on. If the number of protons is increased or diminished in a nucleus, but the charge of the nucleus is still kept unaltered by the addition or the loss of negative electrons, the same element is still obtained but with different atomic weight; a so-called isotope is obtained. Thus e.g. lead is found in several different forms with different weight; and heavy hydrogen, the object of last year's Nobel Prize for Chemistry, is a similar modification of normal hydrogen.

A continued study of the conditions of energy at the disintegration of the nuclei of atoms showed, however, that the theory of the nuclei being composed of protons and electrons could scarcely be brought to agree with theoretical and experimental facts. As often happens in these spheres, it was the discovery of new phenomena, difficult to explain, that gave rise to the solution of the problem about the structure of the nuclei of atoms. In 1930 the scientists Bothe and Becker had found a new strange radiation that appeared, when the substance *beryllium* was bombarded with nuclei of helium. This new radiation, which was called *the radiation of beryllium* proved extremely penetrating. The rays could pierce a brass plate, several centimeters thick, without any noteworthy loss of velocity. When hitting nuclei of atoms, this new radiation caused a disintegration of them, similar to an explosion.

As a matter of course the new rays became at once the object of intensive experimental research, in which today's Nobel Prize winners in Chemistry, the couple Joliot, have taken an active and important part. At that time it was generally supposed that the radiation of beryllium was of the same nature as the electromagnetic waves of extremely short wavelength arising at the disintegration of radioactive substances. This radiation has received the name of γ-radiation and has the same qualities as the well-known X-rays. However, it was found that the new radiation possessed a power considerably superior to that of the strongest radioactive γ-rays; a correspondent radiation from another element, boron, proved, however, still stronger.

During their investigations of the radiation of beryllium, the couple Joliot made the important observation that a block of paraffin or another substance containing hydrogen being bombarded with the new rays, will emit an intensive stream of protons. With the assistance of the expansion chamber, constructed by the Nobel Prize winner Wilson, in which the paths of particles with electric charge – protons or electrons – could be made visible, it was possible to calculate the energy of the protons emitted from paraffin and thus also that of the radiation of beryllium causing the stream of protons. Then it turned out that the values of energy obtained, if the radiation of beryllium was supposed to be a γ-radiation, became absurdly high. Nor could these values of energy be brought to agree with the energy to be reckoned with in the radiation giving rise to the radiation of beryllium.

Chadwick, who had undertaken investigations of the radiation of beryllium, found a similar radiation from quite a number of other elements, e.g. helium, lithium, carbon, nitrogen, and argon. By his extensive studies and calculations on conditions of energy at collisions, he was soon convinced that the radiation of beryllium could not be a γ-radiation.

Already in 1920 Lord Rutherford had suggested that, apart from protons and electrons, there also existed particles of the same weight as a proton but without any electric charge. To this particle was given in advance the name of *neutron*. This neutron had long been searched for but without any result. It is also easily understood how difficult it would be to discover this particle without electric charge. The neutron and the proton are certainly, like the electron, both particles of extremely small dimensions. But owing to their charges, the proton as well as the electron are accompanied by electric fields, which make them act as bodies of considerably larger dimensions, and their charges are influenced by the charges of the atoms they pass; these charged particles are therefore strongly checked when passing through substantial bodies. The neutron, on the contrary, having no electric charge is not affected and is not checked in its way, until it directly hits another particle, which happens extremely seldom owing to the small dimensions of the particles in relation to the distance between them. This explains why a neutron may pass through several kilometers of air, before losing its energy of motion. The motion of a proton or an electron may be observed in the above-mentioned Wilson chamber, and these particles being charged with electricity, their courses will be curved, if they are exposed to electric or magnetic fields. This curve may be studied in the Wilson chamber. The neutron, on the other hand, being without any charge, is not affected by such fields and may be discovered only in the case of a direct collision with the nucleus of an atom.

Chadwick now studied how, at a collision between radiation of beryllium and nuclei of atoms, the exchange of energy would be, supposing that the radiation of beryllium consisted of neutrons flung out from beryllium, and he then found that the experimental results attained agreed well with his own calculations. The same was the case also with radiation from other substances. By these facts the existence of the neutron was beyond all doubt. Chadwick then examined the exchange of mass taking place when by collision the nuclei of different substances are changed into new nuclei, belonging to other substances, and into neutrons. As an example may be mentioned that the nucleus of helium, when meeting that of beryllium, gives rise to a nucleus of carbon plus a neutron. Knowing the masses of different nuclei, it is possible directly to calculate the mass of the neutron. By examining the exchange of mass at a great number of collisions between the nuclei of different elements Chadwick succeeded in determining exactly the mass of the neutron, and as was to be expected, he found it almost the same as that of the proton or that of the nucleus of hydrogen.

On the other hand these researches have given a new method for the exact calculation of the size of masses in the nuclei of different elements. As characteristic for the usefulness of this new method may be mentioned that in this way Chadwick obtained another value for hydrogen than the earlier one observed by Aston with his spectrograph of mass. Aston, having improved his spectrograph, has obtained new values for the mass of hydrogen agreeing with those obtained by Chadwick.

The existence of the neutron having thus been proved, it was no more necessary to suppose compensatory charges of electron in the nuclei. The nucleus of atoms is nowadays considered to be composed of a number of protons and neutrons. Thus the nucleus of helium consists of two protons and two neutrons; about the nucleus there circle in the atom two electrons. Isotopes are formed by surplus or lack of the number of neutrons in the solid atom.

Owing to its weight and its great penetrating power, the neutron has become a powerful resource to bring about the disintegration of atoms and of nuclei of atoms, and during the last few years this power of the neutron to split up atoms and molecules has been largely made use of.

The existence of the neutron having been fully established, scientists have, as has just been mentioned, come to a new conception of the structure of atoms which agrees better with the distribution of energy within the nuclei of atoms. It has proved obvious that the neutron forms one of the building-stones of atoms and molecules and thus also of material universe.

However, there are still many questions to be answered, among others the one about the relations of protons and neutrons to each other. There are certain signs indicating that these two particles are modifications of one and the same primitive particle. The existence of the positive electron, found by Dirac by theoretical research, having now been experimentally proved, the task of physical science will be to examine, more closely, the relations existing between this electron and the parts of the nuclei of atoms – the proton and the neutron; the neutron discovered by Chadwick has here given a powerful instrument for future researches on the structure of atoms and molecules. If the qualities of the neutron are made use of, this will certainly in the immediate future give us a new and deeper knowledge of matter and its transformations.

Professor Chadwick.   The Royal Academy of Sciences has awarded you the Nobel Prize for Physics for your discovery of the neutron.

We congratulate you to this most important result by which has been revealed a new building-stone of matter playing the same fundamental part as the proton and the electron.

By means of a new method, created by you, you have been able to determine the mass of the neutron, and by the same method you have found new, more exact values of the atomic weights of a number of elements.

In the neutron Science has obtained a powerful means of splitting up atoms and molecules which has already given important results.

I now ask you, Mr. Chadwick, to receive the prize from the hands of His Majesty.

JAMES CHADWICK

The neutron and its properties

Nobel Lecture, December 12, 1935

The idea that there might exist small particles with no electrical charge has been put forward several times. Nernst, for example, suggested that a neutral particle might be formed by a negative electron and an equal positive charge, and that these « neutrons » might possess many of the properties of the ether; while Bragg at one time suggested that the γ-rays emitted by radioactive substances consisted of small neutral particles, which, on breaking up, released a negative electron.

The first suggestion of a neutral particle with the properties of the neutron we now know, was made by Rutherford in 1920. He thought that a proton and an electron might unite in a much more intimate way than they do in the hydrogen atom, and so form a particle of no nett charge and with a mass nearly the same as that of the hydrogen atom. His view was that with such a particle as the first step in the formation of atomic nuclei from the two elementary units in the structure of matter – the proton and the electron – it would be much easier to picture how heavy complex nuclei can be gradually built up from the simpler ones. He pointed out that this neutral particle would have peculiar and interesting properties. It may be of interest to quote his remarks:

« Under some conditions, however, it may be possible for an electron to combine much more closely with the H nucleus, forming a kind of neutral doublet. Such an atom would have very novel properties. Its external field would be practically zero, except very close to the nucleus, and in consequence it should be able to move freely through matter. Its presence would probably be difficult to detect by the spectroscope, and it may be impossible to contain it in a sealed vessel. On the other hand, it should enter readily the structure of atoms, and may either unite with the nucleus or be disintegrated by its intense field.

The existence of such atoms seems almost necessary to explain the building up of the nuclei of heavy elements; for unless we suppose the production of charged particles of very high velocities it is difficult to see how any positively charged particle can reach the nucleus of a heavy atom against its intense repulsive field. »

Rutherford's conception of closely combined proton and electron was adopted in pictures of nuclear structure developed by Ono (1926), by Fournier and others, but nothing essentially new was added to it.

No experimental evidence for the existence of neutral particles could be obtained for years. Some experiments were made in the Cavendish Laboratory in 1921 by Glasson and by Roberts, hoping to detect the formation of such particles when an electric discharge was passed through hydrogen. Their results were negative.

The possibility that neutral particles might exist was, nevertheless, not lost sight of. I myself made several attempts to detect them – in discharge tubes actuated in different ways, in the disintegration of radioactive substances, and in artificial disintegrations produced by α-particles.[*] No doubt similar experiments were made in other laboratories, with the same result.

Later, Bothe and Becker showed that γ-radiations were excited in some light elements when bombarded by α-particles. Mr. H. C. Webster, in the Cavendish Laboratory had also been making similar experiments, and he proceeded to examine closely the production of these radiations. The radiation emitted by beryllium showed some rather peculiar features, which were very difficult to explain. I suggested therefore that the radiation might consist of neutral particles and that a test of this hypothesis might be made by passing the radiation into an expansion chamber. Several photographs were taken: some β-particle tracks – presumably recoil electrons – were observed, but nothing unexpected.[**]

The first real step towards the discovery of the neutron was given by a very beautiful experiment of Mme. and M. Joliot-Curie, who were also investigating the properties of this beryllium radiation. They passed the radiation through a very thin window into an ionization vessel containing air. When paraffin wax or any other matter containing hydrogen was placed in front of the window the ionization in the vessel increased. They showed that this increase was due to the ejection from the wax of protons, moving with very high velocities.

This behaviour of the beryllium radiation was very difficult to explain if it were a quantum radiation. I therefore began immediately the study of this new effect using different methods – the counter, the expansion chamber, and the high-pressure ionization chamber.

It appeared at once that the beryllium radiation could eject particles not

[*] Cf. Rutherford and Chadwick, *Proc. Cambridge Phil. Soc.*, 25 (1929) 186.
[**] The failure was partly due to the weakness of the polonium source.

only from paraffin wax but also from other light substances, such as lithium, beryllium, boron, etc., though in these cases the particles had a range of only a few millimetres in air. The experiments showed that the particles are recoil atoms of the element through which the radiation passes, set in motion by the impact of the radiation.

The occurrence of these recoil atoms can be shown most strikingly by means of the expansion chamber. These experiments were carried out by Dr. Feather and Mr. Dee.

Fig. 1.

Fig. 1 is a photograph taken by Dee, which shows the tracks of protons ejected from gelatine on the roof of the expansion chamber. Fig. 2 shows two photographs taken by Feather, using an expansion chamber filled with nitrogen. Two short dense tracks are seen. Each is due to an atom of nitrogen which has been struck by the radiation. One track (Fig. 2b) shows a short spur, due to collision with a nitrogen atom; the angle between the spurs is 90°, as it should be if the initial track is due to a nitrogen atom.

Fig. 2 a.   Fig. 2 b.

The beryllium radiation thus behaved very differently from a quantum radiation. This property of setting in motion the atoms of matter in its path suggests that the radiation consists of particles.

Let us suppose that the radiation consists of particles of mass M moving with velocities up to a maximum velocity V. Then the maximum velocity which can be imparted to a hydrogen atom, mass 1, by the impart of such a particle will be

$$U_p = \frac{2M}{M+1}V$$

and the maximum velocity imparted to a nitrogen atom will be

$$U_n = \frac{2M}{M+14}V$$

Then

$$\frac{M+14}{M+1} = \frac{U_p}{U_n}$$

The velocities U_p and U_n were found by experiment. The maximum range of the protons ejected from paraffin wax was measured and also the ranges of the recoil atoms produced in an expansion chamber filled with nitrogen. From these ranges the velocities U_p and U_n can be deduced approximately: $U_p = $ ca. 3.7×10^9 cm/sec, $U_n = $ ca. 4.7×10^8 cm/sec. Thus we find $M = 0.9$.

We must conclude that the beryllium radiation does in fact consist of particles, and that these particles have a mass about the same as that of a proton. Now the experiments further showed that these particles can pass easily through thicknesses of matter, e.g. 10 or even 20 cm lead. But a proton of the same velocity as this particle is stopped by a thickness of $\frac{1}{4}$ mm of lead. Since the penetrating power of particles of the same mass and speed depends only on the charge carried by the particle, it was clear that the particle of the beryllium radiation must have a very small charge compared with that of the proton. It was simplest to assume that it has no charge at all. All the properties of the beryllium radiation could be readily explained on this assumption, that the radiation consists of particles of mass 1 and charge 0, or neutrons.

The nature of the neutron

I have already mentioned Rutherford's suggestion that there might exist a neutral particle formed by the close combination of a proton and an electron, and it was at first natural to suppose that the neutron might be such a complex particle. On the other hand, a structure of this kind cannot be fitted into the scheme of the quantum mechanics, in which the hydrogen atom represents the only possible combination of a proton and an electron. Moreover, an argument derived from the spins of the particles is against this view. The statistics and spins of the lighter elements can only be given a consistent description if we assume that the neutron is an elementary particle.

Similar arguments make it difficult to suppose that the proton is a combination of neutron and positive electron. It seems at present useless to discuss whether the neutron and proton are elementary particles or not; it may be that they are two different states of the fundamental heavy particle.

In the present view of the β-transformations of radioactive bodies the hypothesis is made that a neutron in the nucleus may transform into a proton and a negative electron with the emission of the electron, or conversely a proton in the nucleus may transform into a neutron and a positive electron with the emission of the positron. Thus

$$n \rightarrow p + e^-$$
$$p \rightarrow n + e^+$$

If spin is to be conserved in this process we must invoke the aid of another particle – Pauli's neutrino; we then write

$$n \rightarrow n + e^- + \text{neutrino}$$
$$p \rightarrow n + e^+ + \text{antineutrino}$$

where the neutrino is a particle of very small mass, no charge, and spin $\frac{1}{2}$.

If we knew the masses of the neutron and proton accurately, these considerations would give the mass of the hypothetical neutrino.

As I have shown, observations of the momenta transferred in collisions of a neutron with atomic nuclei lead to a value of the mass of the neutron but the measurements cannot be made with precision. To obtain an accurate estimate of the neutron mass we must use the energy relations in a disintegration process in which a neutron is liberated from an atomic nucleus. The best estimate at present is obtained from the disintegration of the deuteron by the photoelectric effect of a γ-ray

$$\text{}^{2}_{1}\text{D} + h\nu \rightarrow \text{}^{1}_{1}\text{p} + \text{}^{1}_{0}\text{n}$$

The energy of the protons liberated by a γ-ray quantum of $h\nu = 2.62 \times 10^{6}$ eV has been measured recently by Feather, Bretscher, and myself. It is 180,000 eV. Thus the total kinetic energy set free is 360,000 eV, giving a binding energy of the deuteron of 2.26×10^{6} eV. Using the value of the deuteron mass given by Oliphant, Kempton, and Rutherford, we then obtain a value for the mass of the neutron of 1.0085[*]. The mass of the hydrogen atom is 1.0081. It would seem therefore that a free neutron should be unstable, i.e. it can change spontaneously into a proton + electron + neutrino, unless the neutrino has a mass of the order of the mass of an electron. On the other hand, an argument from the shape of the β-ray spectra suggests that the mass of the neutrino is zero. One must await more exact measurements of the masses of hydrogen and deuterium before speculating further on this matter.

Passage of neutrons through matter

The neutron in its passage through matter loses its energy in collisions with the atomic nuclei and not with the electrons. The experiments of Dee showed that the primary ionization along the track of a neutron in air could not be as much as 1 ion pair in 3 metres' path, while Massey has calculated that it may be as low as 1 ion pair in 10^{5} km. This behaviour is very different from that of a charged particle, such as a proton, which dissipates its energy almost entirely in electron collisions. The collision of a neutron with an atomic nucleus, although much more frequent than with an electron, is also a rare event, for the forces between a neutron and a nucleus are very small except at distances of the order of 10^{-12} cm. In a close collision the neutron may be deflected from its path and the struck nucleus may acquire sufficient energy to produce ions. The recoiling nucleus can then be detected either in an ionization chamber or by its track in an expansion chamber. In some of these collisions, however, the neutron enters the nucleus and a disintegration is

[*] Recent measurements of the mass of deuterium lead to a value of 1.0090 for the mass of the neutron.

produced. Such disintegrations were first observed by Feather in his observations on the passage of neutrons through an expansion chamber filled with nitrogen. An example is shown in Fig. 3. The disintegration process is

$$^{14}_{7}\text{N} + ^{1}_{0}\text{n} \rightarrow ^{11}_{5}\text{B} + ^{4}_{2}\text{He}$$

Since these early experiments many examples of this type of disintegration have been observed by different workers.

Fig. 3.

Fermi and his collaborators have also shown that the phenomenon of artificial radioactivity can be provoked in the great majority of all elements, even in those of large atomic number, by the bombardment of neutrons. They have also shown that neutrons of very small kinetic energy are peculiarly effective in many cases.

In some cases an α-particle is emitted in the disintegration process; in others a proton is emitted; while in others an unstable species of nucleus is formed by the simple capture of the neutron.

Examples of these types are:

$$^{31}_{15}\text{P} + ^{1}_{0}\text{n} \rightarrow ^{28}_{13}\text{Al} + ^{4}_{2}\text{He}$$
$$^{28}_{14}\text{Si} + ^{1}_{0}\text{n} \rightarrow ^{28}_{13}\text{Al} + ^{1}_{1}\text{H}$$
$$^{27}_{13}\text{Al} + ^{1}_{0}\text{n} \rightarrow ^{28}_{13}\text{Al}$$
$$^{127}_{53}\text{I} + ^{1}_{0}\text{n} \rightarrow ^{128}_{53}\text{I}$$

In the cases just cited the nuclei formed in the reaction are unstable, showing the phenomenon of induced activity discovered by Mme. and M. Joliot-Curie, and return to a stable form with the emission of negative electrons.

In the transformations produced in heavy elements by neutrons, the process is, with very few exceptions, one of simple capture. The nucleus so formed, an isotope of the original nucleus, is often unstable but not invariably so. For example the reaction

$$_{48}Cd + _{0}n \rightarrow _{48}Cd + h\nu$$

The cadmium isotope formed is stable, but a γ-ray quantum is emitted of energy corresponding to the binding energy of the neutron.

Other cases of this type of transformation are known.

The great effectiveness of the neutron in producing nuclear transmutations is not difficult to explain. In the collisions of a charged particle with a nucleus, the chance of entry is limited by the Coulomb forces between the particle and the nucleus; these impose a minimum distance of approach which increases with the atomic number of the nucleus and soon becomes so large that the chance of the particle entering the nucleus is very small. In the case of collisions of a neutron with a nucleus there is no limitation of this kind. The force between a neutron and a nucleus is inappreciable except at very small distances, when it increases very rapidly and is attractive. Instead of the potential wall in the case of the charged particle, the neutron encounters a potential hole. Thus even neutrons of very small energy can penetrate into a nucleus. Indeed slow neutrons may be enormously more effective than fast neutrons, for they spend a longer time in the nucleus. The calculations of Bethe show that the chance of capture of a neutron may be inversely proportional to its velocity. The possibility of capture will depend on whether the nucleus possesses an unoccupied p-level or a level with azimuthal quantum number $l = 1$.

In cases where a particle (α-particle or proton) is ejected from the nucleus, the possibility of disintegration will depend on whether the particle can escape through the potential barrier. This will be easier the greater the energy set free in the disintegration process. As a rule disintegration by neutrons will take place with absorption of kinetic energy if a proton is released in the transformation, and may take place with release of kinetic energy if one at least of the products is an α-particle. Thus processes in which a proton is emitted can only occur with fast neutrons, even in collisions with elements of low atomic number; while processes in which α-particles are emitted can occur with slow neutrons in elements of low atomic number, but again only with fast neutrons in elements of higher atomic number. If the atomic number is sufficiently high, the neutrons at present at our disposal have insufficient energy and the particles cannot escape through the potential barrier. Thus with elements of high atomic number, only capture processes are observed, although there may be a few exceptions. There may be, however, special cases in which the particles escape through a resonance level. These would be characterized by the phenomenon that the energy of the escaping particle would be independent of the energy of the incident neutron. These special cases may explain the exceptional disintegrations in which a particle is emitted from a heavy nucleus. They may be of particular interest in giving information about the resonance levels of atomic nuclei.

There is also the possibility of resonance capture of the neutrons, more particularly with very slow neutrons. The capture of neutrons of a certain energy may take place with very great frequency in one species of nucleus while for another neighbouring nucleus the same neutrons may have a long free path. These resonance regions may perhaps be rather broad and therefore comparatively easy to observe experimentally.

The structure of the nucleus

Before the discovery of the neutron we had to assume that the fundamental particles from which an atomic nucleus was built up were the proton and the electron, with the α-particle as a secondary unit. The behaviour of an electron in a space of nuclear dimensions cannot be described on present theory; and other difficulties, e.g. the statistics of the nitrogen nucleus, the peculiarities in the mass defect curve in the region of the heavy elements, also arose. These difficulties are removed if we suppose that the nuclei are built up from protons and neutrons. The forces which determine the stability of a nucleus will then be of three types, the interactions between proton and proton, between proton and neutron, and between neutron and neutron. It is assumed, with Heisenberg and Majorana, that the interaction between neutron and proton is of the exchange type – similar to that between the hydrogen atom and the hydrogen ion – and that the interaction between neutron and neutron is small.

For a nucleus of mass number A and charge Ze we shall have

$$N_n + N_p = A \qquad N_p = Z$$
$$N_n/N_p = (A-Z)/Z$$

The value of N_n/N_p for the most stable nucleus of a given mass number will be determined by the condition that the binding energy is a maximum. The repulsive Coulomb force between the protons tends to diminish the number of protons in a nucleus, while the neutron–proton interaction tends to make $N_n = N_p, Z = A/2$; the neutron–neutron interaction is probably very small. Now in existing nuclei $N_p \sim N_n$, and therefore the neutron–proton interaction must be the predominating force in the nucleus. In heavy elements $N_n > N_p$. This relative increase in the number of neutrons may be due either to an attractive force between neutron–neutron, or more probably to the Coulomb forces between proton–proton.

Thus it appears that the interaction between proton and neutron is of the highest significance in nuclear structure and governs the stability of a nucleus. It is most important to obtain all experimental evidence about the nature of this interaction. The information we have at present is very meagre, but I think that it does to some degree support the view that the interaction is of the exchange type. Dr. Feather and I hope to obtain more definite information on this subject by an extensive study of the collisions of neutrons and protons.

Heisenberg's considerations of nuclear structure point very strongly to this exchange interaction. Such an interaction provides an attractive force at large distances between the particles and a repulsive force at very small distances, thus giving the effect of a more or less definite radius of the particles. A system of particles interacting with exchange forces will keep together due to the attraction, but there will be a minimum distance of approach of the particles; thus the system will not collapse together but will have a more or less definite « radius ».

The exchange forces between a hydrogen atom and a hydrogen ion are large compared with the forces between neutral atoms; by analogy we explain why the neutron–proton interaction is so much stronger than the proton–proton or neutron–neutron interactions.

By a suitable choice of the exchange forces it is possible to obtain a saturation effect, analogous to the saturation of valency bindings between two atoms, when each neutron is bound to two protons and each proton to two neutrons. Thus two neutrons and two protons form a closed system – the α-particle.

These ideas thus explain the general features of the structure of atomic nuclei and it can be confidently expected that further work on these lines may reveal the elementary laws which govern the structure of matter.

Biography

James Chadwick was born in Cheshire, England, on 20th October, 1891, the son of John Joseph Chadwick and Anne Mary Knowles. He attended Manchester High School prior to entering Manchester University in 1908; he graduated from the Honours School of Physics in 1911 and spent the next two years under Professor (later Lord) Rutherford in the Physical Laboratory in Manchester, where he worked on various radioactivity problems, gaining his M.Sc. degree in 1913. That same year he was awarded the 1851 Exhibition Scholarship and proceeded to Berlin to work in the Physikalisch-Technische Reichsanstalt at Charlottenburg under Professor H. Geiger.

During World War I, he was interned in the Zivilgefangenenlager, Ruhleben. After the war, in 1919, he returned to England to accept the Wollaston Studentship at Gonville and Caius College, Cambridge, and to resume work under Rutherford, who in the meantime had moved to the Cavendish Laboratory, Cambridge. Rutherford had succeeded that year in disintegrating atoms by bombarding nitrogen with alpha particles, with the emission of a proton. This was the first artificial nuclear transformation. In Cambridge, Chadwick joined Rutherford in accomplishing the transmutation of other light elements by bombardment with alpha particles, and in making studies of the properties and structure of atomic nuclei.

He was elected Fellow of Gonville and Caius College (1921–1935) and became Assistant Director of Research in the Cavendish Laboratory (1923–1935). In 1927 he was elected a Fellow of the Royal Society.

In 1932, Chadwick made a fundamental discovery in the domain of nuclear science: he proved the existence of *neutrons*–elementary particles devoid of any electrical charge. In contrast with the helium nuclei (alpha rays) which are charged, and therefore repelled by the considerable electrical forces present in the nuclei of heavy atoms, this new tool in atomic disintegration need not overcome any electric barrier and is capable of penetrating and splitting the nuclei of even the heaviest elements. Chadwick in this way prepared the way towards the fission of uranium 235 and towards the creation of the atomic bomb. For this epoch-making discovery he was awarded the Hughes Medal of the Royal Society in 1932, and subsequently the Nobel Prize for Physics in 1935.

He remained at Cambridge until 1935 when he was elected to the Lyon Jones Chair of Physics in the University of Liverpool. From 1943 to 1946 he worked in the United States as Head of the British Mission attached to the Manhattan Project for the development of the atomic bomb. He returned to England and, in 1948, retired from active physics and his position at Liverpool on his election as Master of Gonville and Caius College, Cambridge. He retired from this Mastership in 1959. From 1957 to 1962 he was a part-time member of the United Kingdom Atomic Energy Authority.

Chadwick has had many papers published on the topic of radioactivity and connected problems and, with Lord Rutherford and C. D. Ellis, he is co-author of the book *Radiations from Radioactive substances* (1930).

Sir James was knighted in 1945. Apart from the Hughes Medal (Royal Society) mentioned above, he received the Copley Medal (1950) and the Franklin Medal of the Franklin Institute, Philadelphia (1951). He is an Honorary Fellow of the Institute of Physics and, in addition to receiving honorary doctorate degrees from the Universities of Reading, Dublin, Leeds, Oxford, Birmingham, Montreal (McGill), Liverpool, and Edinburgh, he is a member of several foreign academies, being Associé of the Académie Royale de Belgique; Foreign Member of the Kongelige Danske Videnskabernes Selskab and the Koninklijke Nederlandse Akademie van Wetenschappen; Corresponding Member of the Sächsische Akademie der Wissenschaften, Leipzig; Member of the Pontificia Academia Scientiarum and the Franklin Institute; Honorary Member of the American Philosophical Society and the American Physical Society.

In 1925, he married Aileen Stewart-Brown of Liverpool. They have twin daughters, and live at Denbigh, North Wales. His hobbies include gardening and fishing.

Physics 1936

VICTOR FRANZ HESS

«for his discovery of cosmic radiation»

CARL DAVID ANDERSON

«for his discovery of the positron»

Physics 1936

Presentation Speech by Prof. H. Pleijel, Chairman of the Nobel Committee for Physics of the Royal Swedish Academy of Sciences

Your Majesty, Your Royal Highnesses, Ladies and Gentlemen.

The year 1895 is a turning-point in the history of physics: Röntgen discovered the rays that were to be called after him, and this was rapidly followed by Becquerel's discovery of radioactive radiation, and by the discovery of the negative electron – one of the fundamental elements of atomic structure.

Many research workers have made the radioactive rays discovered by Becquerel the subject of their investigations, starting with the Curies, husband and wife, who discovered the substance radium; these investigations have now come to a natural termination in the discovery by the Joliot-Curies, that normal atoms can be made radioactive by external influences.

The existence of a new, peculiar type of radiation, i.e. cosmic radiation, for the discovery of which Professor Victor Hess will today receive the Nobel Prize for Physics, became manifest during the search for sources of radioactive radiation. A few words on the nature of radioactive radiation may not come amiss. This radiation occurs during the explosion within the atomic nuclei of certain substances of instable structure. As is general knowledge, the rays derive their name from one of these substances, i.e. radium. In the event of an explosion in the atom, parts of the atom are ejected in all directions. The resulting rays are therefore bound to contain heavy, positively charged parts of the nucleus of the atom, and extremely light, negatively charged electrons on the periphery of the atom. When the energy in the atom is liberated, there occurs, apart from these two types of rays, a strong radiation, the so-called gamma rays, which are of the same nature as X-rays. During this explosion of the atom, other elements are formed by it. One element is therefore changed into another. The presence of radioactive rays can be detected from the circumstance that the emitted rays split the molecules of the air into positive and negative components and render the circumambient air electrically conductive, i.e. ionize it. An instrument that is electrically charged, e.g. an electroscope, will therefore lose its electrical charge when it is surrounded by air exposed to radioactive radiation.

The instrument can on the other hand be protected against such radiation by being encased in lead plates of sufficient thickness.

During the years that followed the discovery of radioactive rays a search was made throughout nature for radioactive substances: in the crust of the earth, in the seas, and in the atmosphere; and the instrument just mentioned – the electroscope – was applied. Radioactive rays were found everywhere, whether investigations were made into the waters of deep lakes, or into high mountains. The most surprising discovery that was made was that it was impossible to eliminate the influence of the rays, no matter how thick were the lead plates that encased the instrument. This was inexplicable if the rays were to emanate from radioactive substance in the earth or from the atmosphere, and research workers were therefore compelled to the assumption that there exists another source of radiation unknown to us, with rays of immense powers of penetration.

In searching for this new source of radiation, it was obvious to investigate whether radiation decreased at high levels above the earth's surface. Such experiments were done by various research workers, including some on the Eiffel Tower. The experiments showed some decrease of radiation with increasing distance from the earth's surface, but not at the rate to be expected if radiation emanated from the earth. Observations were extended to greater heights by balloon ascents. In ascents to a height of 4,500 m a slight decrease with height was observed in some cases, but in other cases, ionization remained practically unchanged.

Although no definite results were gained from these investigations, they did show that the omnipresent radiation could not be attributed to radiation of radioactive substances in the earth's crust.

The mystery of the origin of this radiation remained unsolved until Prof. Hess made it his problem. Hess who was from the start of the opinion that the radiation was due to very powerful gamma rays, first investigated in detail the manner in which such rays are weakened on passing through dense layers of air. The sources of error in the instruments used were also investigated. With superb experimental skill Hess perfected the instrumental equipment used and eliminated its sources of error. With these preparations completed, Hess made a number of balloon ascents to heights up to 5,300 m, in 1911 and 1912. His systematic measurements showed that a decrease in ionization did occur up to 1,000 m, but that it increased considerably thereafter, so that at 5,000 m radiation was twice as intensive as on the earth's surface. Later ascents and investigations made by successors of Hess in free balloons equipped with recording instruments showed that at a height of 9,300 m radiation is about 40 times as intensive as on the earth's surface. From these investigations Hess drew the conclusion that there exists an extremely penetrating radiation coming from space which enters the earth's atmosphere. This radiation which has been found to come from all sides in space has been called cosmic radiation. Hess's investigations naturally aroused much interest and were received with much scepticism by many. No regular investigations into cosmic rays were carried out during the World War, but once war was over, investigations were resumed with enthusiasm both in Europe and in the USA, and before long the existence of cosmic radiation was generally accepted.

The new rays surpass in intensity and penetrating power everything previously known. They are capable of penetrating lead plates one metre thick and they have been detected on the floor of lakes with a depth of 500 m. The big question is: where does this radiation come from? During his first balloon ascents Hess observed that there was no particular difference between night and day, and no special influence either was detected in a balloon ascent during a solar eclipse. Cosmic radiation could not therefore originate in the sun.

At a later date Hess made extremely sensitive systematic measurements of the rays and found that they varied in one and the same place during the daily rotation of the earth with the position of the place relative to the fixed stars. The variation is small, only 0.1%. Meanwhile, Compton has shown theoretically that this change may be due to the motion of the sun and therefore of the earth in space. Being part of the galaxy, the solar system participates in the rotation of the galaxy, which imparts to the earth a velocity of about 300 km per second. The earth's motion results in an apparent increase in cosmic radiation, from the side towards which the earth moves, and in an apparent attenuation on the other side. Compton's calculations give the correct figure, from which the conclusion has been drawn that cosmic radiation does not come from our galaxy either, but from stellar systems far beyond it.

We still do not know what processes out in the deep fastnesses of space give rise to this radiation. Many theories have been put forward, but no one has yet been able to provide any detailed explanation of how these rays – over a thousand times more powerful than the strongest radioactivity – come into being. When in the years to come the mysteries thus posed by cosmic radiation have been completely or partially solved, this will surely shed new light on the interaction between energy and matter, and on the origin and disintegration of matter.

Professor Hess.   By virtue of your purposeful researches into the effects of radioactive radiation carried out with exceptional experimental skill you discovered the surprising presence of radiation coming from the depths of space, i.e. cosmic radiation. As you have proved, this new radiation possesses a penetrating power and an intensity of previously unknown magnitude; it has become a powerful tool of research in physics, and has already given us important new results with respect to matter and its composition. The presence of this cosmic radiation has offered us new, important problems on the formation and destruction of matter, problems which open up new fields for research. We congratulate you on your fine achievements.

For your discovery of cosmic radiation, the Royal Academy of Sciences has awarded you the Nobel Prize for Physics, and I now call upon you, Professor Hess, to receive the award from the hands of His Majesty the King.

The experimental discovery of the positive electron, for which discovery Dr. Anderson receives today the Nobel Prize, has such an intimate relation to the cosmic radiation that I must take the liberty to touch once more upon this subject. After the existence of cosmic radiation had been clearly stated there arose the question of the nature of this radiation. On an earlier occasion this day I have had the opportunity of mentioning the various kinds of rays emanating from an atom of a radioactive substance, when this atom explodes. It has been stated that these rays consist partly of heavy, positively charged particles from the nucleus of the atom, partly of light, negative electrons, and finally of so-called gamma rays, which are of the same nature as X-rays and light rays although with an exceedingly short wavelength, and for this reason possessing great penetrating power. The two first kinds of rays, which consist of charged particles, have come to be called corpuscular rays. The question now arose, whether the cosmic radiation was a corpuscular radiation or whether it consisted of gamma rays. It was obvious, in order to settle this question, to examine the rays when passing between the poles of a powerful magnet. In the case that the rays consisted of charged particles, their paths would be changed by the magnetic field in different directions for various kinds of charge. If, on the other hand, they consisted of gamma rays, they would experience no influence from the magnetic field. An excellent instrument for the investigation of the nature of the rays is the Wilson chamber, which consists of a closed vessel filled with super-saturated steam. On account of the condensation caused by the passage of a ray, the path of the ray becomes visible to the eye and can be photographed. The first experiments carried out by means of a magnetic field showed, however, no deviation of the rays. But the high energy which the rays possess requires very strong magnetic fields to produce visible effects. Meanwhile investigations carried out along quite other lines had indicated the probability of the cosmic rays being corpuscular rays. The earth itself is a magnet and above all a big one. It has long been known that a corpuscular radiation consisting of negative electrons emanates from the sun. As Störmer has shown the rays are caused to deviate from the earth by its magnetic field. It is only at the magnetic poles, where the rays have the same direction as the magnetic force, that the rays can penetrate into the atmosphere of the earth, where they give rise to the phenomena called polar lights. On the other hand, the cosmic rays have a much greater penetrating power than the rays from the sun and therefore everywhere make their way down to the surface of the earth. It ought then to be expected that, owing to the influence of the magnetic field of the earth, a certain difference of the intensity of the radiation at the poles and at the equator should be noticeable. To demonstrate this Professor Clay in Amsterdam had, already in 1929, carried out comparative measurements of the cosmic radiation in Holland and Java, and these measurements have shown a distinct latitude effect. It might be mentioned, incidentally, that according to later investigation this effect increases considerably with increasing height above the earth. In order to be able to study more in detail the nature of cosmic radiation Millikan decided to set up, in his institute at Pasadena, an installation for experiments on a large scale containing, among other things, a Wilson chamber equipped with very strong magnets. The planning and direction of the experiments Millikan entrusted to Dr. Anderson. When some years later the installation was ready, the cosmic radiation was recorded day and night every 15 seconds. The result of the rich material thus collected was published in 1931. Upon examination of the photographs there were found, besides the curved paths of negative electrons, also paths deviating in the opposite direction, which accordingly should be attributed to positively charged particles. These paths could as a rule be interpreted as being traces of heavy nuclear residues. On one of the photographs, however, Dr. Anderson found a path with positive deviation, to which this interpretation was not applicable. Owing to their greater weight the nuclei maintain their rectilinear path better than the light electron. The peculiarity is that the path found by Dr. Anderson showed the same deviation as the negative electrons, but in the opposite direction. The most plausible interpretation was to suppose that this was the path of a positive electron with the same mass as the negative one. Previously Dirac had found by theoretical investigation that the equations which determine the electromagnetic field require the existence of such light positively charged particles of the same size as the negative electrons. Since, however, no such particles had been found Dirac formulated the hypothesis that it might be that in other parts of the universe positive and negative charge were reversed. Dr. Anderson now pursued his investigations, introduced certain improvements of the equipment and after having carried out verifying experiments and new measurements he was able to furnish, in the summer of 1932, clear evidence of the existence of the positive electron. The positron Dirac had been searching for was thus found. Now the traces of ray paths appearing in the Wilson chamber could either be due to the cosmic radiation itself or to secondary rays in the chamber or the walls of the chamber caused by rays which, coming from outside, had collided with atoms which were thereby split up into their constituents. It was therefore not yet possible to come to the conclusion that the cosmic rays in part or entirely consisted of charged particles. Several scientists and among them also Dr. Anderson found that the gamma radiation from a radioactive substance containing thorium could release, by interaction, positive as well as negative electrons. The peculiar thing is that then there is often formed a twin pair of electrons consisting of one positive and one negative electron. In this case particles are thus created by the influence of pure radiation energy. It has likewise been found that a positive and a negative particle disappear when united, the only trace left being radiation passing away in every direction.

During these later years an intensive scientific research programme has been carried out concerning the nature and qualities of cosmic radiation. To this work Dr. Anderson has made important contributions. Thus it has been shown that the cosmic radiation consists to a large extent of corpuscles which with enormous energy and velocity enter the atmosphere from all parts of the universe. Positive and negative electrons exist in this radiation in about the same quantities, but the positive electrons soon disappear after having entered the atmosphere, because they coalesce with the atoms. Dr. Anderson has studied the distribution of energy in the cosmic radiation and the loss of energy sustained when it passes through matter.

Doctor Anderson.   In the course of your comprehensive studies on the nature and qualities of cosmic radiation you have made important and material contributions to the elucidation of the questions involved, and by uti-
lizing ingenious devices you have succeeded in finding one of the building-
stones of the universe, the positive electron. We congratulate you on this
great success attained in your young years and we wish to express the hope
that your further investigations will bring to science many new and equally
important results.

For your discovery of the positron the Royal Swedish Academy of
Sciences has awarded you the Nobel Prize in Physics, and I now request
you to receive the prize from the hands of His Majesty.

VICTOR F. HESS

Unsolved problems in physics: tasks for the immediate future in cosmic ray studies

Nobel Lecture, December 12, 1936

From a consideration of the immense volume of newly discovered facts in the field of physics, especially atomic physics, in recent years it might well appear to the layman that the main problems were already solved and that only more detailed work was necessary.

This is far from the truth, as will be shown by one of the biggest and most important newly opened fields of research, with which I am closely associated, that of cosmic rays.

When, in 1912, I was able to demonstrate by means of a series of balloon ascents, that the ionization in a hermetically sealed vessel was reduced with increasing height from the earth (reduction in the effect of radioactive substances in the earth), but that it noticeably increased from 1,000 m onwards, and at 5 km height reached several times the observed value at earth level, I concluded that this ionization might be attributed to the penetration of the earth's atmosphere from outer space by hitherto unknown radiation of exceptionally high penetrating capacity, which was still able to ionize the air at the earth's surface noticeably. Already at that time I sought to clarify the origin of this radiation, for which purpose I undertook a balloon ascent at the time of a nearly complete solar eclipse on the 12th April 1912, and took measurements at heights of two to three kilometres. As I was able to observe no reduction in ionization during the eclipse I decided that, essentially, the sun could not be the source of cosmic rays, at least as far as undeflected rays were concerned.

Many esteemed physicists in Europe and America have tried since then to solve the problems of the origin of cosmic rays. The fluctuations of intensity of the radiation already incidentally observed by me in 1912 have been thoroughly studied using apparatuses which have been constantly improved and perfected. An influence from specific sky zones which individual research workers (1923-1927) believed they had found, could not be confirmed later.

In the autumn of 1931 a small observatory for the continuous recording of the fluctuations in intensity of the cosmic rays was set up by me on a

2,300 m high mountain, the Hafelekar at Innsbruck in Austria. A great number of results are already available from there which will only be mentioned here briefly. The determination of a small, regular, daily fluctuation of radiation according to solar time (maximum at midday), which were attributed to atmospheric influences, particularly electrical and magnetic effects in the highest layers of the atmosphere. Further indications of a still smaller fluctuation according to stellar time, which would speak in favour of Prof. A. H. Compton's hypothesis published a year ago, according to which the cosmic rays come from milky-way systems external to, and far-distant from, our own. Further, evidence of simultaneous radiation fluctuations from day to day at two measuring devices spaced at 6 km from each other at heights of 600 and 2,300 m (fitted with ionization chambers, as well as with counting tubes).

On what can we now place our hopes of solving the many riddles which still exist as to the origin and composition of cosmic rays? It must be emphasized here above all that to attain really decisive progress greater funds must be made available. The further improvement of the method of sending up automatically recording instruments to heights above 25 km using pilot balloons, so successfully employed by Prof. Regener (Stuttgart), must be still further expanded and perfected. In conjunction, the many trial methods of automatic radiotelegraphic transmission of observation data as used in America for stratospheric flights will serve a useful purpose. It may well be said that the answer to the question: Of what do the cosmic rays in fact consist before they produce their familiar secondary radiation phenomena in the earth's atmosphere? can only be obtained from numerous measurements in the stratosphere. In conjunction with this, the study of the occurrence of the so-called showers and Hoffmann's bursts (release of enormous quantities of ions resulting from atomic disintegration processes) of cosmic rays at various heights will provide new knowledge about the effects of these rays.

In addition, the tracing of the occurrence of these « showers » in the depths of the earth, in mines and through the immersion of recording apparatus in water to some hundreds of metres depth will yield very important results.

In order to make further progress, particularly in the field of cosmic rays, it will be necessary to apply all our resources and apparatus simultaneously and side-by-side; an effort which has not yet been made, or at least, only to a limited extent. Simultaneous recording with superimposed ionization chambers and Wilson chambers, ionization chambers and sets of counting tubes, has not yet been carried out. The photographic method of observing the tracks of the particles of cosmic radiation, first succesfully tried out by Prof. Wilkins (Rochester, USA) merits great attention. The application of a strong magnetic field enables the measurement of the energy of the most pene-trating particles to be carried out, and the method may be capable of still further extension and improvement.

The investigation into the possible effects of cosmic rays on living organ-isms will also offer great interest.

The investigation of the tracks of cosmic rays in strong magnetic fields by means of the Wilson cloud chamber method has led to the discovery of the positron (positively charged electrons), that is, one of the hitherto unknown fundamental components of matter; this was carried out by Prof. Carl Anderson (Pasadena) who was in 1936 awarded the Nobel Prize for this work, at the same time as I myself received the award.

It is likely that further research into « showers » and « bursts » of the cosmic rays may possibly lead to the discovery of still more elementary particles, neutrinos and negative protons, of which the existence has been postulated by some theoretical physicists in recent years.

Biography

Victor Franz Hess was born on the 24th of June, 1883, in Waldstein Castle, near Peggau in Steiermark, Austria. His father, Vinzens Hess, was a forester in Prince Öttingen-Wallerstein's service and his mother was Serafine Edle von Grossbauer-Waldstätt.

He received his entire education in Graz: Gymnasium (1893–1901), and afterwards Graz University (1901–1905), where he took his doctor's degree in 1910.

He worked, for a short time, at the Physical Institute in Vienna, where Professor von Schweidler initiated him in recent discoveries in the field of radioactivity. During 1910–1920 he was Assistant under Stephan Meyer at the Institute of Radium Research of the Viennese Academy of Sciences. In 1919 he received the Lieben Prize for his discovery of the « ultra-radiation » (cosmic radiation), and the year after became Extraordinary Professor of Experimental Physics at the Graz University.

From 1921 to 1923, Hess was granted leave of absence, and worked in the United States, where he took a post as Director of the Research Laboratory (created by him) of the U.S. Radium Corporation, at Orange (New Jersey), and as Consulting Physicist for the U.S. Department of the Interior (Bureau of Mines), Washington D.C.

In 1923 he returned to Graz University and in 1925 he was appointed Ordinary Professor of Experimental Physics. In 1931 came his appointment as Professor at Innsbruck University and Director of the newly established Institute of Radiology. He founded the station at the Hafelekar mountain (2,300 m) near Innsbruck for observing and studying cosmic rays.

As well as the Nobel Prize for 1936, which he shared with C. D. Anderson, Hess has been awarded the Abbe Memorial Prize and the Abbe Medal of the Carl Zeiss Institute in Jena (1932); he was also Corresponding Member of the Academy of Sciences in Vienna.

Hess's work which gained him the Nobel Prize, was carried out during the years 1911–1913, and published in the Proceedings of the Viennese Academy of Sciences. In addition he has published some sixty papers and several books, of which the most important were: « Die Wärmeproduktion des Radiums» (The heat production of radium), 1912; «Konvektionserscheinungen in ionisierten Gasen-Ionenwind» (Convection phenomena in ionized gas-ionwinds), 1919–1920; «The measurement of gamma rays», 1916 (with R. W. Lawson); «The counting of alpha particles emitted from radium», 1918 (also with R. W. Lawson); *Elektrische Leitfähigkeit der Atmosphäre und ihre Ursachen* (book), 1926 (in English: *The Electrical Conductivity of the Atmosphere and Its Causes*, 1928); *Ionenbilanz der Atmosphäre* (The ionization balance of the atmosphere–book), 1933; *Luftelektrizität* (Electricity of the air–book, with H. Benndorf), 1928; «Lebensdauer der Ionen in der Atmosphäre» (Average life of the ions in the atmosphere), 1927–1928; «Schwankungen der Intensität in den kosmischen Strahlen» (Intensity fluctuations in cosmic rays), 1929–1936.

Hess has been American citizen since 1944, and is living in New York.

CARL D. ANDERSON

The production and properties of positrons

Nobel Lecture, December 12, 1936

Information of fundamental importance to the general problem of atomic structure has resulted from systematic studies of the cosmic radiation carried out by the Wilson cloud-chamber method.

After Skobelzyn in 1927 had first shown photographs of tracks of cosmic-ray particles, Professor R. A. Millikan and the writer in the spring of 1930 planned a cloud-chamber apparatus suitable for cosmic-ray studies, in particular to measure the energies of cosmic-ray particles by means of their curvatures in a strong magnetic field. The chamber, of dimensions 17 × 17 × 3 cm, was arranged with its long dimension vertical, and incorporated into a powerful electromagnet capable of maintaining a uniform magnetic field up to 24,000 gauss strength.

In the summer of 1931 the first results were obtained with this technique. The direct measurement of the energies of atomic particles was extended from about 15 million electron-volts, the highest energy measured before that time, to 5 billion electron-volts. In the spring of 1932 a preliminary paper on the energies of cosmic-ray particles was published in which energies over 1 billion electron-volts were reported. It was here shown that particles of positive charge occurred about as abundantly as did those of negative charge, and in many cases several positive and negative particles were found to be projected simultaneously from a single center. The presence of positively charged particles and the occurrence of « showers » of several particles showed clearly that the absorption of cosmic rays in material substances is due primarily to a nuclear phenomenon of a new type.

Measurements of the specific ionization of both the positive and negative particles, by counting the number of droplets per unit length along the tracks, showed the great majority of both the positive and negative particles to possess unit electric charge. The particles of negative charge were readily interpreted as electrons, and those of positive charge were at first tentatively interpreted as protons, at that time the only known particle of unit positive charge.

If the particles of positive charge were to be ascribed to protons then those of low energy and sharp curvature in the magnetic field, (e.g. a curvature greater than that corresponding to an electron having an energy of about 500 million electron-volts), should be expected to exhibit an appreciably greater ionization than the negatively charged electrons. In general, however, the positive particles seemed to differ in specific ionization only inappreciably from the negative ones. To avoid the assumption, which appeared very radical at that time, that the positive particles had electronic mass, serious consideration was given to the possibility that the particles which appeared to be positively charged and directed downward into the earth were in reality negatively charged electrons which through scattering had suffered a reversal of direction and were projected upwards away from the earth. Although such a reversal of direction through scattering might be expected to occur occasionally it seemed inadequate to account for the large number of particle tracks which showed a specific ionization anomalously small if they were to be ascribed to protons.

To differentiate with certainty between the particles of positive and negative charge it was necessary only to determine without ambiguity their direction of motion. To accomplish this purpose a plate of lead was inserted across a horizontal diameter of the chamber. The direction of motion of the particles could then be readily ascertained due to the lower energy and therefore the smaller radius of curvature of the particles in the magnetic field after they had traversed the plate and suffered a loss in energy.

Results were then obtained which could logically be interpreted only in terms of particles of a positive charge and a mass of the same order of magnitude as that normally possessed by the free negative electron. In particular one photograph (see Fig. 1) shows a particle of positive charge traversing a 6 mm plate of lead. If electronic mass is assigned to this particle its energy before it traverses the plate is 63 million electron-volts and after it emerges its energy is 23 million electron-volts. The possibility that this particle of positive charge could represent a proton is ruled out on the basis of range and curvature. A proton of the curvature shown after it emerges from the plate would have an energy of 200,000 electron-volts, and according to previously well-established experimental data would have a range of only 5 mm whereas the observed range was greater than 50 mm. The only possible conclusion seemed to be that this track, indeed, was the track of a positively charged electron. Examples similar to this and others in which two or more particles were found to be produced at one center gave additional evidence for the existence of particles of positive charge and mass,

Fig. 1. A 63 million electron-volt positron passing through a 6 mm lead plate and emerging with an energy of 23 million electron-volts. The length of this latter path is at least ten times greater than the possible length of a proton track of this curvature. (Magnetic field 15,000 gauss.) *In all the photographs the magnetic field is directed into the paper.*

small compared with that of the proton. These results formed the basis of the paper published in September 1932 announcing the existence of free positive electrons.

Measurements by the droplet counting method of the magnitude of the specific ionization of the positive and negative electrons which occur with energies low enough to be appreciably curved in the magnetic field have shown that the mass and charge of the positive electron cannot differ by more than 20 percent and 10 percent, respectively, from the mass and charge of the negative electron.

Blackett and Occhialini using an apparatus similar to ours but with the added advantage that through the use of control by Geiger-Müller tube counters their apparatus was made to respond automatically to the passage of a cosmic-ray particle, in the spring of 1933 confirmed the existence of positive electrons, or positrons, and obtained many beautiful photographs of complex electron showers.

That positrons could be produced by an agent other than cosmic rays was first shown by Chadwick, Blackett and Occhialini when they observed that positrons were produced by the radiation generated in the impact of alpha particles upon beryllium. The radiation produced in the beryllium is complex in character, consisting both of neutrons and gamma rays. In their experiment it was not possible to determine which of these rays was responsible for the production of positrons. Curie and Joliot by a similar experiment, in which they interposed blocks of lead and paraffin into the path of the rays from beryllium and measured the yield of positrons as a function of the thickness and material of the absorber concluded that the positrons arose more likely as a result of the gamma rays than of the neutrons.

Direct proof that the hard component of the gamma rays from ThC″ can give rise to positrons was first given by Neddermeyer and the writer, and independently by Curie and Joliot, and by Meitner and Philipp in the spring of 1933. In Figs. 2 and 3 positrons produced by gamma rays from ThC″ are shown.

In addition to the methods of producing positrons already mentioned, i.e. by absorption of cosmic-ray photons and electrons, and by the absorption of sufficiently high energy gamma rays from terrestrial sources, positrons have also been observed among the disintegration products of certain radioactive substances. The artificially produced radioactive elements first discovered by Curie and Joliot in 1934 are found to distintegrate either by the ejection of a positive or negative electron. Those elements whose atomic number is greater than that of the stable elements of the same mass number in general distintegrate by the ejection of a positron. Fig. 4 shows positrons resulting from the disintegration of $^{11}_{6}C$ prepared by bombarding a boron target with deuterons.

Theoretical interpretation

The present electron theory of Dirac provides a means of describing many of the phenomena governing the production and annihilation of positrons. Blackett and Occhialini first suggested that the appearance of pairs of positive and negative electrons could be understood in terms of this theory as the « creation » of a positive-negative electron pair in the neighborhood of an atomic nucleus. The energy corresponding to the proper mass of both of the particles, as well as to their kinetic energies, is, according to this view, sup-

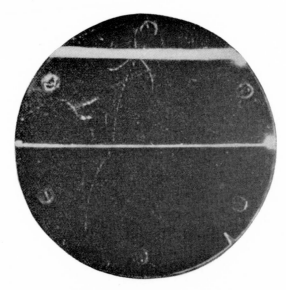

Fig. 2. A positron of 0.82 million electron-volts ejected from a lead plate by gamma rays from ThC″ passes through a 0.5 mm aluminium plate and emerges with an energy of 0.52 million electron-volts. (Magnetic field 430 gauss.)

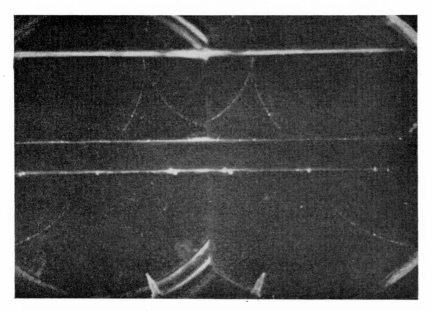

Fig. 3. A positive-negative electron pair produced in a lead plate by the gamma rays from ThC″. (Magnetic field 800 gauss.) *In this and the remaining photographs the direct image is at the left; the right-hand reversed image is taken for stereoscopic observation.*

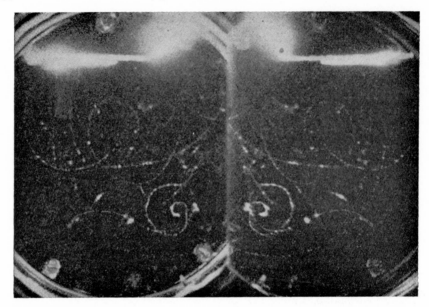

Fig. 4. Positrons produced in the distintegration of radioactive carbon of mass eleven units. (Magnetic field 780 gauss.) (The radioactive carbon was kindly supplied by Professor C.C. Lauritsen and his collaborators who prepared it by bombarding with deuterons a target containing boron.)

plied by the incident radiation. Since the energy corresponding to the proper mass of a pair of electrons is approximately one million electron-volts one should expect gamma rays of energy greater than this amount to produce positrons in their passage through matter, and further that the sum of the kinetic energies of the positive and negative electrons should be equal to the energy of the radiation producing them diminished by approximately one million electron-volts.

Experiments by Neddermeyer and the writer, and by Chadwick, Blackett and Occhialini, and others, have shown this relation to obtain in the production of positrons by ThC″ gamma rays, providing evidence for the correctness of this view of the origin of positive-negative electron pairs.

The theory of Dirac requires further that a positron, when it finds itself in a very ordinary environment, as, for example, in passing through common substances, will, on the average, have only a very short life, of the order of one billionth of a second or less. The positrons and negative electrons will mutually annihilate one another in pairs, and in their stead will appear a pair of photons, each of approximately one-half million electron-volts energy.

Although the lifetime of positrons has not been actually measured, it has been shown to be very short, and the radiation which results from their annihilation has been observed. The first to do this were Joliot and Thibaud. The annihilation radiation is of the proper intensity and the energy of its individual corpuscles is approximately the required amount of one-half million electron-volts, corresponding to the complete annihilation of the positrons.

Positrons of high energy

The experimental results on the production of positrons out of radiation have been shown to be in approximate agreement with the theory for those processes where the quantum energies are not too high. Gamma radiations of quantum energy extending up to some 15 million electron-volts arise in certain nuclear transformations produced in the laboratory. Measurements of the absorption of these radiations and of the numbers and distribution in energy of the positive and negative electrons produced by these radiations are in sufficiently good agreement with the calculations of Oppenheimer, Heitler, and Bethe based on the Dirac theory to provide evidence for the essential correctness of the theory of absorption of gamma radiations in the range of quantum energy up to some 15 million electron-volts.

In the broad range of energies, however, which lies above 15 million electron-volts and extends up to at least 20,000 million electron-volts, such as the energies with which the cosmic-ray particles are endowed, the experiments have only very recently provided strong evidence leading to a detailed understanding of the absorption of photons and electrons in this range of energies and to an explanation of the cosmic-ray showers.

Closely related to the process of the production of positive and negative electrons out of radiation, is the one which may be considered its inverse, namely, the production of radiation through nuclear impacts by a positive or negative electron in its passage through matter. Direct measurements on the energy loss of electrons, in the energy range up to about 400 million electron-volts, in their traversals through thin plates of lead, have shown that the loss in energy due to direct ionization by the electrons is but a small fraction of the total energy loss, and that the loss in energy over that due to ionization is in good accord with that to be expected theoretically through the production of radiation by nuclear impact. Furthermore a small number of measurements at energies up to 1,000 million electron-volts has shown no significant deviation from the theoretical loss. These data on energy loss of high-energy electrons afford strong evidence that, at least in part, the origin of the cosmic-ray showers of photons and positive and negative electrons can be understood in terms of a chain of successive processes of photon production by radiative impacts with nuclei on the part of the high-energy positive and negative electrons, and the subsequent absorption of these photons in nuclear collisions resulting in the production of numerous positive-negative electron pairs which appear as the cosmic-ray showers. After more detailed theoretical computations have been carried out on the rate of building-up of positive and negative electron secondaries resulting from these multiple processes, and their subsequent removal through absorption, will a more adequate test of the theory be possible. At present, however, it is very difficult to doubt that the highly absorbable component of the primary cosmic-ray beam consists largely of electrons absorbed principally through the mechanisms discussed above, which give rise to the electron showers.

Until quite recently it was not clear that the high-energy positive and negative electrons which have now been shown to exhibit a high absorbability, behaved in a manner essentially differently from the cosmic-ray particles of highly penetrating character. These highly penetrating particles, although not free positive and negative electrons, appear to consist of both positive and negative particles of unit electric charge, and will provide interesting material for future study.

Figs. 5–11 show examples of cosmic-ray showers of positive and negative electrons, and Fig. 12* an example of a large energy loss of a fast positive electron. Figs. 5, 6, 7, 8, and 11 were photographed at 4,300 meters above sea level, the remainder near sea level.

It is a pleasure to express my sincere gratitude to Professor Millikan and to Dr. Neddermeyer for the great part they have played in these investigations on the properties of positrons, and to the Carnegie Institution of Washington, whose funds administered to Professor Millikan have made the investigations possible.

---

* No reproduction of this figure was given in the original.

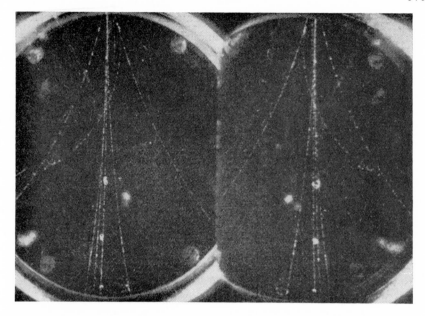

Fig. 5. A small cosmic-ray shower of positive and negative electrons. (Magnetic field 7,900 gauss.)

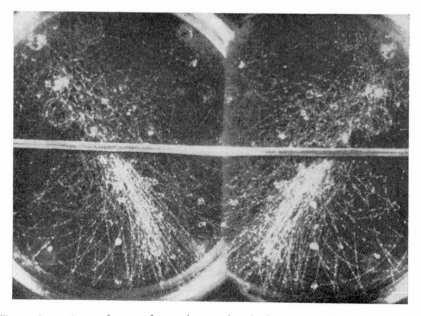

Fig. 6. A cosmic-ray shower of more than one hundred positive and negative electrons. (Magnetic field 7,900 gauss.)

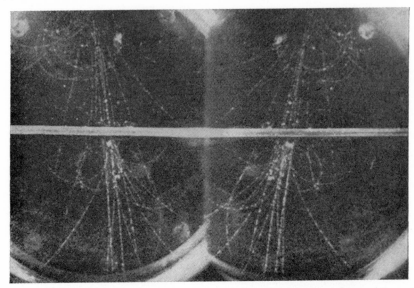

Fig. 7. A shower in which eight electrons (+ and −) strike the upper surface of a 0.35 cm lead plate, and more than fifteen emerge from its lower surface. This photograph is an example of the multiplication of shower tracks in a thin piece of absorbing material, due to the production by radiative impacts of photons and their absorption through pair-production (Magnetic field 7,900 gauss.)

Fig. 8. A positive-negative electron pair (energies of negative and positive 4.6 and 140 million electron-volts respectively) generated in the gas (argon) of the chamber by a photon associated with the cosmic rays. (Magnetic field 7,900 gauss.)

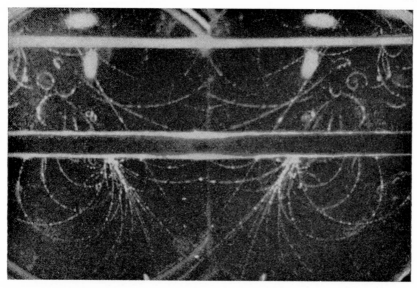

Fig. 9. A cosmic-ray shower of 22 positive and negative electrons produced by one or more photons initially incident on the upper surface of a 1 cm lead plate. (Magnetic field 17,000 gauss.)

Fig. 10. Three high-energy cosmic-ray electrons incident on the upper surface of a 1 cm platinum plate. A shower of more than 20 positive and negative electrons emerges from the lower surface of the plate from a region below two of the three incident electrons. The shower appears as a result of the production of photons by radiative impacts and their absorption by pair-production in the platinum plate. (Magnetic field 7,900 gauss.)

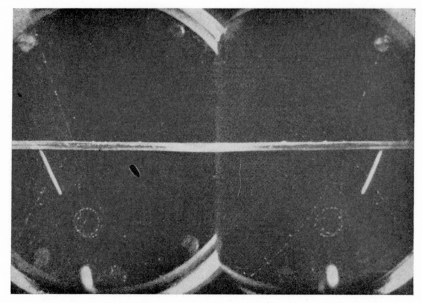

Fig. 11. A positron of 480 million electron-volts strikes a 0.35 cm lead plate. Below the plate three electrons appear having energies (in million electron-volts) respectively: positron 45, negatron 45, and positron 31. One of the tracks below the plate presumably represents the incident positron after passage through the plate, and the other two tracks a pair generated by the absorption of a photon generated in the plate. The energy lost in the plate by the incident positron is at least 435 million electron-volts and since the loss by ionization in a plate of this thickness should not be greater than 10 million electron-volts, the greater part of the energy lost by the positron in this instance must have appeared in the form of radiation. (Magnetic field 7,900 gauss.)

Biography

Carl David Anderson, who was born of Swedish parents –his father was Carl David Anderson and his mother Emma Adolfina Ajaxson– in New York City (USA) on 3rd September, 1905, has spent the bulk of his life in the United States. He graduated from the California Institute of Technology in 1927 with a B.Sc. degree in Physics and Engineering, and was awarded his Ph.D. degree by the same Institute, in 1930. For the period 1930–1933 he was Research Fellow there, subsequently (1933) Assistant Professor of Physics, and Professor of Physics (1939). During the war years (1941–1945) he was also active on projects for the National Defence Research Committee and the Office of Scientific Research and Development.

His early researches were in the field of X-rays. For his doctoral thesis he studied the space distribution of photoelectrons ejected from various gases by X-rays. In 1930, with Professor Millikan, he began his cosmic-ray studies which led in 1932 to the discovery of the positron. He has studied the energy distribution of cosmic-ray particles and the energy loss of very high speed electrons in traversing matter. In 1933 he and Dr. Neddermeyer obtained the first direct proof that gamma rays from ThC″ generate positrons in their passage through material substances. Since 1933 he has continued his work on radiation and fundamental particles. Most of Anderson's researches and discoveries have been published in *The Physical Review* and *Science*.

Among the scientific honours bestowed upon him, in addition to the Nobel Prize, may be mentioned the following: Gold Medal of the American Institute of City of New York (1935); Sc.D. of Colgate University (1937); Elliott Cresson Medal of the Franklin Institute (1937); Presidential Certificate of Merit (1945); LL.D. Temple University (1949); John Ericsson Medal of the American Society of Swedish Engineers (1960).

In 1946 Anderson married Lorraine Bergman; they have two sons, Marshall and David.

Physics 1937

CLINTON JOSEPH DAVISSON

GEORGE PAGET THOMSON

«for their experimental discovery of the diffraction of electrons by crystals»

Physics 1937

Presentation Speech by Professor H. Pleijel, Chairman of the Nobel Committee for Physics of the Royal Swedish Academy of Sciences

Your Majesty, Your Royal Highnesses, Ladies and Gentlemen.

The Nobel Prize for Physics for the year 1937 will today be delivered to Dr. C. J. Davisson and Professor G. P. Thomson for their discovery of the interference phenomena arising when crystals are exposed to electronic beams.

The study of the dispersion and diffraction phenomena produced by beams of electrons impinging on crystal surfaces was begun already in 1922 by Davisson and his collaborator Kunsman. These investigations soon obtained special actuality in connection with the theory of mechanical waves pronounced in 1923 by the Nobel Prize winner Prince de Broglie. According to this theory material particles are always linked with a system of travelling waves, a « wave-packet », forming the constituent parts of matter and determining its movements. We might get a popular picture of the relation between a material particle and the associated mechanical waves, if we assume space filled with wave systems travelling with somewhat different velocities. In general these waves neutralize one another, but at certain points it happens that a great number of waves are in such a position as to reinforce one another and form a marked wave crest. This wave crest then corresponds to a material particle. Since, however, the waves travel with different velocity they will part from one another, and the wave crest disappears to be found again at a nearby point. The material particle has moved. The wave crest will thus travel, but the velocity with which this is done is quite different from the one with which the underlying wave systems move. The material particle in general moves at right angles to the surfaces of the mechanical waves, just as a ray of light is, as a rule, directed at right angles to the surface planes of the light waves.

The theory of de Broglie derived from analogies between the laws ruling the movement of a material particle and those applying in the case of the passage of a ray of light.

A great number of phenomena observed in optics can neither be explained nor described by the aid of rays of light, and this holds true especially of the diffraction and dispersion phenomena produced when light passes through a narrow slit or by a sharp edge. To explain those phenomena it is necessary to have recourse to the hypothesis of the propagation of light by means of waves.

In recent times, the existence of diffraction and interference phenomena has settled a dispute regarding the nature of a certain radiation. This time the X-rays were concerned. The question was whether these rays consist of particles ejected with great velocity or of electromagnetic waves.

The mechanical grids utilized for studying interference phenomena in optics let through the X-rays without diffraction. This might be due to the wavelength of these rays being so short that the grids became too wide. The Nobel Prize winner von Laue then got the ingenious idea to use as grids, crystals, the regularly arranged atoms of which could serve as diffraction centres. It was also stated that the X-rays in those grids gave rise to diffraction and interference phenomena; the X-rays consequently consisted of waves.

The mechanical waves of de Broglie now correspond to the waves of light and the path of the material particle to the passage of the ray of light.

In his theory de Broglie found a simple relation between the velocity of the material particle and the wavelength of the « wave-packet » associated with this particle. The greater the velocity of the particle the shorter is the wavelength. If the velocity of the particle is known, it is then possible to calculate, by means of the formula indicated by de Broglie, the wavelength and *vice versa*.

The theory of de Broglie of mechanical waves and the development of wave mechanics have been of radical importance to modern atom theory.

It is therefore quite natural that this revolutionary theory should become the object of assiduous research as to its consequences and of efforts to prove experimentally the existence of mechanical waves.

As has already been mentioned, Davisson had, together with his collaborator Kunsman, in the year before the theory of de Broglie was presented, started a series of experiments on the diffraction phenomena produced when a beam of electrons impinges with a certain velocity on the surface of a crystal. These experiments which were continued during the following years, gave, however, at the beginning results rather strange and hard to explain, probably due to the great experimental difficulties connected with the apparatus arrangement. In 1928, however, the investigations met with such a success that Davisson and his collaborator Germer were able to present the incontestable evidence, reached by experiments, of the existence of mechanical waves and of the correctness of the theory of de Broglie. Four months later Professor Thomson, who had been studying the same problem independently of Davisson and by the aid of a different apparatus equipment for his experiments, also confirmed de Broglie's theory.

For their experiments Davisson and Germer availed themselves of a cubic nickel crystal. Here the atoms are symmetrically arranged in planes parallel to the end surfaces of the crystal, the atoms forming a quadratic network in the planes. However, as radiation surface was not used the end plane of the cube but the triangular plane obtained, if an angle of the cube is symmetrically cut off. The atoms in this plane form a triangular network.

A minute bundle of electrons of determined velocity were emitted perpendicularly upon this plane. If we assume the incoming electrons replaced by mechanical waves, the planes of which are thus parallel to the surface of the crystal, these mechanical waves will strike the atoms lying in the surface simultaneously, and these atoms as centres will, in their turn, emit new mechanical waves in all directions. The waves going out in a certain direction can be studied and measured by the aid of a so-called Faraday chamber placed in this direction. In this chamber the mechanical waves cause the same effect as the corresponding electrons. In order to describe better how the outgoing radiation arises, let us suppose the receiving device placed so as to capture the waves going out parallel to the crystal plane and at right angles to one of the sides of the triangle. Parallel to this side the atoms lie in parallel rows with a certain distance between the rows, this distance having been determined beforehand by the aid of X-ray investigations. Every row now emits its wave. But the waves from the inner rows arrive later, due to the longer way they have to pass to reach the edge of the triangle. As a rule an irregular system of waves is thus obtained in which the waves neutralize each other, and consequently no outgoing wave is produced. If on the other hand the mechanical waves should be of such a wavelength that the distance between the rows of atoms becomes equal to the wavelength or to a multiple thereof, all the outgoing waves will be in phase and reinforce one another. In this case a wave system going out in the direction indicated is obtained or, if preferable, a bundle of outgoing electronic beams.

The experiments now showed at what velocities of the incoming electrons outgoing beams are produced, and these have, according to what has been stated above, a wavelength equal to the distance between the rows of atoms. Since thus the wavelength of the mechanical waves had been found and since the velocity of the corresponding electron was known, it was possible to check the formula of de Broglie. Davisson found that the theory agreed with the experiments except for 1 to 2%. Davisson and Germer examined the reflection of the electronic beams in various directions and obtained results which agreed with the wave theory.

During his experiments Davisson used electron beams with rather a low velocity corresponding to the one obtained when an electron is made to pass a voltage between 50 and 600 volts.

Thomson, on the other hand, for his experiments availed himself of swift electrons with a velocity corresponding to voltages between 10,000 and 80,000 volts. These swift electrons have afterwards proved to be of great use in connection with studies on the structure of matter.

For his experiments Thomson made use of exceedingly thin films of celluloid, gold, platinum, or aluminium. He made the electron beam fall perpendicularly upon the film and examined the diffraction figures produced on a fluorescent screen placed behind the film, or else had them reproduced on a photographic plate. The thickness of the films used for the experiments amounted to between 1/10,000 and 1/100,000 of a millimetre. Such a film now consists of innumerable small crystals of various directions. In accordance with what the theory indicates, there is generally obtained on the screen a series of concentric rings corresponding to the various directions of the planes in a crystal where a regularly arranged network of atoms can be found. From the diametre of a ring, the wavelength of the mechanical wave can be determined, and to make possible the production of a ring this wavelength must be in accordance with the spacing of the planes in the system of planes to which the ring corresponds. A similar method has been applied previously by Debye-Scherrer for X-rays analysis of the structure of crystals. Thomson found very good agreement with the theory of de Broglie. He further found that a magnetic field influencing the beams having passed the film produced a lateral movement of the image on the screen, which shows that these beams consist of bundles of electrons.

For the above-mentioned experiments electrons have been employed as matter; later investigations have confirmed the correctness of de Broglie's theory also for such cases where beams of molecules, atoms, and atom nuclei have been used.

The purpose of the said experiments was to verify the theory of de Broglie, and to this end was utilized the knowledge of the arrangement of the atoms in a crystal, this knowledge having been previously acquired as a result of investigations by means of X-rays. Now that the law of de Broglie has become known and acknowledged, the opposite way has been taken. From the law of de Broglie we know the wavelength of the mechanical waves accompanying an electronic beam with a certain velocity of the electrons. By changing this velocity we can then obtain electronic waves with known wavelengths. By application of one or the other of the investigation methods mentioned above we can find the distances between the various atom planes within the crystal and thus also the structure of the crystal. The procedure is here the same as the one previously applied to determine the structure of crystals by means of X-rays. We have thus obtained a new method for such investigation, but the two methods have found very different fields of application due to the different nature of the beams employed. The X-rays are pure electromagnetic rays like the rays of light, and they therefore influence but slightly the atoms of the crystal, and owing to this circumstance easily traverse the crystal structure. From the same reason the diffracted rays are comparatively feeble, and many hours' exposure is therefore required to record X-ray diagrams. The mechanical waves, on the other hand, are associated with electrical charges which are very strongly influenced by the charges of the crystal atoms. The mechanical waves will therefore be rapidly absorbed in the crystal, and the interference figures obtained only come from an exceedingly thin surface layer. In return the intensity of the diffracted or reflected bundles of electrons becomes very great, and the time of exposure required is consequently extremely short, in many cases only a fraction of a second. These properties of the electronic beams make them an exceedingly important complement to the X-rays as far as researches on the structure of matter are concerned. At the important investigations of the structure of surfaces good results can be attained only by the new method, since the images of the X-rays are influenced by the matter lying behind the surface layer. By the aid of electronic beams it has thus been possible to explain how the structure of the surfaces of metals is changed by various mechanical, thermal, or chemical treatment. It has also been possible to ascertain the properties of thin layers of gases and powder. On account of the rapid exposure which the electronic beams permit, we can follow the course of the changes occurring in connection with the oxidization of metals and also observe the corrosion phenomenon in iron and steel for various thermal treatment as well as the chemical process ensuing when metals are attacked by corrosive substances. The intensity of radiation is so great that one can easily carry out investigations of the structure of crystals with a mass of less than a millionth of a gram. This has made it possible to discover in certain substances exceedingly minute crystalline structures, which it would not have been possible to find by means of X-ray investigations.

It would bring us too far here to enter upon the multitude of experimental results furnished by the method with electronic beams, especially as new fields of application of the electron beam are incessantly being opened up within the spheres of physical and chemical research.

Dr. Davisson.   When you found that electron beams touching crystals give rise to phenomena of diffraction and interference, this signified in itself a discovery that widened essentially our knowledge of the nature of electrons. But this discovery has proved to be of still greater importance. Your researches concerning these phenomena resulted in your presenting the first positive, experimental evidence of the wave nature of matter. The investigation methods that you and Professor Thomson have elaborated and the further research work carried out by both of you have provided science with a new, exceedingly important instrument for examining the structure of matter, an instrument constituting a very valuable complement to the earlier method which makes use of the X-ray radiation. The new investigations have already furnished manifold new, significant results within the fields of physics and chemistry and of the practical application of these sciences.

On behalf of the Royal Swedish Academy of Sciences I congratulate you on your important discoveries, and I now ask you to receive your Nobel Prize from the hands of His Majesty.

The Royal Swedish Academy of Sciences much regrets that Professor Thomson has not had the opportunity of being present on this occasion to receive in person his Nobel Prize. The prize will now instead be delivered to His Excellency the Minister of Great Britain.

Your Excellency.   Permit me to request you to receive on behalf of Professor Thomson the Nobel Prize for Physics from the hands of His Majesty.

CLINTON J. DAVISSON

The discovery of electron waves

Nobel Lecture, December 13, 1937

That streams of electrons possess the properties of beams of waves was discovered early in 1927 in a large industrial laboratory in the midst of a great city, and in a small university laboratory overlooking a cold and desolate sea. The coincidence seems the more striking when one remembers that facilities for making this discovery had been in constant use in laboratories throughout the world for more than a quarter of a century. And yet the coincidence was not, in fact, in any way remarkable. Discoveries in physics are made when the time for making them is ripe, and not before; the stage is set, the time is ripe, and the event occurs – more often than not at widely separated places at almost the same moment.

The setting of the stage for the discovery of electron diffraction was begun, one may say, by Galileo. But I do not propose to emulate the gentleman who began a history of his native village with the happenings in the Garden of Eden. I will take, as a convenient starting-point, the events which led to the final acceptance by physicists of the idea that light for certain purposes must be regarded as corpuscular. This idea after receiving its quietus at the hands of Thomas Young in 1800 returned to plague a complacent world of physics in the year 1899. In this year Max Planck put forward his conception that the energy of light is in some way quantized. A conception which, if accepted, supplied, as he showed, a means of explaining completely the distribution of energy in the spectrum of black-body radiation. The quantization was such that transfers of energy between radiation and matter occurred abruptly in amounts proportional to the radiation frequency. The factor of proportionality between these quantities is the ever-recurring Planck constant, h. Thus was reborn the idea that light is in some sense corpuscular.

How readily this circumstantial evidence for a corpuscular aspect of light would have been accepted as conclusive must remain a matter of conjecture, for already the first bits of direct evidence pointing to the same conclusion were being taken down from the scales and meters of the laboratory; the truth about light was being wrung from Nature – at times, and in this case, a most reluctant witness.

In an extended examination carried on chiefly by Richardson and K. T. Compton, Hughes, and Millikan, it was brought out that light imparts energy to individual electrons in amounts proportional to its frequency and finally that the factor of proportionality between energy and frequency is just that previously deduced by Planck from the black-body spectrum. The idea of pressing the witness on the latter point had come from Einstein who outplancked Planck in not only accepting quantization, but in conceiving of light quanta as actual small packets or particles of energy transferable to single electrons *in toto*.

The case for a corpuscular aspect of light, now exceedingly strong, became overwhelmingly so when in 1922 A. H. Compton showed that in certain circumstances light quanta – photons as they were now called – have elastic collisions with electrons in accordance with the simple laws of particle dynamics. What appeared, and what still appears to many of us as a contradiction in terms had been proved true beyond the least possible doubt – light was at once a flight of particles and a propagation of waves; for light persisted, unreasonably, to exhibit the phenomenon of interference.

Troubles, it is said, never come singly, and the trials of the physicist in the early years of this century give grounds for credence in the pessimistic saying. Not only had light, the perfect child of physics, been changed into a gnome with two heads – there was trouble also with electrons. In the open they behaved with admirable decorum, observing without protest all the rules of etiquette set down in Lorentz' manual, but in the privacy of the atom they indulged in strange and unnatural practices; they oscillated in ways which no well-behaved mechanical system would deem proper. What was to be said of particles which were ignorant apparently of even the rudiments of dynamics? Who could apologize for such perversity – rationalize the data of spectroscopy? A genius was called for, and a genius appeared. In 1913 Niels Bohr gave us his strange conception of «stationary» orbits in which electrons rotated endlessly without radiating, of electrons disappearing from one orbit and reappearing, after brief but unexplained absences, in another. It was a weird picture – a picture to delight a surrealist – but one which fascinated the beholder, for in it were portrayed with remarkable fidelity the most salient of the orderly features which spectroscopic data were then known to possess; there was the Balmer series! and there the Rydberg constant! – correct to the last significant digit! It was a masterpiece. It is important to note that in achieving this *tour de force* Bohr made judicious use of the constant which Planck had extracted from the black-body spectrum, the constant h.

It looked at this time – in the year 1913 – as if the authentic key to the spectra had at last been found, as if only time and patience would be needed to resolve their riddles completely. But this hope was never fulfilled. The first brilliant triumphs of the theory were followed by yet others, but soon the going became distressingly difficult, and finally, despite the untiring efforts of countless helpers, the attack came virtually to a standstill. The feeling grew that deeply as Bohr had dived he had not, so to speak, touched bottom. What was wanted, it was felt, was a new approach, a new theory of the atom which would embrace necessarily all the virtues of the Bohr theory and go beyond it – a theory which would contain some vaguely sensed unifying principle which, it was felt, the Bohr theory lacked.

Such an underlying principle had been sought for almost from the first. By 1924 one or two ideas of promise had been put forward and were being assiduously developed. Then appeared the brilliant idea which was destined to grow into that marvelous synthesis, the present-day quantum mechanics. Louis de Broglie put forward in his doctor's thesis the idea that even as light, so matter has a duality of aspects; that matter like light possesses both the properties of waves and the properties of particles. The various « restrictions » of the Bohr theory were viewed as conditions for the formation of standing electron wave patterns within the atom.

Reasoning by analogy from the situation in optics and aided by the clue that Planck's constant is a necessary ingredient of the Bohr's theory, de Broglie assumed that this constant would connect also the particle and wave aspects of electrons, if the latter really existed. De Broglie assumed that, as with light, the correlation of the particle and wave properties of matter would be expressed by the relations:

(Energy of particle)$E = h\nu$(frequency, i.e. waves/unit time)
(Momentum of particle)$p = h\sigma$(wave number, i.e. waves/unit distance)

The latter may be written in the more familiar form $\lambda = h/p$, where λ represents wavelength.

Perhaps no idea in physics has received so rapid or so intensive development as this one. De Broglie himself was in the van of this development but the chief contributions were made by the older and more experienced Schrödinger.

In these early days – eleven or twelve years ago – attention was focussed on electron waves in atoms. The wave mechanics had sprung from the atom, so to speak, and it was natural that the first applications should be to the atom. No thought was given at this time, it appears, to electrons in free flight. It was implicit in the theory that beams of electrons like beams of light would exhibit the properties of waves, that scattered by an appropriate grating they would exhibit diffraction, yet none of the chief theorists mentioned this interesting corollary. The first to draw attention to it was Elsasser, who pointed out in 1925 that a demonstration of diffraction would establish the physical existence of electron waves. The setting of the stage for the discovery of electron diffraction was now complete.

It would be pleasant to tell you that no sooner had Elsasser's suggestion appeared than the experiments were begun in New York which resulted in a demonstration of electron diffraction – pleasanter still to say that the work was begun the day after copies of de Broglie's thesis reached America. The true story contains less of perspicacity and more of chance. The work actually began in 1919 with the accidental discovery that the energy spectrum of secondary electron emission has, as its upper limit, the energy of the primary electrons, even for primaries accelerated through hundreds of volts; that there is, in fact, an elastic scattering of electrons by metals.

Out of this grew an investigation of the distribution-in-angle of these elastically scattered electrons. And then chance again intervened; it was discovered, purely by accident, that the intensity of elastic scattering varies with the orientations of the scattering crystals. Out of this grew, quite naturally, an investigation of elastic scattering by a single crystal of predetermined orientation. The initiation of this phase of the work occurred in 1925, the year following the publication of de Broglie's thesis, the year preceding the first great developments in the wave mechanics. Thus the New York experiment was not, at its inception, a test of the wave theory. Only in the summer of 1926, after I had discussed the investigation in England with Richardson, Born, Franck and others, did it take on this character.

The search for diffraction beams was begun in the autumn of 1926, but not until early in the following year were any found – first one and then twenty others in rapid succession. Nineteen of these could be used to check the relationship between wavelength and momentum and in every case the correctness of the de Broglie formula, $\lambda = h/p$ was verified to within the limit of accuracy of the measurements.

I will recall briefly the scheme of the experiment. A beam of electrons of predetermined speed was directed against a (111) face of a crystal of nickel as indicated schematically in Fig. 1. A collector designed to accept only elastically scattered electrons and their near neighbors, could be moved on an arc about the crystal. The crystal itself could be revolved about the axis of the incident beam. It was possible thus to measure the intensity of elastic scattering in any direction in front of the crystal face with the exception of those directions lying within 10 or 15 degrees of the primary beam.

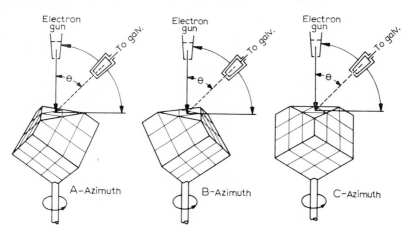

Fig. 1. Schematic diagram showing disposition of primary beam, nickel crystal, and collector. Crystal shown revolved to bring one principal azimuth after another into plane of observation.

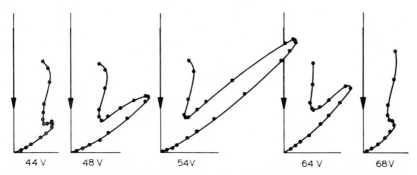

Fig. 2. Polar diagram showing intensity of elastic scattering in A-azimuth (Fig. 1) as function of latitude angle, for series of primary-beam voltages.

The curves reproduced in Fig. 2 show the distribution-in-angle of intensity for a particular azimuth of the crystal. The curves are for a series of electron speeds, therefore, for a series of electron wavelengths. For a particular wavelength a diffraction beam shines out. Setting the collector on this beam at its brightest, and revolving the crystal, the intensity was found to vary in azimuth as illustrated in Fig. 3. The high peak on the left represents the cross-section-in-azimuth of the beam shown in Fig. 2. Two similar peaks mark the positions of companion beams which with the first form a set of three, as required by the threefold symmetry of the crystal about its (111) directions – the direction of the incident beam. The lesser intermediate peaks are due to a different set of beams which is not here fully developed.

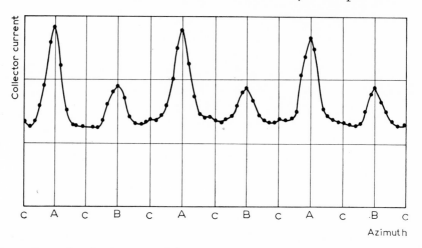

Fig. 3. Curve showing intensity of elastic scattering of 54-volt primary beam as function of azimuth for latitude of peak in 54-volt curve of Fig. 2.

The de Broglie relation was tested by computing wavelengths from the angles of the diffraction beams and the known constant of the crystal, and comparing these with corresponding wavelengths computed from the formula $\lambda = h/p$, where p, the momentum of the electrons, was obtained from the potential used to accelerate the beam and the known value of e/m for electrons. If wavelengths computed from the formula agreed with those obtained from the diffraction data, the de Broglie relation would be verified. How nearly the theoretical values agreed with the experimental is illustrated in Fig. 4. For perfect agreement all points would fall on the line drawn through the origin.

You will realize without my telling you that this series of experiments extending in time over a period of eight or nine years and requiring the construction and manipulation of intricate apparatus was not made by me alone. From first to last a considerable number of my colleagues contributed to the investigation. Chief among these were my two exceptionally able collaborators, Dr. C. H. Kunsman and Dr. L. H. Germer. Dr. Kunsman worked with me throughout the early stages of the investigation, and Dr. Germer,

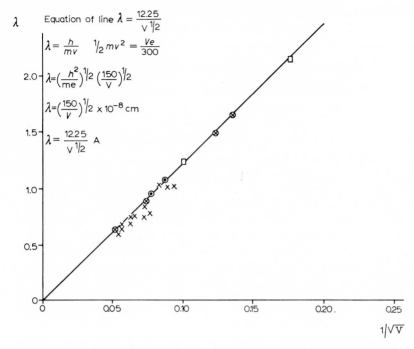

Fig. 4. Test of the de Broglie formula $\lambda = h/p = h/mv$. Wavelength computed from diffraction data plotted against $1/V^{\frac{1}{2}}$, (V, primary-beam voltage). For precise verification of the formula all points should fall on the line $\lambda = 12.25/V^{\frac{1}{2}}$ plotted in the diagram. ($\times$ From observations with diffraction apparatus; $\circ$ same, particularly reliable; $\square$ same, grazing beams. $\otimes$ From observations with reflection apparatus.)

to whose skill and perseverance a great part of the success of the definitive experiments is due, succeeded Dr. Kunsman in 1924.

I would like also at this time to express my admiration of the late Dr. H. D. Arnold, then Director of Research in the Bell Telephone Laboratories, and of Dr. W. Wilson, my immediate superior, who were sufficiently far-sighted to see in these researches a contribution to the science of communication. Their vision was in fact accurate, for today in our, as in other industrial laboratories, electron diffraction is applied with great power and efficacy for discerning the structures of materials.

But neither of this nor of the many beautiful and important researches which have been made in electron diffraction in laboratories in all parts of the world since 1927 will I speak today. I will take time only to express my admiration of the beautiful experiments – differing from ours in every respect – by which Thomson in far-away Aberdeen also demonstrated electron diffraction and verified de Broglie's formula at the same time as we in New York. And to mention, as closely related to the subject of this discourse, the difficult and beautifully executed experiments by which Stern and Estermann in 1929 showed that atomichy drogen also is diffracted in accordance with the de Broglie-Schrödinger theory.

Important and timely as was the discovery of electron diffraction in inspiring confidence in the physical reality of material waves, our confidence in this regard would hardly be less today, one imagines, were diffraction yet to be discovered, so great has been the success of the mechanics built upon the conception of such waves in clarifying the phenomena of atomic and subatomic physics.

Biography

Clinton Joseph Davisson was born at Bloomington, Illinois, U.S.A., October 22, 1881, son of Joseph Davisson, an artisan, native of Ohio, descendant of early Dutch and French settlers of Virginia, Union veteran of the American Civil War, and Mary Calvert, a school-teacher, native of Pennsylvania, of English and Scotch parentage.

He attended the Bloomington public schools, and on graduation from High School in 1902 was granted a scholarschip by the University of Chicago for proficiency in mathematics and physics. In September of that year he entered the University of Chicago and came at once under the influence of Professor R. A. Millikan. Unable for financial reasons to continue at Chicago the following year he found employment with a telephone company in his home town. In January 1904 he was appointed assistant in physics at Purdue University on recommendation of Professor Millikan. He returned to Chicago in June 1904 and remained in residence at the University until August 1905. In September 1905, again on the recommendation of Professor Millikan, he was appointed part-time instructor in physics at Princeton University. This post he held until 1910, studying, as his duties permitted, under Professor Francis Magie, Professor E. P. Adams, Professor (later Sir) James Jeans and particularly under Professor O. W. Richardson. During a part of this period Davisson returned to the University of Chicago for the summer sessions and in August 1908 received a B.S. degree from that institution.

He was awarded a Fellowship in Physics at Princeton for the year 1910–1911 and during that year completed requirements for the degree of Ph.D. which he received June 1911. His thesis, under Professor Richardson, was *On The Thermal Emission of Positive Ions From Alkaline Earth Salts.*

From September 1911 until June 1917 he was an instructor in the Department of Physics at the Carnegie Institute of Technology, Pittsburgh, Pa. During the summer of 1913 he worked in the Cavendish Laboratory under Professor (later Sir) J. J. Thomson.

In April 1917 he was refused enlistment in the United States Army. In

June of the same year he accepted war-time employment in the Engineering Department of the Western Electric Company (later Bell Telephone Laboratories), New York City – at first for summer, then, on leave of absence from Carnegie Tech., for the duration of the World War. At the end of the war he resigned an assistant professorship to which he had been appointed at Carnegie Tech. to continue as a Member of the Technical Staff of the Telephone Laboratories.

The series of investigations which led to the discovery of electron diffraction in 1927 was begun in 1919 and was continued into 1929 with the collaboration first of Dr. C. H. Kunsman, and from 1924 on, of Dr. L. H. Germer. During the same period researches were carried on in thermal radiation with the collaboration of Mr. J. R. Weeks, and in thermionics with Dr. H. A. Pidgeon and Dr. Germer.

From 1930–1937 Dr. Davisson devoted himself to the study of the theory of electron optics and to applications of this theory to engineering problems. He then investigated the scattering and reflection of very slow electrons by metals. During World War II he worked on the theory of electronic devices and on a variety of crystal physics problems.

In 1946 he retired from Bell Telephone Laboratories after 29 years of service. From 1947 to 1949, he was Visiting Professor of Physics at the University of Virginia, Charlottesville, Va.

In 1928 he was awarded the Comstock Prize by the National Academy of Sciences, in 1931 the Elliott Cresson Medal by the Franklin Institute, and in 1935 the Hughes Medal by the Royal Society (London), and in 1941 the Alumni Medal by the University of Chicago. He held honorary doctorates from Purdue University, Princeton University, the University of Lyon and Colby College.

In 1911 he married Charlotte Sara Richardson, a sister of Professor Richardson. He died in Charlottesville on February 1, 1958, at the age of 76, and was survived by his wife, three sons and one daughter.

GEORGE P. THOMSON

Electronic waves

Nobel Lecture, June 7, 1938

Ever since last November, I have been wanting to express in person my gratitude to the generosity of Alfred Nobel, to whom I owe it that I am privileged to be here today, especially since illness prevented me from doing so at the proper time. The idealism which permeated his character led him to make his magnificent foundation for the benefit of a class of men with whose aims and viewpoint his own scientific instincts and ability had made him naturally sympathetic, but he was certainly at least as much concerned with helping science as a whole, as individual scientists. That his foundation has been as successful in the first as in the second, is due to the manner in which his wishes have been carried out. The Swedish people, under the leadership of the Royal Family, and through the medium of the Royal Academy of Sciences, have made the Nobel Prizes one of the chief causes of the growth of the prestige of science in the eyes of the world, which is a feature of our time. As a recipient of Nobel's generosity I owe sincerest thanks to them as well as to him.

The goddess of learning is fabled to have sprung full-grown from the brain of Zeus, but it is seldom that a scientific conception is born in its final form, or owns a single parent. More often it is the product of a series of minds, each in turn modifying the ideas of those that came before, and providing material for those that come after. The electron is no exception.

Although Faraday does not seem to have realized it, his work on electrolysis, by showing the unitary character of the charges on atoms in solution, was the first step. Clerk Maxwell in 1873 used the phrase a «molecule of electricity» and von Helmholtz in 1881 speaking of Faraday's work said «If we accept the hypothesis that elementary substances are composed of atoms, we cannot well avoid concluding that electricity also is divided into elementary portions which behave like atoms of electricity.» The hypothetical atom received a name in the same year when Johnstone Stoney of Dublin christened it «electron», but so far the only property implied was an electron charge.

The last year of the nineteenth century saw the electron take a leading place amongst the conceptions of physics. It acquired not only mass but universality, it was not only electricity but an essential part of all matter. If among the many names associated with this advance I mention that of J. J. Thomson I hope you will forgive a natural pride. It is to the great work of Bohr that we owe the demonstration of the connection between electrons and Planck's quantum which gave the electron a dynamics of its own. A few years later, Goudsmit and Uhlenbeck, following on an earlier suggestion by A. H. Compton showed that it was necessary to suppose that the electron had spin. Yet even with the properties of charge, mass, spin and a special mechanics to help it, the electron was unable to carry the burden of explaining the large and detailed mass of experimental data which had accumulated. L. de Broglie, working originally on a theory of radiation, produced as a kind of by-product the conception that any particle and in particular an electron, was associated with a system of waves. It is with these waves, formulated more precisely by Schrödinger, and modified by Dirac to cover the idea of spin, that the rest of my lecture will deal.

The first published experiments to confirm de Broglie's theory were those of Davisson and Germer, but perhaps you will allow me to describe instead those to which my pupils and I were led by de Broglie's epoch-making conception.

A narrow beam of cathode rays was transmitted through a thin film of matter. In the earliest experiment of the late Mr. Reid this film was of celluloid, in my own experiment of metal. In both, the thickness was of the order of 10^{-6} cm. The scattered beam was received on a photographic plate normal to the beam, and when developed showed a pattern of rings, recalling optical halos and the Debye-Scherrer rings well known in the corresponding experiment with X-rays. An interference phenomenon is at once suggested. This would occur if each atom of the film scattered in phase a wavelet from an advancing wave associated with the electrons forming the cathode rays. Since the atoms in each small crystal of the metal are regularly spaced, the phases of the wavelets scattered in any fixed direction will have a definite relationship to one another. In some directions they will agree in phase and build up a strong scattered wave, in others they will destroy one another by interference. The strong waves are analogous to the beams of light diffracted by an optical grating. At the time, the arrangement of the atoms in celluloid was not known with certainty and only general conclusions could be drawn, but for the metals it had been determined previously by the use of X-rays. According to de Broglie's theory the wavelength associated with an electron is h/mv which for the electrons used (cathode rays of 20 to 60,000 volts energy) comes out from 8×10^{-9} to 5×10^{-9} cm. I do not wish to trouble you with detailed figures and it will be enough to say that the patterns on the photographic plates agreed quantitatively, in all cases, with the distribution of strong scattered waves calculated by the method I have indicated. The agreement is good to the accuracy of the experiments which was about 1%. There is no adjustable constant, and the patterns reproduce not merely the general features of the X-ray patterns but details due to special arrangements of the crystals in the films which were known to occur from previous investigation by X-rays. Later work has amply confirmed this conclusion, and many thousands of photographs have been taken in my own and other laboratories without any disagreement with the theory being found. The accuracy has increased with the improvement of the apparatus, perhaps the most accurate work being that of v. Friesen of Uppsala who has used the method in a precision determination of e in which he reaches an accuracy of 1 in 1,000.

Before discussing the theoretical implications of these results there are two modifications of the experiments which should be mentioned. In the one, the electrons after passing through the film are subject to a uniform magnetic field which deflects them. It is found that the electrons whose impact on the plate forms the ring pattern are deflected equally with those which have passed through holes in the film. Thus the pattern is due to electrons which have preserved unchanged the property of being deflected by a magnet. This distinguishes the effect from anything produced by X-rays and shows that it is a true property of electrons. The other point is a practical one, to avoid the need for preparing the very thin films which are needed to transmit the electrons, an apparatus has been devised to work by reflection, the electrons striking the diffracting surface at a small glancing angle. It appears that in many cases the patterns so obtained are really due to electrons transmitted through small projections on the surface. In other cases, for example when the cleavage surface of a crystal is used, true reflection occurs from the Bragg planes.

The theory of de Broglie in the form given to it by Schrödinger is now known as wave mechanics and is the basis of atomic physics. It has been applied to a great variety of phenomena with success, but owing largely to mathematical difficulties there are not many cases in which an accurate comparison is possible between theory and experiment. The diffraction of fast electrons by crystals is by far the severest numerical test which has been made and it is therefore important to see just what conclusions the excellent agreement between theory and these experiments permits us to draw.

The calculations so far are identical with those in the corresponding case of the diffraction of X-rays. The only assumption made in determining the directions of the diffracted beams is that we have to deal with a train of wave of considerable depth and with a plane wave-front extending over a considerable number of atoms. The minimum extension of the wave system sideways and frontways can be found from the sharpness of the lines. Taking v. Friesen's figures, it is at least 225 waves from back to front over a front of more than 200 Å each way.

But the real trouble comes when we consider the physical meaning of the waves. In fact, as we have seen, the electrons blacken the photographic plate at those places where the waves would be strong. Following Bohr, Born, and Schrödinger, we can express this by saying that the intensity of the waves at any place measures the *probability* of an electron manifesting itself there. This view is strengthened by measurements of the relative intensities of the rings, which agree well with calculations by Mott based on Schrödinger's equation. Such a view, however successful as a formal statement is at variance with all ordinary ideas. Why should a particle appear only in certain places associated with a set of waves? Why should waves produce effects only through the medium of particles? For it must be emphasized that in these experiments each electron only sensitizes the photographic plate in one minute region, but in that region it has the same powers of penetration and photographic action as if it had never been diffracted. We cannot suppose that the energy is distributed throughout the waves as in a sound or water wave, the wave is only effective in the one place where the electron appears. The rest of it is a kind of phantom. Once the particle has appeared the wave disappears like a dream when the sleeper wakes. Yet the motion of the electron, unlike that of a Newtonian particle, is influenced by what happens over the whole front of the wave, as is shown by the effect of the size of the crystals on the sharpness of the patterns. The difference in point of view is fundamental, and we have to face a break with ordinary mechanical ideas. Particles have not a unique track, the energy in these waves is not continuously distributed, probability not determinism governs nature.

But while emphasizing this fundamental change in outlook, which I believe to represent an advance in physical conceptions, I should like to point out several ways in which the new phenomena fit the old framework better than is often realized. Take the case of the influence of the size of the crystals on the sharpness of the diffracted beams, which we have just mentioned. On the wave theory it is simply an example of the fact that a diffraction grating with only a few lines has a poor resolving power. Double the number of the lines and the sharpness of the diffracted beams is doubled also. However if there are already many lines, the *angular* change is small. But imagine a particle acted on by the material which forms the slits of the grating, and suppose the forces such as to deflect it into one of the diffracted beams. The forces due to the material round the slits near the one through which it passes will be the most important, an increase in the number of slits will affect the motion but the angular deflection due to adding successive slits will diminish as the numbers increase. The law is of a similar character, though no simple law of force would reproduce the wave effect quantitatively.

Similarly for the length of the wave train. If this were limited by a shutter moving so quickly as to let only a short wave train pass through, the wave theory would require that the velocity of the particle would be uncertain over a range increasing with the shortness of the wave train, and corresponding to the range of wavelengths shown by a Fourier analysis of the train. But the motion of the shutter might well be expected to alter the velocity of a particle passing through, just before it closed.

Again, on the new view it is purely a matter of chance in which of the diffracted beams of different orders an electron appears. If the phenomenon were expressed as the classical motion of a particle, this would have to depend on the initial motion of the particle, and there is no possibility of determining this initial motion without disturbing it hopelessly. There seems no reason why those who prefer it should not regard the diffraction of electrons as the motion of particles governed by laws which simulate the character of waves, but besides the rather artificial character of the law of motion, one has to ascribe importance to the detailed initial conditions of the motion which, as far as our present knowledge goes, are necessarily incapable of being determined. I am predisposed by nature in favour of the most mechanical explanations possible, but I feel that this view is rather clumsy and that it might be best, as it is certainly safer, to keep strictly to the facts and regard the wave equation as merely a way of predicting the result of experiments. Nevertheless, the view I have sketched is often a help in thinking of these problems. We are curiously near the position which Newton took over his theory of optics, long despised but now seen to be far nearer the truth than that of his rivals and successors.

« Those that are averse from assenting to any new Discoveries, but such as they can explain by an Hypothesis, may for the present suppose, that as Stones by falling upon water put the Water into an undulating Motion, and all Bodies by percussion excite vibrations in the Air: so the Rays of Light, by impinging on any refracting or reflecting Surface, excite vibrations in the refracting or reflecting Medium or Substance, much after the manner that vibrations are propagated in the Air for causing Sound, and move faster than the Rays so as to overtake them; and that when any Ray is in that part of the vibration which conspires with its Motion, it easily breaks through a re- fracting Surface, but when it is in the contrary part of the vibration which impedes its Motion, it is easily reflected; and, by consequence, that every Ray is successively disposed to be easily reflected, or easily transmitted, by every vibration which overtakes it. But whether this Hypothesis be true or false I do not here consider.»

Although the experiments in diffraction confirm so beautifully the de Broglie-Schrödinger wave theory, the position is less satisfactory as regards the extended theory due to Dirac. On this theory the electron possesses magnetic properties and the wave requires four quantities instead of one for its specification. This satisfies those needs of spectroscopy which led to the invention of the spinning electron. It suggests however that electronic waves could be polarized and that the polarized waves might interact with matter in an anisotropic manner. In fact detailed calculations by Mott indicate that if Dirac electrons of 140 kV energy are scattered twice through 90° by the nuclei of gold atoms the intensity of the scattered beam will differ by 16% according to whether the two scatterings are in the same or in opposite direc- tions. Experiments by Dymond and by myself have established independent- ly that no effect of this order of magnitude exists, when the scattering is done by gold foils. While there is a slight possibility that the circumnuclear elec- trons, or the organization of the atoms into crystals might effect the result, it seems very unlikely. Some of the theorists have arrived at results con- flicting with Mott, but I understand that their work has been found to con- tain errors. At present there seems no explanation of this discrepancy which throws doubt on the validity of the Dirac equations in spite of their success in predicting the positive electron.

I should be sorry to leave you with the impression that electron diffraction was of interest only to those concerned with the fundamentals of physics. It has important practical applications to the study of surface effects. You know how X-ray diffraction has made it possible to determine the arrangement of the atoms in a great variety of solids and even liquids. X-rays are very penetrating, and any structure peculiar to the surface of a body will be likely to be overlooked, for its effect is swamped in that of the much greater mass of underlying material. Electrons only affect layers of a few atoms, or at most tens of atoms, in thickness, and so are eminently suited for the purpose. The position of the beams diffracted from a surface enables us, at least in many cases, to determine the arrangement of the atoms in the surface. Among the many cases which have already been studied I have only time to refer to one, the state of the surface of polished metals. Many years ago Sir George Beilby suggested that this resembled a supercooled liquid which had flowed under the stress of polishing. A series of experiments by electron diffraction carried out at the Imperial College in London has confirmed this conclusion. The most recent work due to Dr. Cochrane has shown that though this amorphous layer is stable at ordinary temperature as long as it remains fixed to the mass of the metal, it is unstable when removed, and recrystalizes after a few hours. Work by Professor Finch on these lines has led to valuable conclusions as to the wear on the surfaces of cylinders and pistons in petrol engines.

It is in keeping with the universal character of physical science that this single small branch of it should touch on the one hand on the fundamentals of scientific philosophy and on the other, questions of everyday life.

Biography

George Paget Thomson was born in 1892 at Cambridge, the son of the late Sir J. J. Thomson (then Professor of Physics at Cambridge University), a Nobel Prize winner who, more than anyone else, was responsible for the discovery of the electron, and Rose Elisabeth Paget, daughter of the late Sir George Paget, Regius Professor of Medicine at Cambridge.

George Thomson went to school in Cambridge, and then up to the University. As an undergraduate at Trinity College he took mathematics followed by physics, and had done a year's research under his father when the 1914–1918 war broke out.

He joined the Queen's Regiment of Infantry as a Subaltern and served for a short time in France, but returned to work on the stability of aeroplanes and other aerodynamical problems at Farnborough, and continued to work on this kind of problem at various establishments throughout the war, apart from eight months in the United States attached to the British War Mission.

After the war he spent three years as Fellow and Lecturer at Corpus Christi College, Cambridge, and continued his research on physics. He was then appointed Professor of Natural Philosophy (as physics is called in Scotland) at the University of Aberdeen, a post he held for eight years. At Aberdeen he carried out experiments on the behaviour of electrons going through very thin films of metals, which showed that electrons behave as waves in spite of being particles. For this work he later shared the Nobel Prize in Physics with C. J. Davisson of the Bell Telephone Laboratories, who had arrived at the same conclusions by a different kind of experiment. The process of electron diffraction which these experiments established to be possible has been widely used in the investigation of the surfaces of solids.

In the winter of 1929–1930 Thomson visited Cornell University, Ithaca, N.Y. as a « non-resident» lecturer. In 1930 he was appointed Professor at Imperial College in the University of London; he held this post until 1952, when he became Master of Corpus Christi College, Cambridge, retiring from the latter in 1962.

During his time at Imperial College he became interested in nuclear physics, and when the fission of uranium by neutron was discovered at the beginning of 1939 he was struck by its military and other possibilities, and persuaded the British Air Ministry to procure a ton of uranium oxide for experiments. These experiments were incomplete at the outbreak of war, when Thomson went back to the Royal Aircraft Establishment to work on a series of war problems, including magnetic mines. A year later he was made Chairman of the British Committee set up to investigate the possibilities of atomic bombs. This committee reported in 1941 that a bomb was possible, and Thomson was authorized to give this report to the American scientists Vannevar Bush and James Conant.

He spent the next year as Scientific Liaison Officer at Ottawa, and for part of this time was in close touch with the American atomic bomb effort. On returning to England he was appointed Vice-Chairman of the Radio Board and later became Scientific Adviser to the Air Ministry.

After the war he returned to work at Imperial College, and early in 1946 became interested in the possibilities of nuclear power from deuterium (heavy hydrogen). Some experiments bearing on this were started at Imperial College under Dr. Ware, but Thomson's work was theoretical. Later, because of the requirements of secrecy, this work was transferred to the Associated Electrical Industry's Research Laboratories at Aldermaston, where Thomson continued to act as Consultant.

Sir George Thomson is a Fellow of the Royal Society, and has received the Royal Medal and the Hughes Medal of that Society. He is a Doctor of Science at Cambridge, Hon. D.Sc. (Lisbon), Hon. LL.D. (Aberdeen), Hon. Sc. D. (Dublin), Sheffield, University of Wales and Reading. He has written a book on aerodynamics and other scientific works. His published works also include a popular book on *The Atom* and *The Foreseeable Future*, published in 1955, and *The Inspiration of Science*, published in 1962. He is a Foreign Member of the American Academy of Arts and Sciences and of the Lisbon Academy, and a Corresponding Member of the Austrian Academy.

In 1924 he married Kathleen Buchanan, daughter of the Very Rev. Sir George Adam Smith. They have two sons and two daughters. Ship models form part of his recreations.

Physics 1938

ENRICO FERMI

«for his demonstrations of the existence of new radioactive elements produced by neutron irradiation, and for his related discovery of nuclear reactions brought about by slow neutrons»

Physics 1938

Presentation Speech by Professor H. Pleijel, Chairman of the Nobel Committee for Physics of the Royal Swedish Academy of Sciences

Your Majesty, Your Royal Highnesses, Ladies and Gentlemen.

With what we know today of the structure of atoms, we understand perfectly the hopeless task undertaken by alchemists of old, striving to transmute the different elements one to another, and to transform lead and mercury into gold. With the means at their command, they could not work on the essential part of the atom, that is to say the nucleus. The chemical binding forces and most of the physical phenomena, such as radiation, etc., originate in the outermost parts of the atom, in the light, negatively charged electrons orbiting around the nucleus. The characteristic feature of atoms and what makes atoms different from each other, however, is the number of positive unit charges of electricity, or the number of protons, contained in the nucleus. It is this charge which holds together the light, negative electrons that spread, like the planets round the sun, in circular layers round the central nucleus.

At the present level of our knowledge, everything points to the fact that the nuclei of the atoms are composed of particles of two types, one being a heavy particle that has been given the name of *neutron* as it lacks electric charge, and the other being called *proton*, of the same mass as the neutron but with a positive unit charge. A proton is nothing but the nucleus of the lightest atom, i.e. hydrogen. A helium nucleus has two protons and two neutrons; the atom of carbon has six protons and six neutrons, and so on. The atoms are numbered according to the number of protons, or unit charges in the nucleus, with hydrogen as number 1 and uranium as nummer 92, which is the heaviest element known to date.

Meanwhile, it has been found that the nucleus of an atom can contain a number of neutrons less than or in excess of the normal. These atoms, that present the same physical and chemical qualities as the normal atom except that the weight is different, have received the name of *isotopes*. As an example of an isotope, we can cite the heavy-hydrogen atom discovered by Urey which is a constituent of so-called heavy water. There exist hydrogen isotopes with one or two neutrons in the nucleus.

After all the fruitless attempts at the transmutation of one element into another, the firm conviction grew last century that the different atoms, 92 in number, were indestructible and immutable units of the structure of matter. There was thus great sensation when the Frenchman Becquerel, in 1892, discovered that the element uranium distintegrated giving off strong radiation. Research on this radiation proved that it consisted among others of the helium nuclei that were emitted at very high speed from the uranium atoms. Thus, when one part of the uranium nuclei disintegrates explosively, new substances are formed that disintegrate in their turn, giving off radiations, and so on, until a final stable product is formed which is found to be lead. Among the substances included in this chain, there is the highly radioactive substance radium, which Madame Curie discovered and succeeded in producing. Soon after the radioactivity of uranium was discovered, it was established that this same characteristic occurred in another element, thorium, and later it appeared that this was also the case with the element called actinium. The end-product of the disintegration of these two last-named elements is lead also. However, the lead obtained in these three series is not identical, in so far as the number of constituent neutrons is concerned. The lead that comes from the uranium has 124 neutrons in the nucleus, that which comes from thorium has 126 and that which comes from actinium has 125. So we have three isotopes of lead. Lead as found in nature is usually a mixture of these three types.

It must be noted in this respect that however strong the effect of a substance that is radioactive, it is in many instances only a very small part of the number of atoms that disintegrates. Thus, for a half of the number of uranium atoms to disintegrate, it would take four and a half thousand million years. For radium, the corresponding length of time would be one thousand six hundred years. Other radioactive materials would by contrast only take seconds or days for half of the number of atoms to disintegrate.

As the idea of immutability of the atoms of the elements had to be abandoned, one was back at the age-old problem of the alchemists, the transmutation of the elements. Lord Rutherford was the first to put forward the idea that it would be possible, with the help of the heavy-helium nuclei that are thrown off at great speed by the natural radioactive substances, to split atoms. He met with success in several cases. For the sake of example, we will be content to mention that if a nitrogen nucleus has been struck by the bombarding helium nuclei, a hydrogen nucleus is ejected from the former, and that the rests together with the captured helium nucleus form an oxygen nucleus. By this means helium and nitrogen were thus changed into oxygen and hydrogen. The atom of oxygen that was obtained by this method was however not the ordinary oxygen atom, an atom that has eight neutrons in the nucleus, but an oxygen atom with nine neutrons. This meant that an oxygen isotope had been obtained. This occurs in nature, although rarely; among 12,500 ordinary oxygen atoms, one oxygen isotope is found.

Rutherford's experiments on the splitting of atoms have later been continued by the husband-and-wife team Joliot-Curie, among others, who also used helium nuclei as projectiles. They found that often when new isotopes were formed, these isotopes were radioactive, and distintegrated emitting radioactive radiations. This discovery was of great importance, for it opened up the possibility of obtaining, by artificial processes, substances capable of replacing radium, a material that was both very costly and hard to come by.

Using helium nuclei and also hydrogen nuclei as projectiles, however, one can not split atoms with atomic numbers higher than 20; therefore, only part of the lighter elements of the series of atoms can so be split.

It was granted to today's Nobel Prize winner, Professor Fermi, to succeed in shattering even the heavier and the heaviest elements in the Periodic System.

Fermi used neutrons as projectiles in his experiments.

We have earlier spoken of the neutron as one of the two building-stones in atom nuclei. The existence of the neutron is however only a recent discovery. Rutherford had suspected the existence of a heavy particle without electric charge and had even given it the name neutron; it was given to one of his pupils, Chadwick, to find the neutron in the extremely strong radiation given off by beryllium subjected to the effect of a radioactive substance. The neutron has qualities that make it particularly suitable as a projectile in atomic fission. Both the helium nucleus and the hydrogen nucleus carry electric charges. The strong electric forces of repulsion developed when such a charged particle comes within reach of an atomic nucleus, deflect the projectile. The neutron being uncharged continues on its course without suffering any hindrance until it is stopped by direct impact on a nucleus. As the dimensions of the nuclei are extremely small compared with the distances that separates the different parts of the atoms, such impacts are of rare occurrence. As a result, beams of neutrons, experiment has shown, can pass through armour-plates metres thick without appreciable reduction in speed taking place.

The result which Fermi was able to achieve by using neutron bombardments have proved to be of inestimable value, and have shed new light on the structure of atom nuclei.

At first, the source of radiation was a mixture of beryllium powder and a radioactive substance. Today, neutrons are artifically produced by bombarding beryllium or lithium with heavy-hydrogen nuclei, whereby these substances emit neutrons with high energy. The neutron beams so produced are particularly powerful.

When using neutrons as projectiles, these are captured in the nucleus. In the case of the lighter elements, a hydrogen nucleus or a helium nucleus is ejected instead. With the heavier elements, however, the forces that interlink the atomic parts are so strong that, at least with neutron speeds that can be obtained by present methods, there is no ejection of any material part. The surplus energy disappears in the form of electromagnetic radiations (γ-radiations). As there is no variation in the charge, an isotope is obtained of the initial substance. This isotope, in many cases unstable, disintegrates giving off radioactive radiations. Radioactive materials are thus obtained as a rule.

It was some six months after their first experiment with neutron irradiation that Fermi and his co-workers came by chance on a new discovery which proved to be of the greatest importance. They observed namely that the effect of neutron irradiation was often extremely increased, when the rays were allowed to pass through water or paraffin. Minute study of this phenomenon showed that the speed of the neutrons was slowed down on impact with the hydrogen nuclei which were present in these substances. Contrary to what one had reasons to believe, it appeared that the slow neutrons had a much more powerful effect than the fast neutrons. It was further found that the strongest effect was achieved at a certain speed, which is different for different substances. This phenomenon has therefore been compared with resonance found in optics and acoustics.

With low-speed neutrons, Fermi and his co-workers were successful in producing radioactive isotopes of all the elements with the exception of hydrogen and helium and part of the radioactive substances. More than four hundred new radioactive substances have thus been obtained. A certain number of these has effects stronger than radium as regards radioactivity. Of these substances, more than half were products of bombardment by neutrons. The half-lives of these artificial radioactive substances appear comparatively short, varying from one second to several days.

As we have said, during the irradiation of heavy elements by neutrons, the neutrons are captured and incorporated in the nucleus, and an isotope is thus formed of the primary substance, and this isotope is radioactive. When the isotope decays, however, negative electrons–as can be proved–are projected and new substances are formed with higher positive charges, and therefore substances with higher rank number.

This general pattern that Fermi has found to be the rule when heavy substances are subjected to irradiation by neutrons, took on special interest when applied by him to the last element in the series of elements, viz. uranium, which has rank number 92. Following this process, the first product of disintegration should be an element with 93 positive electric charges and a new element would thus have been found, lying outside the old series. Fermi's researches on uranium made it most probable that a series of new elements could be found, which exist beyond the element up to now held to be the heaviest, namely uranium with rank number 92. Fermi even succeeded in producing two new elements, 93 and 94 in rank number. These new elements he called Ausenium and Hesperium.

Along with Fermi's significant discoveries, and to a certain extent equivalent, can be placed his experimental skill, his brilliant inventiveness and his intuition. These qualities have found expression in the creation of refined research methods which made it possible to demonstrate the existence of these newly formed substances, which occur in extremely small quantities. The same goes for the measurement of the speed at which the different radioactive products disintegrate, particularly since in many cases several disintegration products with different half-lives are simultaneously involved.

Professor Fermi. The Royal Swedish Academy of Sciences has awarded you the Nobel Prize for Physics for 1938 for your discovery of new radioactive substances belonging to the entire field of the elements and for the discovery, which you made in the course of your studies, of the selective powers of the slow neutrons.

We offer our congratulations and we express the most vivid admiration for your brilliant researches, which throw new light on the structure of atomic nuclei and which open up new horizons for the future development of atomic investigation.

We ask you now to receive the Nobel Prize from the hands of His Majesty the King.

ENRICO FERMI

Artifical radioactivity produced by neutron bombardment

Nobel Lecture, December 12, 1938

Although the problem of transmuting chemical elements into each other is much older than a satisfactory definition of the very concept of chemical element, it is well known that the first and most important step towards its solution was made only nineteen years ago by the late Lord Rutherford, who started the method of the nuclear bombardments. He showed on a few examples that, when the nucleus of a light element is struck by a fast α-particle, some disintegration process of the struck nucleus occurs, as a consequence of which the α-particle remains captured inside the nucleus and a different particle, in many cases a proton, is emitted in its place. What remains at the end of the process is a nucleus different from the original one; different in general both in electric charge and in atomic weight.

The nucleus that remains as disintegration product coincides sometimes with one of the stable nuclei, known from the isotopic analysis; very often, however, this is not the case. The product nucleus is then different from all «natural» nuclei; the reason being that the product nucleus is not stable. It disintegrates further, with a mean life characteristic of the nucleus, by emission of an electric charge (positive or negative), until it finally reaches a stable form. The emission of electrons that follows with a lag in time the first practically instantaneous disintegration, is the so-called artificial radioactivity, and was discovered by Joliot and Irène Curie at the end of the year 1933.

These authors obtained the first cases of artificial radioactivity by bombarding boron, magnesium, and aluminium with α-particles from a polonium source. They produced thus three radioactive isotopes of nitrogen, silicon and phosphorus, and succeeded also in separating chemically the activity from the bulk of the unmodified atoms of the bombarded substance.

The neutron bombardment

Immediately after these discoveries, it appeared that α-particles very likely did not represent the only type of bombarding projectiles for producing artificial radioactivity. I decided therefore to investigate from this point of view the effects of the bombardment with neutrons.

Compared with α-particles, the neutrons have the obvious drawback that the available neutron sources emit only a comparatively small number of neutrons. Indeed neutrons are emitted as products of nuclear reactions, whose yield is only seldom larger than 10^{-4}. This drawback is, however, compensated by the fact that neutrons, having no electric charge, can reach the nuclei of all atoms, without having to overcome the potential barrier, due to the Coulomb field that surrounds the nucleus. Furthermore, since neutrons practically do not interact with electrons, their range is very long, and the probability of a nuclear collision is correspondingly larger than in the case of the α-particle or the proton bombardment. As a matter of fact, neutrons were already known to be an efficient agent for producing some nuclear disintegrations.

As source of neutrons in these researches I used a small glass bulb containing beryllium powder and radon. With amounts of radon up to 800 millicuries such a source emits about 2×10^7 neutrons per second. This number is of course very small compared to the yield of neutrons that can be obtained from cyclotrons or from high-voltage tubes. The small dimensions, the perfect steadiness and the utmost simplicity are, however, sometimes very useful features of the radon + beryllium sources.

Nuclear reactions produced by neutrons

Since the first experiments, I could prove that the majority of the elements tested became active under the effect of the neutron bombardment. In some cases the decay of the activity with time corresponded to a single mean life; in others to the superposition of more than one exponential decay curve.

A systematic investigation of the behaviour of the elements throughout the Periodic Table was carried out by myself, with the help of several collaborators, namely Amaldi, d'Agostino, Pontecorvo, Rasetti, and Segrè. In most cases we performed also a chemical analysis, in order to identify the chemical element that was the carrier of the activity. For short living substances, such an analysis must be performed very quickly, in a time of the order of one minute.

The results of this first survey of the radioactivities produced by neutrons can be summarized as follows: Out of 63 elements investigated, 37 showed an easily detectable activity; the percentage of the activatable elements did not show any marked dependence on the atomic weight of the element. Chemical analysis and other considerations, mainly based on the distribution of the isotopes, permitted further to identify the following three types of nuclear reactions giving rise to artificial radioactivity:

$$_Z^M A + _0^1 n = _{Z-2}^{M-3} A + _2^4 He \tag{1}$$

$$_Z^M A + _0^1 n = _{Z-1}^{M} A + _1^1 H \tag{2}$$

$$_Z^M A + _0^1 n = _Z^{M+1} A \tag{3}$$

where $_Z^M A$ is the symbol for an element with atomic number Z and mass number M; n is the symbol of the neutron.

The reactions of the types (1) and (2) occur chiefly among the light elements, while those of the type (3) are found very often also for heavy elements. In many cases the three processes are found at the same time in a single element. For instance, neutron bombardment of aluminium that has a single isotope ^{27}Al, gives rise to three radioactive products: ^{24}Na, with a half-period of 15 hours by process (1); ^{27}Mg, with a period of 10 minutes by process (2); and ^{28}Al with a period of 2 to 3 minutes by process (3).

As mentioned before, the heavy elements usually react only according to process (3) and therefore, but for certain complications to be discussed later, and for the case in which the original element has more than one stable isotope, they give rise to an exponentially decaying activity. A very striking exception to this behaviour is found for the activities induced by neutrons in the naturally active elements thorium and uranium. For the investigation of these elements it is necessary to purify first the element as thoroughly as possible from the daughter substances that emit β-particles. When thus purified, both thorium and uranium emit spontaneously only α-particles, that can be immediately distinguished, by absorption, from the β-activity induced by the neutrons.

Both elements show a rather strong, induced activity when bombarded with neutrons; and in both cases the decay curve of the induced activity shows that several active bodies with different mean lives are produced. We attempted, since the spring of 1934, to isolate chemically the carriers of these activities, with the result that the carriers of some of the activities of uranium are neither isotopes of uranium itself, nor of the elements lighter than uranium down to the atomic number 86. We concluded that the carriers were one or more elements of atomic number larger than 92; we, in Rome, use to call the elements 93 and 94 Ausenium and Hesperium respectively. It is known that O. Hahn and L. Meitner have investigated very carefully and extensively the decay products of irradiated uranium, and were able to trace among them elements up to the atomic number 96.*

It should be noticed here, that besides processes (1), (2), and (3) for the production of artificial radioactivity with neutrons, neutrons of sufficiently high energy can react also as follows, as was first shown by Heyn: The primary neutron does not remain bound in the nucleus, but knocks off instead, one of the nuclear neutrons out of the nucleus; the result is a new nucleus, that is isotopic with the original one and has an atomic weight less by one unit. The final result is therefore identical with the products obtained by means of the nuclear photoeffect (Bothe), or by bombardment with fast deuterons. One of the most important results of the comparison of the active products obtained by these processes, is the proof, first given by Bothe, of the existence of isomeric nuclei, analogous to the isomers UX_2 and UZ, recognized long since by O. Hahn in his researches on the uranium family. The number of well-established cases of isomerism appears to increase rather rapidly, as investigation goes on, and represents an attractive field of research.

The slow neutrons

The intensity of the activation as a function of the distance from the neutron source shows in some cases anomalies apparently dependent on the objects that surround the source. A careful investigation of these effects led to the unexpected result that surrounding both source and body to be activated with masses of paraffin, increases in some cases the intensity of activation by a very large factor (up to 100). A similar effect is produced by water, and in general by substances containing a large concentration of hydrogen. Substances not containing hydrogen show sometimes similar features, though extremely less pronounced.

The interpretation of these results was the following. The neutron and the

* The discovery by Hahn and Strassmann of barium among the disintegration products of bombarded uranium, as a consequence of a process in which uranium splits into two approximately equal parts, makes it necessary to reexamine all the problems of the transuranic elements, as many of them might be found to be products of a splitting of uranium.

proton having approximately the same mass, any elastic impact of a fast neutron against a proton initially at rest, gives rise to a distribution of the available kinetic energy between neutron and proton; it can be shown that a neutron having an initial energy of 10^6 volts, after about 20 impacts against hydrogen atoms has its energy already reduced to a value close to that corresponding to thermal agitation. It follows that, when neutrons of high energy are shot by a source inside a large mass of paraffin or water, they very rapidly lose most of their energy and are transformed into « slow neutrons ». Both theory and experiment show that certain types of neutron reactions, and especially those of type (3), occur with a much larger cross-section for slow neutrons than for fast neutrons, thus accounting for the larger intensities of activation observed when irradiation is performed inside a large mass of paraffin or water.

It should be remarked furthermore that the mean free path for the elastic collisions of neutrons against hydrogen atoms in paraffin, decreases rather pronouncedly with the energy. When therefore, after three or four impacts, the energy of the neutron is already considerably reduced, its probability of diffusing outside of the paraffin, before the process of slowing down is completed, becomes very small.

To the large cross-section for the capture of slow neutrons by several atoms, there must obviously correspond a very strong absorption of these atoms for the slow neutrons. We investigated systematically such absorptions, and found that the behaviour of different elements in this respect is widely different; the cross-section for the capture of slow neutrons varies, with no apparent regularity for different elements, from about 10^{-24} cm^2 or less, to about a thousand times as much. Before discussing this point, as well as the dependence of the capture cross-section on the energy of the neutrons we shall first consider how far down the energy of the primary neutrons can be reduced by the collisions against the protons.

The thermal neutrons

If the neutrons could go on indefinitely diffusing inside the paraffin, their energy would evidently reach finally a mean value equal to that of thermal agitation. It is possible, however, that, before the neutrons have reached this lowest limit of energy, either they escape by diffusion out of the paraffin, or are captured by some nucleus. If the neutron energy reaches the thermal value, one should expect the intensity of the activation by slow neutrons to depend upon the temperature of the paraffin.

Soon after the discovery of the slow neutrons, we attempted to find a temperature dependence of the activation, but, owing to insufficient accuracy, we did not succeed. That the activation intensities depend upon the temperature was proved some months later by Moon and Tillman in London; as they showed, there is a considerable increase in the activation of several detectors, when the paraffin, in which the neutrons are slowed down, is cooled from room temperature to liquid-air temperature. This experiment definitely proves that a considerable percentage of the neutrons actually reaches the energy of thermal agitation. Another consequence is that the diffusion process must go on inside the paraffin for a relatively long time.

In order to measure, directly at least, the order of magnitude of this time, an experiment was attempted by myself and my collaborators. The source of neutrons was fastened at the edge of a rotating wheel, and two identical detectors were placed on the same edge, at equal distances from the source, one in front and one behind with respect to the sense of rotation. The wheel was then spun at a very high speed inside a fissure in a large paraffin block. We found that, while, with the wheel at rest, the two detectors became equally active, when the wheel was in motion during the activation, the detector that was behind the source became considerably more active than the one in front. From a discussion of this experiment was deduced, that the neutrons remain inside the paraffin for a time of the order of 10^{-4} seconds.

Other mechanical experiments with different arrangements were performed in several laboratories. For instance Dunning, Fink, Mitchell, Pegram, and Segrè in New York, built a mechanical velocity selector, and proved by direct measurement, that a large amount of the neutrons diffusing outside of a block of paraffin, have actually a velocity corresponding to thermal agitation.

After their energy is reduced to a value corresponding to thermal agitation, the neutrons go on diffusing without further change of their average energy. The investigation of this diffusion process, by Amaldi and myself, showed that thermal neutrons in paraffin or water can diffuse for a number of paths of the order of 100 before being captured. Since, however, the mean free path of the thermal neutrons in paraffin is very short (about 0.3 cm) the total displacement of the thermal neutrons during this diffusion process is rather small (of the order of 2 or 3 cm). The diffusion ends when the thermal neutron is captured, generally by one of the protons, with production of a

deuteron. The order of magnitude for this capture probability can be calculated, in good agreement with the experimental value, on the assumption
that the transition from a free-neutron state to the state in which the neutron
is bound in the deuteron is due to the magnetic dipole moments of the proton and the neutron. The binding energy set free in this process, is emitted
in the form of γ-rays, as first observed by Lea.

All the processes of capture of slow neutrons by any nucleus are generally
accompanied by the emission of γ-rays: Immediately after the capture of the
neutron, the nucleus remains in a state of high excitation and emits one or
more γ-quanta, before reaching the ground state. The γ-rays emitted by
this process were investigated by Rasetti and by Fleischmann.

Absorption anomalies

A theoretical discussion of the probability of capture of a neutron by a
nucleus, under the assumption that the energy of the neutron is small compared with the differences between neighbouring energy levels in the nucleus, leads to the result that the cross-section for the capture process should
be inversely proportional to the velocity of the neutron. While this result
is in qualitative agreement with the high efficiency of the slow-neutron bombardment observed experimentally, it fails on the other hand to account for
several features of the absorption process, that we are now going to discuss.

If the capture probability of a neutron were inversely proportional to its
velocity, one would expect two different elements to behave in exactly the
same way as absorbers of the slow neutrons, provided the thicknesses of the
two absorbers were conveniently chosen, so as to have equal absorption for
neutrons of a given energy. That the absorption obeys instead more complicated laws, was soon observed by Moon and Tillman and other authors
who showed that the absorption by a given element appears, as a rule, to be
larger when the slow neutrons are detected by means of the activity induced
in the same element. That the simple law of inverse proportionality does not
hold, was also proved by a direct mechanical experiment by Dunning, Pegram, Rasetti, and others in New York.

In the winter of 1935–1936 a systematic investigation of these phenomena
was carried out by Amaldi and myself. The result was, that each absorber of
the slow neutrons has one or more characteristic absorption bands, usually
for energies below 100 volts. Besides this or these absorption bands, the ab-

sorption coefficient is always large also for neutrons of thermal energy. Some elements, especially cadmium, have their characteristic absorption band overlapping with the absorption in the thermal region. This element absorbs therefore very strongly the thermal neutrons, while it is almost transparent to neutrons of higher energies. A thin cadmium sheet is therefore used for filtering the thermal neutrons out of the complex radiation that comes out of a paraffin block containing a neutron source inside.

Bohr and Breit and Wigner proposed independently to explain the above anomalies, as due to resonance with a virtual energy level of the compound nucleus (i.e. the nucleus composed of the bombarded nucleus and the neutron). Bohr went much farther in giving also a qualitative explanation of the large probability for the existence of at least one such level, within an energy interval of the order of magnitide of 100 volts corresponding to the energy band of the slow neutrons. This band corresponds, however, to an excitation energy of the compound nucleus of many million volts, representing the binding energy of the neutron. Bohr could show that, since nuclei, and especially heavy nuclei, are systems with a very large number of degrees of freedom, the spacing between neighbouring energy levels decreases very rapidly with increasing excitation energy. An evaluation of this spacing shows that whereas for low excitation energies the spacing is of the order of magnitude of 10^5 volts, for high excitation energies, of the order of ten million volts, it is reduced (for elements of mean atomic weight) to less than one volt. It is therefore a very plausible assumption that one (or more) such level lies within the slow-neutron band, thus explaining the large frequency of the cases in which absorption anomalies are observed.

Before concluding this review of the work on artificial radioactivity produced by neutrons, I feel it as a duty to thank all those who have contributed to the success of these researches. I must thank in particular all my collaborators that have already been mentioned; the Istituto di Sanità Pubblica in Rome and especially Prof. G. C. Trabacchi, for the supply of all the many radon sources that have been used; the Consiglio Nazionale delle Richerche for several grants.

Biography

Enrico Fermi was born in Rome on 29th September, 1901, the son of Alberto Fermi, a Chief Inspector of the Ministry of Communications, and Ida de Gattis. He attended a local grammar school, and his early aptitude for mathematics and physics was recognized and encouraged by his father's colleagues, among whom A. Amidei. In 1918, he won a fellowship of the Scuola Normale Superiore of Pisa. He spent four years at the University of Pisa, gaining his doctor's degree in physics in 1922, with Professor Puccianti.

Soon afterwards, in 1923, he was awarded a scholarship from the Italian Government and spent some months with Professor Max Born in Göttingen. With a Rockefeller Fellowship, in 1924, he moved to Leyden to work with P. Ehrenfest, and later that same year he returned to Italy to occupy for two years (1924–1926) the post of Lecturer in Mathematical Physics and Mechanics at the University of Florence.

In 1926, Fermi discovered the statistical laws, nowadays known as the « Fermi statistics », governing the particles subject to Pauli's exclusion principle (now referred to as «fermions », in contrast with « bosons » which obey the Bose-Einstein statistics).

In 1927, Fermi was elected Professor of Theoretical Physics at the University of Rome (a post which he retained until 1938, when he – immediately after the receipt of the Nobel Prize – emigrated to America, primarily to escape Mussolini's fascist dictatorship).

During the early years of his career in Rome he occupied himself with electrodynamic problems and with theoretical investigations on various spectroscopic phenomena. But a capital turning-point came when he directed his attention from the outer electrons towards the atomic nucleus itself. In 1934, he evolved the β-decay theory, coalescing previous work on radiation theory with Pauli's idea of the neutrino. Following the discovery by Curie and Joliot of artificial radioactivity (1934), he demonstrated that nuclear transformation occurs in almost every element subjected to neutron bombardment. This work resulted in the discovery of slow neutrons that same year, leading to the discovery of nuclear fission and the production of elements lying beyond what was until then the Periodic Table.

In 1938, Fermi was without doubt the greatest expert on neutrons, and he continued his work on this topic on his arrival in the United States, where he was soon appointed Professor of Physics at Columbia University, N.Y. (1939–1942).

Upon the discovery of fission, by Hahn and Strassmann early in 1939, he immediately saw the possibility of emission of secondary neutrons and of a chain reaction. He proceeded to work with tremendous enthusiasm, and directed a classical series of experiments which ultimately led to the atomic pile and the first controlled nuclear chain reaction. This took place in Chicago on December 2, 1942 – on a volley-ball field situated beneath Chicago's stadium. He subsequently played an important part in solving the problems connected with the development of the first atomic bomb (He was one of the leaders of the team of physicists on the Manhattan Project for the development of nuclear energy and the atomic bomb.)

In 1944, Fermi became American citizen, and at the end of the war (1946) he accepted a professorship at the Institute for Nuclear Studies of the University of Chicago, a position which he held until his untimely death in 1954. There he turned his attention to high-energy physics, and led investigations into the pion–nucleon interaction.

During the last years of his life Fermi occupied himself with the problem of the mysterious origin of cosmic rays, thereby developing a theory, according to which a universal magnetic field – acting as a giant accelerator – would account for the fantastic energies present in the cosmic ray particles.

Professor Fermi was the author of numerous papers both in theoretical and experimental physics. His most important contributions were:
«Sulla quantizzazione del gas perfetto monoatomico», Rend. Accad. Naz. Lincei, 1935 (also in Z. Phys., 1936), concerning the foundations of the statistics of the electronic gas and of the gases made of particles that obey the Pauli Principle.

Several papers published in Rend. Accad. Naz. Lincei, 1927–28, deal with the statistical model of the atom (Thomas–Fermi atom model) and give a semiquantitative method for the calculation of atomic properties. A resumé of this work was published by Fermi in the volume: Quantentheorie und Chemie, edited by H. Falkenhagen, Leipzig, 1928.

«Über die magnetischen Momente der Atomkerne», Z. Phys., 1930, is a quantitative theory of the hyperfine structures of spectrum lines. The magnetic moments of some nuclei are deduced therefrom.

« Tentativo di una teoria dei raggi β », *Ricerca Scientifica*, 1933 (also *Z. Phys.*, 1934) proposes a theory of the emission of β-rays, based on the hypothesis, first proposed by Pauli, of the existence of the neutrino.

The Nobel Prize for Physics was awarded to Fermi for his work on the artificial radioactivity produced by neutrons, and for nuclear reactions brought about by slow neutrons. The first paper on this subject « Radioattività indotta dal bombardamento di neutroni » was published by him in *Ricerca Scientifica*, 1934. All the work is collected in the following papers by himself and various collaborators: « Artificial radioactivity produced by neutron bombardment », *Proc. Roy. Soc.*, 1934 and 1935; « On the absorption and diffusion of slow neutrons », *Phys. Rev.*, 1936. The theoretical problems connected with the neutron are discussed by Fermi in the paper « Sul moto dei neutroni lenti», *Ricerca Scientifica*, 1936.

His *Collected Papers* are being published by a Committee under the Chairmanship of his friend and former pupil, Professor E. Segrè (Nobel Prize winner 1959, with O. Chamberlain, for the discovery of the antiproton).

Fermi was member of several academies and learned societies in Italy and abroad (he was early in his career, in 1929, chosen among the first 30 members of the Royal Academy of Italy).

As lecturer he was always in great demand (he has also given several courses at the University of Michigan, Ann Arbor; and Stanford University, Calif.). He was the first recipient of a special award of $\$ 50,000$ – which now bears his name – for work on the atom.

Professor Fermi married Laura Capon in 1928. They had one son Giulio and one daughter Nella. His favourite pastimes were walking, mountaineering, and winter sports.

He died in Chicago on 29th November, 1954.

Physics 1939

ERNEST ORLANDO LAWRENCE

« for the invention and development of the cyclotron and for results obtained with it, especially with regard to artificial radioactive elements»

Physics 1939

The following account of Lawrence's work is by Professor K. M. G. Siegbahn, member of the Nobel Committee for Physics of the Royal Swedish Academy of Sciences

In 1919 Lord Rutherford discovered that nitrogen can be brought to emit protons by bombardment with alpha particles, according to the nuclear-reaction equation:

$$^{14}_{7}N + ^{4}_{2}He \rightarrow ^{17}_{8}O + ^{1}_{1}H$$

This discovery meant the initiation of a new era in natural sciences. However, as long as one was limited to the use of alpha radiation of naturally radioactive substances for carrying out nuclear reactions, very strict limits were set to further development both with regard to the substances which could produce these reactions, as well as to the quantitative yield of the reactions.

How then would it be possible, by some method other than the use of radioactive substances, to make available projectiles with sufficient energies to bring about nuclear reactions in an artificial way? Fortunately, the quantum-mechanical treatment of this problem, developed in the meantime, implied that the energy of the particles need not be as high as might be expected from classical theories. Among all the proposals and experiments carried out in different quarters to produce sufficiently fast particles for nuclear experiments, those carried out at the Cavendish Laboratory on Rutherford's initiative were the first to yield a positive result (1932). In this case use was made of a high electrical voltage, up to about 600 kV, to accelerate protons which, upon bombarding lithium, caused a nuclear reaction:

$$^{7}_{3}Li + ^{1}_{1}H \rightarrow 2 \; ^{4}_{2}He$$

Two years earlier (September, 1930), however, Lawrence had indicated an entirely new method to obtain fast particles, i.e. the so-called magnetic resonance acceleration. This method is based on a brilliant combination of a constant homogeneous magnetic field and an oscillating electrical field with constant frequency, whereby the ions move about in circular orbits with ever-increasing radii, through stepwise acceleration. The communication on the first simple experimental model of the «cyclotron» was published in the same year as the aforementioned experiment with artificially produced nuclear reactions at the Cavendish Laboratory. Under Lawrence's guidance and with the assistance of a large number of skilled collaborators the cyclotron method soon proved suitable for rapid development towards an exceptionally effective tool for research in this field. The energies of the particles, successively obtained by the further development of the cyclotron method, surpassed significantly that which had been obtained by other means. The maximum energy of the particles accelerated in the cyclotron even considerably exceeded the energy values present in alpha rays of naturally radioactive substances. While the latter energy is of the order of magnitude of 7 to 8 MeV, the energy of alpha particles supplied by the cyclotron is, according to latest reports (November, 1939), up to 38 MeV.

Experiments with heavy hydrogen nuclei as projectiles, with which Lawrence and his collaborators could produce nuclear reactions with practically all elements, proved to be particularly successful.

With regard to the intensities of the radiation produced in the cyclotron, it can be mentioned that a current of over 150 microamperes has been attained, corresponding to the alpha radiation of *30 kg radium*. As a comparison it may be mentioned that the entire world stock of purified radium can be estimated at 1 kg.

With the powerful means given to nuclear research by the cyclotron, an explosive development took place in this field. Nowadays, cyclotron installations are built or planned in a large number of laboratories throughout the world. The number of publications on the results obtained with the use of cyclotrons has grown with the speed of an avalanche.

The greatest significance the cyclotron has had is in the production of artificially radioactive substances. True, the discovery of active isotopes was made by the Curie-Joliots in 1933 with the use of alpha particles from naturally radioactive substances, but only with the cyclotron was it possible to produce active isotopes in large quantities. This was, among other things, an essential condition for the use of active elements for biological and medical purposes. On this terrain, where such splendid achievements had already been made, a new field for research and practical applications has been opened, thanks to the cyclotron. To appreciate the strength of the radioactive sources produced for the last-mentioned purposes, the following data may be given. Using deuterium in his cyclotron Lawrence was able, already in 1936, to produce daily quantities of *active sodium*, which, with regard to gamma radiation, were equivalent to 200 mg radium. The later cyclotrons of larger dimensions (1939) have a production capacity of about 10 times this value.

Finally, it may be mentioned that the cyclotron offers possibilities of producing neutron radiation of great intensity, as a result of which quantitative research on the physical and biological effects of this radiation has been carried out. With regard to therapeutic applications, these preliminary investigations are rather encouraging.

Within the history of the development of experimental physics, the cyclotron takes an exceptional position. It is, without comparison, the most extensive and complicated apparatus construction carried out so far. As to the scientific results achieved, we can scarcely find anything similar among the other experimental tools in physics. It is also evident that the operation and testing of an apparatus of this type, with such a multitude of details, cannot be the merit of one man alone. As promotor and leader of this almost gigantic work, Lawrence has shown such merits in the field of physics that the Royal Swedish Academy of Sciences has considered him as having fulfilled to the highest degree the requirements implied in the award of the Nobel Prize*.

* Owing to the war conditions, the Prize was handed over to Professor Lawrence at a ceremony in Berkeley on February 29, 1940. Among the speeches delivered was a thorough account of Professor Lawrence's work by the physicist R. T. Birge. A report of the ceremonies in Berkeley has been published in «Les Prix Nobel en 1939», Stockholm, 1942.

ERNEST O. LAWRENCE

The evolution of the cyclotron

Nobel Lecture, December 11, 1951

The development of the cyclotron was begun more than twenty years ago and perhaps it is appropriate on this occasion to give something of an historical account. The story goes back to 1928 when I had the good fortune of becoming a member of the Faculty of the University of California. At that time it seemed opportune to review my plans for research, to see whether I might not profitably go into nuclear research, for the pioneer work of Rutherford and his school had clearly indicated that the next great frontier for the experimental physicist was surely the atomic nucleus.

It seemed equally obvious also at that time that a prerequisite to a successful experimental attack on the nucleus was the development of means of accelerating charged particles to high velocities – to energies measured in millions of electron volts, a task which appeared formidable indeed! Accordingly, I devoted considerable time and thought to the technical problem of ways and means of reaching millions of electron volts in the laboratory. The problem seemed to reduce itself to two parts, (a) the production of high voltages, and (b) the development of accelerating tubes capable of withstanding such high voltages.

Since transformers and rectifiers for such high voltages seemed rather out of the question for various reasons, not the least of which were connected with financial limitations, I naturally looked for alternative means of producing high voltages: the surge generator which was used by Brasch and Lange; the electrostatic generator which Professor W. F. G. Swann was working on when I was a student under him at the University of Minnesota in 1924 and which was later brought to practical development by Van de Graaff; and the Tesla coil source of high voltage which Tuve, Breit, and Hafstad brought to a fruitful stage of development.

One evening early in 1929 as I was glancing over current periodicals in the University library, I came across an article in a German electrical engineering journal by Wideröe on the multiple acceleration of positive ions. Not being able to read German easily, I merely looked at the diagrams and photographs of Wideröe's apparatus and from the various figures in the article was able to determine his general approach to the problem – i.e. the multiple acceleration of the positive ions by appropriate application of radio-frequency oscillating voltages to a series of cylindrical electrodes in line. This new idea immediately impressed me as the real answer which I had been looking for to the technical problem of accelerating positive ions, and without looking at the article further I then and there made estimates of the general features of a linear accelerator for protons in the energy range above one million volt electrons. Simple calculations showed that the accelerator tube would be some meters in length which at that time seemed rather awkwardly long for laboratory purposes. And accordingly, I asked myself the question, instead of using a large number of cylindrical electrodes in line, might it not be possible to use two electrodes over and over again by sending the positive ions back and forth through the electrodes by some sort of appropriate magnetic field arrangement. Again a little analysis of the problem showed that a uniform magnetic field had just the right properties – that the angular velocity of the ions circulating in the field would be independent of their energy so that they would circulate back and forth between suitable hollow electrodes in resonance with an oscillating electrical field of a certain frequency which now has come to be known as the « cyclotron frequency ».

Now this occasion affords me a felicitous opportunity in some measure to correct an error and an injustice. For at that time I did not carefully read Wideröe's article and note that he had gotten the idea of multiple accelera-

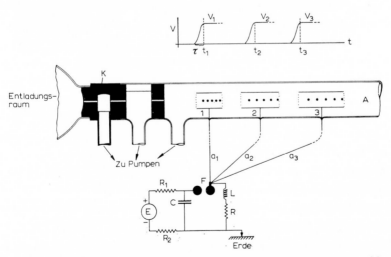

Fig. 1. Diagram of linear accelerator from Professor G. Ising's pioneer publication (1924) of the principle of multiple acceleration of ions.

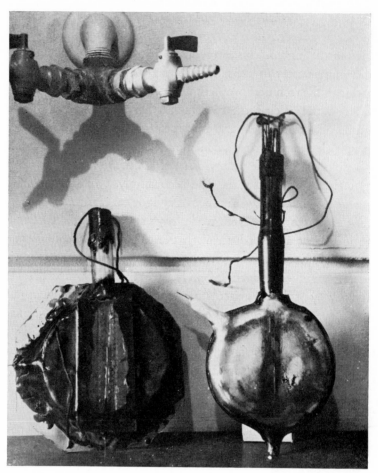

Fig. 2. First crude models of the cyclotron constructed by Edlefsen in 1930.

tion of ions from one of your distinguished colleagues, Professor G. Ising, who in 1924 published this important principle. It was only after several years had passed that I became aware of Professor Ising's prime contribution. I should like to take this opportunity to pay tribute to his work for he surely is the father of the developments of the methods of multiple acceleration.

Perhaps you will permit me first of all to show a slide of the diagram of the linear accelerator in his original publication (Fig. 1).

I hope I have not belabored excessively these early incidents of history and now I should like to trace rapidly the evolution of the cyclotron by showing examples of the apparatus in our laboratory as it was developed in the course of time. In doing so, I am afraid I shall not be able to mention all those who

Fig. 3. Working model of cyclotron constructed by M. Stanley Livingston which pointed the way to later developments.

deserve great credit for the developments – as from the beginning the work has been a team effort involving many able and devoted co-workers in many laboratories. As I am sure you will appreciate, a great many diverse talents are involved in such developments and whatever measure of success is achieved is dependent on close and effective collaboration.

Although the cyclotron was, so to speak, invented early in 1929, actual experimental work on its development was begun in the spring of 1930 when one of my students, Nels Edlefsen, constructed two crude models shown in Fig. 2. One of the models which gave slight evidence of working consisted of two copper duants waxed together on a glass plate with a filament source along the diameter at the center much like later models.

In the fall, another student, M. Stanley Livingston, continued the development and quickly constructed the model shown in Fig. 3 which, as you see, had all the features of early cyclotrons and which worked very well indeed as 80,000 volt protons were produced with less than 1,000 volts on the semi-circular accelerating electrode – now called the « dee ».

The next milestone in the development was the construction of a larger model (Figs. 4 and 5) which produced protons of the desired energies – in the region of one million electron volts. Livingston and I had the remarkable good fortune of observing that this apparatus was rather more successful than we had expected. For, as you can well imagine, we were concerned about how many of the protons would succeed in spiralling around a great many times without getting lost on the way. We soon recognized that the focussing actions of the electric and magnetic fields were responsible for the relatively large currents of protons that reached the periphery of the apparatus; but we must acknowledge that here again experiment preceded theory!

We were busy with further improvements of the apparatus to produce larger currents at higher voltages when we received word of the discovery by Cockcroft and Walton, which this year has been recognized by the Nobel Prize in Physics. We were overjoyed with this news, for it constituted definite assurance that the acceleration of charged particles to high speeds was a worth-while endeavor. As you can imagine, we went ahead with all speed, and it was not long before the disintegration of lithium by protons had been observed with the apparatus.

Now we may proceed rapidly with examples of later developments. Figs. 6 and 7 show the first two-dee 27″ cyclotron which produced protons and deuterons of several million volts and was used extensively in early investigations of nuclear reactions involving neutrons and artificial radioactivity.

Again, with this apparatus the discoveries of Chadwick and the Curie-Joliots were promptly confirmed. Indeed, looking back it is remarkable that we managed to avoid the discovery of artificial radioactivity prior to their epoch-making announcement: for we tried at first to use Geiger counters in observing nuclear radiations produced by the cyclotron and observed that their background was always variable and large. In those days Geiger counters had the reputation of being unreliable and, rather than looking into the matter of their apparent misbehavior, we turned to ion chambers and linear amplifiers to observe heavy-particle nuclear reactions. Of course, the Geiger counters were simply being faithful to duty and recording the radiations from the artificial radioactive substances, and this became immediately ap-

Fig. 4. General view of first cyclotron used in nuclear transformations.

Fig. 5. Vacuum chamber of cyclotron (Fig. 4) which produced 1 million volt protons.

Fig. 6. General view of 27″ cyclotron built by young physicists including M.S. Livingston (*left*) and E. O. Lawrence (*right*). (The lack of good engineering design is quite evident!)

Fig. 7. The chamber of the 27″ cyclotron showing two dees.

Fig. 8. Early photograph of 60″ cyclotron showing first evidence of good engineering practice, introduced into our laboratory by W. M. Brobeck (*right*) and Donald Cooksey (*left*).

parent after the Curie-Joliot announcement. Again, we were overjoyed at the richness of the domain in the nucleus accessible to particles of several million electron volts energy and there followed a happy period of intensive experimental investigations, which indeed through the years has gained ever-increasing tempo in laboratories the world over.

The next milestone in our laboratory was the construction of the 60″ cyclotron, and this undertaking was greatly strengthened by the joining of our team of William Brobeck, a truly outstanding engineer. Brobeck brought to our laboratory sound engineering practice which from the day he joined us has had a profound effect on developments. To him, more than to any other one individual, goes the credit for the success of the 60″ cyclotron and all subsequent developments. As you can see in Fig. 8, the cyclotron for the first time began to look like a well-engineered machine. It was with this machine that the discoveries of the transuranium elements were made which have been rewarded this year by the award of the Nobel Prize in Chemistry to McMillan and Seaborg. Perhaps the finest example of a 60″

cyclotron is now in operation at the Nobel Institute here in Stockholm.

Soon our objective was the production of protons and deuterons of much higher energies, and Bethe pointed out the difficulty introduced by the relativistic increase in mass of the particles as they increase in energy in the course of acceleration which causes them to get out of resonance with an oscillating electric field in a uniform magnetic field.

However, Thomas devised a magnetic field that avoided the limitation discussed by Bethe, and also, of course, it was recognized that one might modulate the frequency in step with the changing angular frequency of the accelerated particles. These two solutions of the technical problem of yet higher energies – the region of 100 million volts – seemed impractical; at least much less practicable than simply so designing the cyclotron that a million volts or more could be applied to the dees, so that the particles would need to circulate around relatively few times in reaching the desired high energies.

Accordingly, just before the war, Brobeck and co-workers designed the great 184″ cyclotron shown in Fig. 9.

As is well known, the war prevented the building of this machine and immediately afterwards McMillan, and Veksler independently a few months earlier, came forward with the principle of phase stability which transformed the conventional cyclotron to a much more powerful instrument for higher energies – the synchrocyclotron. Fig. 10 shows the main features of the Berkeley 184″ synchrocyclotron which produces 340 MeV protons, while there are later and more modern installations, notably at Columbia University and University of Chicago, which produce somewhat higher energies. As I am sure this audience is well aware, a beautifully engineered synchrocyclotron is nearing completion at Uppsala.

On completion of the 184″ synchrocyclotron, it was natural that Brobeck should turn his attention to the engineering problem of applying the synchrotron principle to the acceleration of heavy ions, particularly protons, to much higher energies – in the range of billions of electron volts. It was not long before his engineering studies indicated the practicability of producing protons in the energy range well above one billion electron volts.

With the extensive developments in the atomic energy field, large funds became available for research purposes – much larger than seemed possible before the war – and indeed, as soon as all concerned were convinced of the practicality of building a proton synchrotron for several billion electron volts, the construction of two installations was begun, one at Brookhaven for

Fig. 9. Artist's sketch of 184″ cyclotron designed by Brobeck before the war to produce 100 million electron volt protons.

Fig. 10. General view of 184″ synchrocyclotron which produces 340 MeV protons. (The concrete shielding, partially removed in this photograph, is 15′ in thickness.)

Fig. 11. One-quarter scale operating model of 6 BeV proton synchrotron.

about 3 billion electron volts and a second at Berkeley for about twice this energy.

The first step in these large undertakings was to build a substantial operating model to test out the theory of the proton synchrotron, as well as the engineering principles of design. Accordingly, a quarter-scale operating model was constructed and is shown in Fig. 11. A small cyclotron was designed to produce large current pulses of 1 MeV protons which were injected into the « race track » of the synchrotron by an appropriate magnetic and electrostatic deflecting system which can be seen in the foreground of Fig. 11. This model worked as expected and provided a great deal of practical data giving confidence that the full-scale machines will function successfully and satisfactorily.

It is hardly appropriate here to describe either the Brookhaven or Berkeley proton synchrotrons (the former is called the *cosmotron* and the latter is called the *bevatron*) but perhaps it is of interest to show a number of photographs which display the general features of this great machine (Figs. 12, 13, 14, 15 and 16).

Now that we shall soon have 5 or 10 BeV particles in the laboratory, what possibilities are there for going on higher to 50 or 100 BeV? One answer is that the limitation of the bevatron is largely a financial one. With a correspondingly larger expenditure, higher energies surely can be reached.

But I should like to close by emphasizing that a more feasible, if not more interesting, approach to the problem of higher-energy nuclear projectiles is the acceleration of multiply charged heavier ions such as C^{6+}, or Ne^{10+}. Already extraordinarily interesting nuclear reactions have been produced by the acceleration of C^{6+} ions to 120 MeV in the 60″ cyclotron, and such particles in the Berkeley bevatron would be accelerated to more than 36 BeV Since in the cosmic radiation such heavy particles play an important role, they will surely be produced in the bevatron some day, contributing to further progress in our understanding of Nature.

Fig. 12. General view of «race track» magnet in process of assembly for 6.3 BeV proton synchrotron or «bevatron».

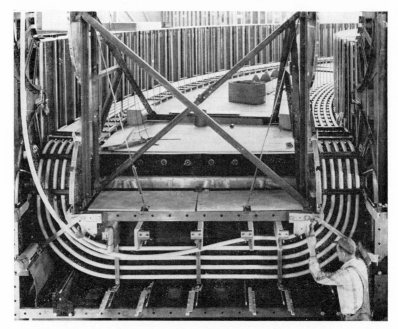

Fig. 13. Showing coil winding of bevatron magnet.

Fig. 14. The size of the bevatron magnet is here indicated .(*Left to right*: E. O. Lawrence,
W. M. Brobeck, H. A. Fidler, and D. Cooksey).

Fig. 15. Bevatron motor generator equipment.

Fig. 16. Ignitrons and associated switchgear for bevatron motor generator.

Biography

Ernest Orlando Lawrence was born on 8th August, 1901, at Canton, South Dakota (United States). His parents, Carl Gustavus and Gunda (*née* Jacobson) Lawrence, were the children of Norwegian immigrants, his father being a Superintendant of Schools. His early education was at Canton High School, then St. Olaf College. In 1919 he went to the University of South Dakota, receiving his B.A. in Chemistry in 1922. The following year he received his M.A. from the University of Minnesota. He spent a year at Chicago University doing physics and was awarded his Ph.D. from Yale University in 1925. He continued at Yale for a further three years, the first two as a National Research Fellow and the third as Assistant Professor of Physics. In 1928 he was appointed Associate Professor of Physics at the University of California, Berkeley, and two years later he became Professor, being the youngest professor at Berkeley. In 1936 he became Director of the University's Radiation Laboratory as well, remaining in these posts until his death.

During World War II he made vital contributions to the development of the atomic bomb, holding several official appointments in the project. After the war he played a part in the attempt to obtain international agreement on the suspension of atomic-bomb testing, being a member of the U.S. delegation at the 1958 Geneva Conference on this subject.

Lawrence's research centred on nuclear physics. His early work was on ionization phenomena and the measurement of ionization potentials of metal vapours. In 1929 he invented the cyclotron, a device for accelerating nuclear particles to very high velocities without the use of high voltages. The swiftly moving particles were used to bombard atoms of various elements, disintegrating the atoms to form, in some cases, completely new elements. Hundreds of radioactive isotopes of the known elements were also discovered. His brother, Dr. John Lawrence, who became Director of the University's Medical Physics Laboratory, collaborated with him in studying medical and biological applications of the cyclotron and himself became a consultant to the Institute of Cancer Research at Columbia.

Larger and more powerful versions of the cyclotron were built by Lawrence. In 1941 the instrument was used to generate artificially the cosmic particles called mesons, and later the studies were extended to antiparticles.

Lawrence was a most prolific writer: during 1924–1940 his name appeared on 56 papers (an average of $3\frac{1}{2}$ papers a year), showing his exceptional breadth of interest. He was also the inventor of a method for obtaining time intervals as small as three billionths of a second, to study the discharge phenomena of an electric spark. In addition he devised a very precise method for measuring the e/m ratio of the electron, one of the fundamental constants of Nature. Most of his work was published in *The Physical Review* and the *Proceedings of the National Academy of Sciences*.

Among his many awards may be mentioned the Elliott Cresson Medal of the Franklin Institute, the Comstock Prize of the National Academy of Sciences, the Hughes Medal of the Royal Society, the Duddell Medal of the Royal Physical Society, the Faraday Medal, and the Enrico Fermi Award. He was decorated with the Medal for Merit and was an Officer of the Legion of Honour. He held honorary doctorates of thirteen American and one British University (Glasgow). He was a member or fellow of many American and foreign learned societies.

Lawrence married Mary Kimberly Blumer, daughter of the Emeritus Dean at Yale Medical School, in May 1932. They had six children. His recreations were boating, tennis, ice-skating, and music. He died on 27th August, 1958, at Palo Alto, California.

Physics 1940

Prize not awarded.

Physics 1941

Prize not awarded.

Name Index

Subject Index

Index of Biographies